MODULAR SERIES
ON SOLID STATE DEVICES

Gerold W. Neudeck and Robert F. Pierret, Editors

D1547129

Advanced
MOS Devices

DIETER K. SCHRODER

Arizona State University

ADDISON-WESLEY PUBLISHING COMPANY

READING, MASSACHUSETTS
MENLO PARK, CALIFORNIA · DON MILLS, ONTARIO
WOKINGHAM, ENGLAND · AMSTERDAM · SYDNEY
SINGAPORE · TOKYO · MADRID · BOGOTÁ
SANTIAGO · SAN JUAN

This book is in the
Addison-Wesley Modular Series on Solid State Devices

Library of Congress Cataloging-in-Publication Data

Schroder, Dieter K.
  Advanced MOS devices.

  (Modular series on solid state devices)
  Includes bibliographies and index.
  1. Metal oxide semiconductors.   2. Charge coupled
devices.   3. Metal oxide semiconductor field-effect
transistors.   I. Title.   II. Series.
TK7871.99.M44S47   1987   621.3815'2   85-28585
ISBN 0-201-16506-6

ABCDEFGHIJ-MA-89876

Foreword

Metal-oxide semiconductor (MOS) devices dominate the integrated circuit industry, both in numbers produced and in the variety of their application. They have always been dominant in semiconductor memories and microcomputers, but recently they have become important as power transistors and, through the use of complementary MOS technology, are the key to low-power circuits. For charge-coupled devices, the MOS approach has dominated from the very beginning.

This volume is devoted entirely to MOS devices. It is a natural extension of earlier volumes in *Modular Series on Solid State Devices* by G. W. Neudeck and R. F. Pierret, in which the basics of the most common semiconductor devices were treated. Volumes I to III laid the groundwork for *pn* junctions and bipolar transistors, and Volume IV treated the basics of MOS devices. The work of Volume IV is further extended here by treating nonequilibrium MOS devices in more detail. The nonequilibrium MOS capacitor is at the heart of the dynamic random-access memory and the charge-coupled device. Memory devices are the basis of the computer industry and are produced in great quantities all over the world. Charge-coupled devices are beginning to be a major factor in consumer products associated with the television industry, both as components in TV sets and as sensors in TV cameras.

The common thread throughout this volume is the nonequilibrium MOS device. Chapter 1 provides the necessary charge, capacitance, and voltage fundamentals of the nonequilibrium MOS-capacitor (MOS-C) and the necessary background of carrier generation and recombination. In Chapter 2, the use of the nonequilibrium or deep-depletion MOS-C as a test structure is treated. Its most common applications in that mode are the measurement of the generation lifetime and the doping-concentration profile. In Chapters 3 and 4, the charge-coupled device is discussed. Both its fundamentals and its applications in signal processing and imaging are treated. Semiconductor memories are the subject of Chapter 5. In Chapter 6 some properties of MOSFET's, not discussed in first-level texts, are addressed. For example, effects of short channels and narrow gates, threshold voltage adjustment by ion implantation, mobility reduction by the gate voltage, and hot electron effects on device performance are described.

I have tried to keep within the spirit of the earlier volumes by stressing device concepts through physical insight. In that process I have attempted to keep mathematical manipulations to a level consistent with a good understanding without letting complicated mathematics and derivations stand in the way of conceptual explanations. I have found that in teaching semiconductors, device understanding is sometimes relegated to second place by clouding the concepts with sophisticated mathematical derivations. I hope that in this book the concepts come across as more important than the equations.

This book is aimed at seniors and first-year graduate students, as well as industrial researchers who cannot find the topics of this volume in traditional textbooks. Their only recourse has been to published journals and to chapters in advanced books. I have attempted here to put together the most relevant concepts and descriptions, along with appropriate references. The references at the ends of the chapters were helpful during the writing of the book, but they are by no means exhaustive of all the topics.

The concepts presented in this volume have come about through numerous discussions with many colleagues, particularly at the Westinghouse Research Laboratories and at Arizona State University. Many questioning students at Carnegie-Mellon University, the University of Pittsburgh, and Arizona State University have contributed to a better understanding of semiconductor devices for me. Of the many colleagues, teachers, and co-workers, I am especially indebted to C. T. Sah, who first introduced me to semiconductor devices at the University of Illinois; to H. C. Nathanson at Westinghouse, with whom I had many discussions of which first-order ideas always formed the framework; and to R. F. Pierret of Purdue University for suggesting that I write this volume. His ideas and lecture notes were very helpful in the formulation of this book. J. S. Kang, one of my graduate students, helped with the problems in this volume.

I wish especially to thank my wife Beverley and my sons Mark and Derek for their assistance in numerous ways during the preparation of the manuscript.

Prof. Dieter K. Schroder
Arizona State University
Dept. of Electrical &
    Computer Engineering
Tempe, AZ 85287

Contents

3 Charge-Coupled Devices – Fundamentals

4 Charge-Coupled Devices – Applications

5 Semiconductor Memories

6 Advanced MOSFET Concepts

Introduction

This volume treats advanced concepts of MOS devices, and in that sense it is a continuation of Volume IV in this series. We assume the reader to be familiar with the material in that volume. However, certain parts will be reviewed whenever necessary. The basic theme running through most of this book is the deep-depletion Metal-Oxide-Semiconductor Capacitor (MOS-C). It has found applications both as a test structure and as the building block for a variety of devices. As a test structure, it reveals a remarkable amount of information about the oxide and the semiconductor. As a building block, it is the unit cell of the Charge-Coupled Device (CCD) and the Dynamic Random Access Memory (DRAM). Moreover, the region between the source and the drain in a conventional Metal-Oxide-Semiconductor Field-Effect Transistor (MOSFET) is nothing more than a deep-depletion MOS-C.

In Chapter 1 we present the fundamentals of the MOS-C. We review a few of the concepts of Volume IV and then derive the appropriate electrostatic equations for the deep-depletion condition. The charge-voltage and capacitance-voltage relationships are presented. We also briefly review the necessary recombination and generation fundamentals as they affect the devices discussed in the rest of the book. Chapter 2 is devoted to the MOS-C as a test structure. The pulsed and linear sweep capacitance-voltage methods for lifetime extraction are given, and doping concentration measurements are discussed. The gate-controlled diode is described because it is closely related to the nonequilibrium MOS capacitor.

Charge-coupled devices are introduced in Chapter 3. They are important because they form the basis for most solid-state imagers and for some selected signal processing applications. We introduce the concepts of charge packets, charge input and output, as well as charge transfer. The terminal characteristics of most semiconductor devices are described by their current and voltage. The CCD is the first device in which charge and its motion are the main descriptors, not current and voltage. This leads to some interesting concepts. Some of these concepts are discussed in Chapter 4, where CCD applications are described. We treat signal processing and imaging applications. Signal processing is illustrated by the comb and the transversal filters. Both line and area arrays are used as solid-state imagers.

Semiconductor memories are described in Chapter 5. After a brief overview of memories, both static and dynamic random access memories are discussed. The DRAM is a device based largely on CCD concepts. It is the core of the ubiquitous semiconductor memory. Finally, a number of advanced MOSFET concepts are described in Chapter 6. For example, the threshold voltage of most MOSFET's is adjusted by ion implantation, and the MOSFET mobility is always significantly lower than that of bulk material. As the dimensions of the MOSFET continue to shrink, a number of interesting phenomena are observed that are not seen in large devices. The threshold voltage becomes a function of the gate length, and hot electron effects become noticeable. These aspects are addressed in Chapter 6.

1 / MOS and Generation-Recombination Fundamentals

1.1 THE MOS CAPACITOR

1.1.1 Introduction

This chapter is devoted to the fundamentals of the *nonequilibrium* or *deep-depletion* metal-oxide-semiconductor capacitor (MOS-C) and to the *recombination* and *generation* of electron-hole pairs (ehp). In this sense it is a continuation of Volumes IV[1] and VI[2] of this series. For completeness we review the more pertinent MOS-C equilibrium concepts and equations to lay the groundwork for the deep-depletion device. We use the term "metal-oxide" even if the gate is not a metal and the insulator is not an oxide. The term "gate-insulator-semiconductor" is more generic, but we conform to common usage and will use "MOS" throughout this volume. We also use the terms "nonequilibrium" and "deep-depletion" interchangeably. Both apply to a device **not** in equilibrium.

The MOS-C is the only semiconductor device that is in equilibrium when a voltage is applied to it. This makes its analysis very simple. In all other devices there is a current flow. Their analysis is more complex, because the Fermi-level concept no longer holds and therefore the spatial or temporal electron and hole distributions are generally not known. The MOS-C is only an equilibrium device, however, when the voltage applied to it does not change with time. As soon as the voltage changes, a current flows and the equilibrium concepts no longer hold. The current flows as a conduction current in the semiconductor and connecting wires, and as a displacement current through the oxide.

When MOS capacitors are used as semiconductor elements, they operate in the deep-depletion mode. They are also widely used as test structures to characterize a wide variety of semiconductor material and device parameters. We address both aspects of MOS-C's in this volume. For example, we show how they are used to measure bulk and surface generation properties and the doping concentration of the substrate, and then go on to discuss their application as circuit elements.

The exact electrostatic solutions are derived for both equilibrium and nonequilibrium devices. These solutions are subsequently simplified through the delta-depletion approximation. This simplification allows closed-form equations to be written. The charge-voltage and capacitance-voltage relationships are then developed because they are required for the analyses of Chapter 2.

In the second part of this chapter we review those aspects of generation-recombination statistics that are relevant to deep-depletion MOS-C's. We stress the generation parameters in particular, because the device is primarily used to measure the generation lifetime.

1.1.2 The Equilibrium MOS Capacitor

The MOS capacitor is the only semiconductor device to which equilibrium equations can be applied, provided that the gate voltage is constant or changes sufficiently slowly to be approximated as being constant. This allows exact solutions with a minimum of complexity, because the Fermi level is well defined. For illustrative purposes we use a p-type substrate throughout. The concepts developed here, of course, apply equally well to n-type substrates. Only changes in the signs, and a few other minor changes, are required.

The device cross section, energy-band diagram, and charge-distribution plot for an MOS-C are shown in Fig. 1.1. The substrate is provided with an ohmic contact held at ground or reference potential. This contact provides the transition for *majority* carriers from the metallic conductor to the semiconductor substrate. On the energy-band diagram, the contact to the semiconductor is made at the Fermi energy level, E_F. On the same band diagram, E_c, E_v, and E_i are the conduction-band, valence-band, and intrinsic energies, respectively.

A negative gate voltage causes the surface to be accumulated with majority holes, indicated by the open circles in Fig. 1.1a and b and the sharply peaked, narrow charge density Q_P in Fig. 1.1c. Charge-neutrality considerations require an equal density of negative gate charges. The negatively charged electrons are shown by the solid circles in Fig. 1.1a and b and by the narrow charge spike, Q_G, in Fig. 1.1c. For the present, we assume the structure to be ideal, with zero oxide charges and interface states and no metal-semiconductor work-function difference.

Let us now briefly review the various bias states of the capacitor. For simplicity, however, we will not show all the detail of Fig. 1.1 in the following diagrams. Instead we will restrict ourselves to the band diagrams and charge-density plots of Fig. 1.2. They will be described in conjunction with the C-V_G curves of Fig. 1.3.

Figure 1.2a is a repeat of Fig. 1.1 and shows the device in accumulation at $V_G = -V_{G1}$. The capacitance (a) in Fig. 1.3 is the oxide capacitance C_o. At a gate voltage of zero volts, the device is at flatband with its flatband capacitance, C_{FB}. There is no charge induced on the gate or in the semiconductor. This is true for the dc voltage shown in Fig. 1.2b. For capacitance measurements, a small ac signal voltage is superimposed on the dc gate voltage. The ac voltage periodically induces a small charge in the semiconductor. The equivalent space-charge region (scr) width is the extrinsic Debye length, and the capacitance C_{FB} is less than the oxide capacitance. As the dc

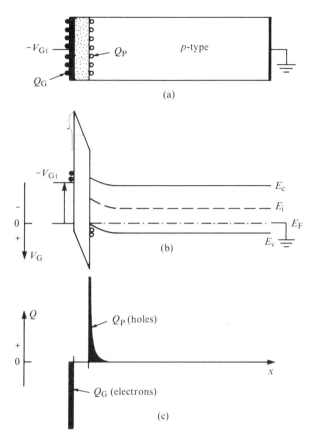

Fig. 1.1 Cross section (a), energy-band diagram (b), and charge-distribution plot (c) of a p-type substrate MOS capacitor in accumulation.

gate voltage is made positive, at V_{G2} the semiconductor near the surface is depleted of majority holes to an scr width W, shown in Fig. 1.2c and by point (c) in Fig. 1.3. The scr charge consists of negatively charged ionized acceptors and an equal positive gate charge. A further gate voltage increase to V_{G3} at point (d) in Fig. 1.3 not only gives an increased scr width and lower capacitance, but in addition attracts minority electrons, Q_{N3}, to the surface. V_{G3} is such that E_i at the semiconductor surface has moved as much below E_F as it was above E_F at flatband. This point is usually defined as the onset of heavy inversion and corresponds to a surface electron volume concentration (electrons/cm^3) equal to the hole volume concentration in the bulk. In other words, $n(x = 0) = p(\text{bulk})$. The scr width at this point is defined as W_T and the corresponding capacitance as C_T.

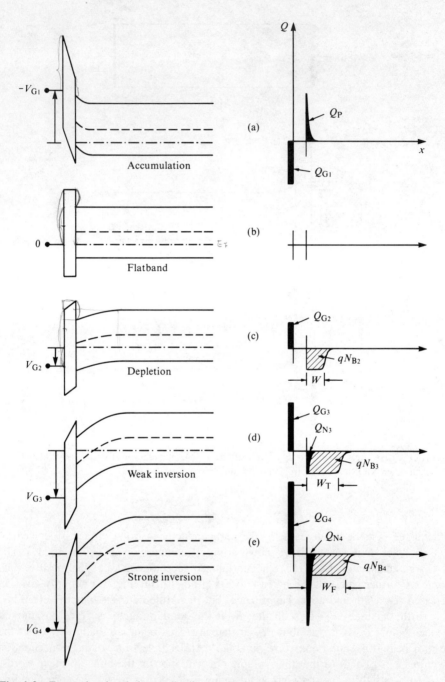

Fig. 1.2 Energy-band and charge-distribution diagrams for an MOS-C on a *p*-type substrate in (a) accumulation, (b) flatband, (c) depletion, (d) weak inversion, and (e) strong inversion.

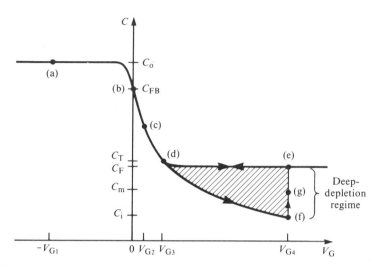

Fig. 1.3 Capacitance–gate voltage curves for the MOS-C whose charge distributions are shown in Figs. 1.2 and 1.5.

Raising the gate voltage further to V_{G4} increases both the gate and semiconductor charge. In the semiconductor it is primarily the inversion charge that increases, with only a small increase in the scr bulk charge. The inversion layer effectively shields the body of the semiconductor from gate-voltage changes, and the scr width is effectively pinned at W_F and the capacitance at C_F, shown by (e) in Figs. 1.2 and 1.3. We call W_F the final scr width. It is slightly wider than W_T, but it is W_T that is generally used in device analyses, because it is well defined by the surface potential being twice the Fermi potential. We discuss this further in Section 1.1.4. W_F is more difficult to calculate, because the surface potential is not well defined.

1.1.3 The Deep-Depletion MOS Capacitor

The C-V_G curve (a) to (e) or (e) to (a) in Fig. 1.3 is experimentally obtained by sweeping the gate voltage very slowly. Although the device is in the nonequilibrium state whenever the gate voltage is changed, if such changes are sufficiently slow, the capacitor can be considered to be in quasiequilibrium and the considerations of the previous section apply. For devices with low generation rates or long generation lifetimes, it is very difficult to obtain the true inversion curve because the sweep rate has to be exceedingly slow. In that case it is easier to set the gate voltage, wait for the device capacitance to settle, and then record its value. This procedure is then repeated to generate the experimental curve point by point. If this is not done, the following situation frequently develops. Sweeping the gate voltage toward more positive values in the inversion regime causes the capacitance to be **below** its equilibrium value, because the inversion charge cannot be generated rapidly enough to follow the sweep rate. When the gate voltage is swept toward more negative voltages in the inversion regime, minority carriers are injected from the inversion layer into the bulk. This forces the gate-induced junction, consisting of the n-inversion layer and the p-bulk, to be forward biased, and the measured capacitance will be **above** its equilibrium value. Note that the true equilibrium C-V_G curve is not measured for either sweep direction. These considerations apply only in the inversion part of the C-V_G curve. In the depletion and accumulation regimes there are no such limitations, because there are very few or no minority carriers.

If the gate voltage is swept rapidly from negative to positive potentials, the device is driven into deep depletion to point (f) in Fig. 1.3. Consider the device to be biased at zero volts and, at $t = 0$, the gate voltage V_{G4} to be suddenly applied. In practice this is done by closing a switch or applying a pulse. Majority holes are repelled from the surface to the depth W_i shown in Figs. 1.4f and 1.5f. This happens in a very short time determined by the carrier velocity and the scr width. Using the carrier thermal velocity of 10^7 cm/s gives $t = W_i/v_{th} = 10^{-11}$ s for a W_i of one micron. The time may be longer if a measurement RC time constant is dominant. In any case, on the time scale that we are concerned with during deep-depletion MOS-C measurements, this time is negligibly small and can be neglected.

From Fig. 1.5f we see that the Fermi level has split into the hole and electron quasi-Fermi levels and that the semiconductor charge consists to first order of ionized acceptor bulk charge only. The few minority carriers that were in the semiconductor volume, defined by W_i and the gate area, **before** gate voltage V_{G4} was applied will be attracted to the interface **after** the voltage is applied. However, their density is small compared with the ionized acceptor density and can be neglected. It does, however, keep the surface electron quasi-Fermi level approximately at the same energy in the band gap, where the Fermi level was at flatband.

Once the MOS-C is in the deep-depletion state, it returns to equilibrium through electron-hole pair generation. The electrons so generated drift to the interface to form an inversion layer. The scr width decreases as the inversion layer forms. Some of the thermally generated holes neutralize the ionized acceptors of the diminishing scr, and some holes flow onto the gate to supply the additional positive gate charge required to balance the increased negative inversion charge. The scr width decreases and some time later will reach an intermediate value shown as W_m in Figs. 1.4g and 1.5g and as C_m in Fig. 1.3. The bulk charge qN_{B4} decreases as the inversion charge Q_{N4} increases. The ehp-generation process continues until the device reaches equilibrium, shown as (e) in Fig. 1.3 and as Fig. 1.4e and Fig. 1.5e. The capacitance can range anywhere from C_i to C_F in the deep-depletion state, with C_i corresponding to zero inversion charge and C_F to the device strongly inverted and in equilibrium.

The deep-depletion state for gate voltage V_{G4} is anywhere along the curve (d) to (f) to, but not including, (e) in Fig. 1.3. The equilibrium state corresponds to the path (d) to (e). If the gate voltage is not restricted to V_{G4}, but is allowed to assume any value between V_{G3} and V_{G4}, then the deep-depletion state corresponds to the entire shaded region in Fig. 1.3, excluding the line (d) to (e).

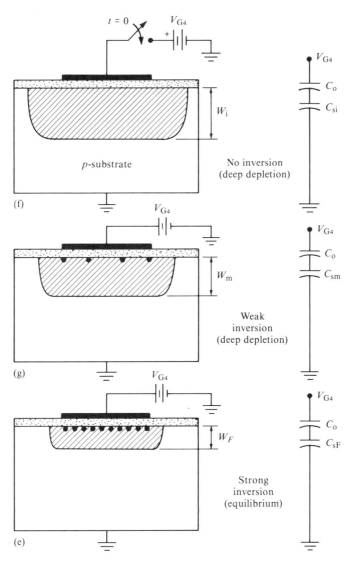

Fig. 1.4 Schematic representation of the space-charge region (scr) widths and capacitances during various times of the *C-t* transient. The letters (f, g, e) correspond to those in Figs. 1.3 and 1.5.

1.1.4 Semiconductor Electrostatics

1.1.4.1 Definition of Parameters

Following the qualitative description of the previous section, here we review the quantitative aspects of the MOS-C. First we define the terms, then examine the exact

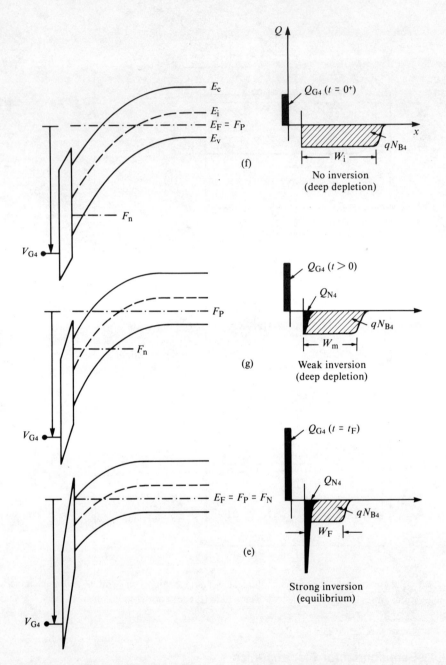

Fig. 1.5 Energy-band diagrams and charge-distribution plots for an MOS-C in deep depletion. The corresponding capacitances are shown in Fig. 1.3, and the letters (f,g,e) correspond to those in Figs. 1.3 and 1.4.

formulation, and finally discuss the delta-depletion approximation of MOS-C electrostatics. We give the key concepts and equations only, because the details have already been treated in Volume IV. The reader interested in a more detailed treatment of the "equilibrium MOS-C" is advised to consult that volume. For the "nonequilibrium MOS-C" we develop the relevant equations here.

The potentials and the spatial coordinate system are defined in Fig. 1.6. Let x be the depth into the semiconductor, measured from the oxide/semiconductor interface. The substrate is assumed to be sufficiently thick for the electric field to vanish in the bulk. This is mathematically equivalent to letting x extend from 0 to ∞. Consistent with most of the published literature, we choose zero potential to be in the semicon-

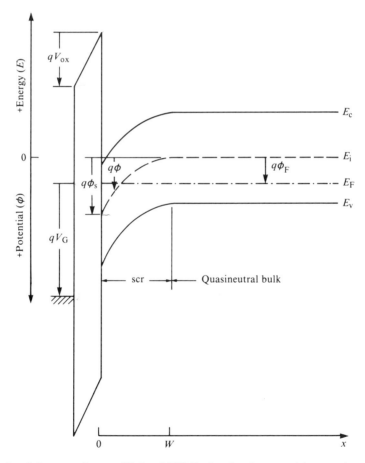

Fig. 1.6 Band diagram of an equilibrium MOS-C, showing the potentials, energies, and spatial dimension.

ductor bulk at the intrinsic energy E_i. Remember that the electrostatic potential is arbitrary to within a constant. We use ϕ for the potential rather than the V of Volume IV, because we will use the surface potential a great deal later on. It is generally designated by ϕ_s. The potential ϕ, shown in Fig. 1.6, is the potential or voltage anywhere in the semiconductor, measured from the bulk zero reference. At the surface it is called the surface potential ϕ_s, and it is the total voltage drop across the semiconductor, measured from the surface to the bulk reference.

We use both normalized and non-normalized potentials, whenever appropriate. The two are related to each other by

$$\phi(x) = [E_i(\text{bulk}) - E_i(x)]/q \qquad U(x) = \phi(x)/(kT/q) \quad (1.1a, b)$$

$$\phi_F = [E_i(\text{bulk}) - E_F]/q \qquad U_F = \phi_F/(kT/q) \quad (1.2a, b)$$

$$\phi_s = \phi(x = 0) \qquad U_s = U(x = 0) \quad (1.3a, b)$$

$$\phi(x \to \infty) = 0 \qquad U(x \to \infty) = 0 \quad (1.4a, b)$$

The normalized Fermi potentials are given by

$$U_F = -\ln(n_{\text{bulk}}/n_i) \approx -\ln(N_D/n_i) \quad \text{for } n\text{-type substrates} \qquad (1.5)$$

$$U_F = +\ln(p_{\text{bulk}}/n_i) \approx +\ln(N_A/n_i) \quad \text{for } p\text{-type substrates} \qquad (1.6)$$

The "$\approx$" is used in place of the "$=$" to indicate that, in general, $n \neq N_D$ and $p \neq N_A$. However, for the common substrate doping concentrations lying in the 10^{14} to 10^{17} cm^{-3} range, the equality is a very good approximation. This is no longer true for higher doping concentrations.

Substituting these doping concentrations into eq. (1.5) or (1.6) reveals the range of normalized Fermi potentials as $9 \leq |U_F| \leq 16$ for silicon at room temperature where $n_i \approx 10^{10}$ cm^{-3}. We mentioned earlier that the generally accepted definition of strong inversion is one where the surface concentration of minority carriers is equal in magnitude to the bulk concentration of majority carriers. From the band diagram of Fig. 1.6, this means that the surface potential is as much below as the bulk potential is above the Fermi level. In other words,

$$\phi_s = 2\phi_F \qquad U_s = 2U_F \qquad (1.7a, b)$$

For the p-type substrate, we use in our analyses $U_s < 0$ for accumulation, $0 < U_s < U_F$ for depletion, $U_F \leq U_s < 2U_F$ for weak inversion, and $U_s \geq 2U_F$ for strong inversion. For n-type substrates, the inequalities are reversed. The surface potential lies within the band gap between the conduction and the valence band under equilibrium conditions. For deep-depletion conditions it can take on much larger values, as we shall see later.

1.1.4.2 The Exact Solution–Equilibrium

An exact solution for the equilibrium state is briefly derived here to set the stage for the delta-depletion solution and for the deep-depletion device. The charge/unit volume for the structure of Fig. 1.6 is given by

$$\rho = q(p - n + N_D - N_A) \tag{1.8}$$

Substituting eqs. (1.5) and (1.6) into eq. (1.8) and using definitions for n and p of $n = n_i \exp(U - U_F)$ and $p = n_i \exp(U_F - U)$ gives

$$\rho = qn_i[\exp(U_F - U) - \exp(U - U_F) + \exp(-U_F) - \exp(U_F)] \tag{1.9}$$

The electric field and potential distributions are obtained from Poisson's equation:

$$d\mathscr{E}/dx = -d^2\phi/dx^2 = \rho/K_s\varepsilon_0 \tag{1.10}$$

With the charge density from eq. 1.9 and the boundary conditions

$$U = U_s \quad \text{at } x = 0 \quad \text{and} \quad dU/dx = 0 \quad \text{at } x = \infty \tag{1.11}$$

the electric field becomes

$$\mathscr{E} = \hat{U}_s(kT/q)F(U, U_F)/L_D \tag{1.12}$$

where the dimensionless electric field, F, is defined by

$$F(U, U_F) = \{\exp(U_F)[\exp(-U) + U - 1] + \exp(-U_F)[\exp(U) - U - 1]\}^{1/2} \tag{1.13}$$

The symbol $\hat{U}_s$ stands for the sign of the surface potential and is given by

$$\hat{U}_s = 1 \quad \text{if } U_s > 0, \quad \text{and} \quad \hat{U}_s = -1 \quad \text{if } U_s < 0 \tag{1.14}$$

$$L_D = (K_s\varepsilon_0 kT/2q^2 n_i)^{1/2} \tag{1.15}$$

is the intrinsic Debye length. The F-function can be thought of as a normalized electric field. However, it is not just normalized by kT/q as the normalized potentials are, but is also divided by L_D as seen in eq. (1.12).

The total semiconductor charge is given by

$$Q_s = -K_s\varepsilon_0 \mathscr{E}_s \tag{1.16}$$

Actually, Q_s is the charge/unit area—i.e., the charge density. However, for simplicity we will refer to it as the **charge** throughout this volume. Whenever there is uncertainty about the charge, the charge/unit area, or the charge/unit volume, we will clarify it. The surface electric field, $\mathscr{E}_s$, is given by eq. (1.12) when the normalized surface potential U_s is substituted for U in the F-function. In accumulation, the semiconductor charge is the majority hole accumulation charge, in depletion it is the ionized acceptor bulk depletion charge in the scr, and in inversion it is the sum of electron inversion and bulk scr depletion charges.

1.1.4.3   The Exact Solution–Deep Depletion

We will first consider the deep-depletion MOS-C immediately after a depleting voltage has been applied to the device. The band diagram is that of Fig. 1.7. The chief problem in the deep-depletion analysis is the Fermi level splitting into two quasi-Fermi levels, because we are dealing with a nonequilibrium condition. In order to retain a closed-form expression, we will make some assumptions about the quasi-Fermi levels.

We assume the majority carrier quasi-Fermi level, F_P, to remain constant throughout the semiconductor at its bulk value. We also assume the minority carrier quasi-Fermi level, F_N, to remain constant in the near-surface region. But where is F_N likely to be located in the band gap? The Fermi level at flatband is well defined (see Fig. 1.2b), because we know the majority- and minority-carrier concentrations exactly. When a depleting voltage step drives the device into deep depletion, the minority electrons within the scr width W drift to the interface. Their concentration at the surface increases somewhat over what it was at flatband. F_N shifts slightly above E_F(flatband). We do not know, however, just how much it shifts. Since the minority-carrier concentration, now in the form of a very weak inversion layer, is still low, we assume that F_N(surface) = E_F(flatband) immediately after the depleting voltage step has been applied. Recall that potentials are proportional to the logarithm of the carrier concentration, and that a factor of 10 in concentration is an equivalent potential of $2.3kT/q$.

With these assumptions we can write the potentials as

$$\phi = [E_i(\text{bulk}) - E_i(x)]/q \qquad U = \phi/(kT/q) \qquad (1.17a, b)$$

$$\phi_{FP} = [E_i(\text{bulk}) - F_P]/q \qquad U_{FP} = \phi_{FP}/(kT/q) \qquad (1.18a, b)$$

$$\phi_{FN} = [E_i(\text{bulk}) - F_N]/q \qquad U_{FN} = \phi_{FN}/(kT/q) \qquad (1.19a, b)$$

$$\phi_s = \phi(\text{at } x = 0) \qquad U_s = U(\text{at } x = 0) \qquad (1.20a, b)$$

The charge/unit volume now takes the form

$$\rho = q(p - n + N_D - N_A)$$
$$= qn_i[\exp(U_{FP} - U) - \exp(U - U_{FN}) + \exp(-U_{FN}) - \exp(U_{FP})] \qquad (1.21)$$

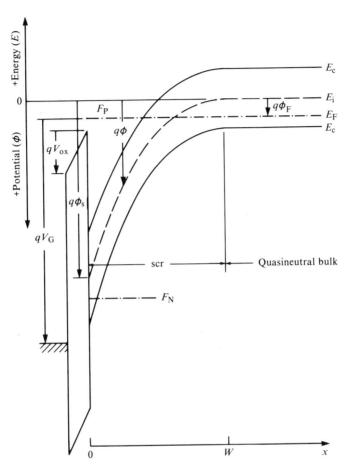

Fig. 1.7 Band diagram of a nonequilibrium MOS-C immediately after a deep-depletion gate voltage step, showing the potentials, energies, and spatial dimension.

resulting in the electric field

$$\mathscr{E} = \hat{U}_s(kT/q)F(U, U_{FP}, U_{FN})/L_D \tag{1.22}$$

where the F-function is modified to

$$F(U, U_{FP}, U_{FN}) = \{\exp(U_{FP})[\exp(-U) + U - 1] + \exp(-U_{FN})[\exp(U) - U - 1]\}^{1/2} \tag{1.23}$$

and, as in eq. (1.16), the semiconductor charge is given by

$$Q_s = -K_s \varepsilon_0 \mathcal{E}_s \tag{1.24}$$

All the equations we have derived so far deal with potentials **within** the semiconductor. The voltage applied to the device is applied not to the semiconductor but to the gate. So we need a relationship between the gate voltage and the surface potential. The gate voltage of an MOS-C, V_G, divides between the voltage drop across the oxide, V_{ox}, and the voltage drop across the semiconductor, ϕ_s. We designate the gate voltage of an ideal device with no interface states, no oxide charges, and zero metal-semiconductor work-function difference as V_G'. A real device has all of these, and the two gate voltages are related to each other through the flatband voltage V_{FB}:

$$V_G' = V_G - V_{FB} \tag{1.25}$$

which is also given by

$$V_G' = \phi_s + V_{ox} \tag{1.26}$$

In effect, a nonideal device is made ideal by eq. (1.25). The use of the primed gate voltage simplifies the equations by eliminating the need to write V_{FB} each time.

The oxide voltage is

$$V_{ox} = Q_G/C_o = -Q_s/C_o \tag{1.27}$$

since $Q_G + Q_s = 0$. Any oxide or interface charges do not appear in this expression, because they are already incorporated into the flatband voltage. From eq. (1.24) we have $Q_s = -K_s \varepsilon_0 \mathcal{E}_s$. Furthermore, using eq. (1.12) or (1.22) allows eq. (1.27) to be expressed as

$$V_{ox} = K_s \varepsilon_0 \mathcal{E}_s/C_o = \hat{U}_s(K_s x_o/K_o)(kT/q)F/L_D \tag{1.28}$$

This in turn gives the gate voltage–surface potential relationship

$$\boxed{V_G' = \phi_s + \hat{U}_s(K_s x_o/K_o)(kT/q)F/L_D} \tag{1.29}$$

The F-function is written simply as "F," allowing either eq. (1.13) or eq. (1.23) to be substituted.

1.1.4.4   The Delta-Depletion Solution–Equilibrium

The delta-depletion solution, also treated in greater detail in Volume IV, simplifies the foregoing analysis by recognizing that the majority-carrier accumulation charges and the minority-carrier inversion charges reside in a very shallow region in the semi-conductor at the oxide/semiconductor interface. Detailed calculations have shown these thicknesses to be around several hundred angstroms or less. Here we approximate the charges by delta functions at $x = 0$. They are assumed to be charge sheets of zero width but finite charge density. A second assumption is an scr depleted of mobile carriers and abruptly terminated at $x = W$. This, of course, applies only for the depletion and inversion states, not for the accumulation condition. The "zero mobile carriers in the scr" assumption may seem somewhat extreme for the equilibrium MOS-C, but it is certainly more justified for the deep-depletion case.

The charge/unit volume is now written as

$$\rho = -q(N_A - N_D) = -qN_B \quad \text{for } 0 \le x \le W \tag{1.30}$$

We take the general case of a p-type substrate that not only contains acceptors, but is slightly compensated with donors. This is true for every semiconductor wafer. No wafer has only one doping type, but the compensating impurity is usually negligibly small. Nevertheless we retain it, keeping in mind that $N_B \approx N_A$ for the type of p-substrates generally used. A solution of Poisson's equation with the boundary condition of $\mathcal{E} = 0$ and $\phi = 0$ at $x = W$ leads to the electric field expression

$$\mathcal{E}(x) = qN_B(W - x)/K_s\varepsilon_0 \quad \text{for } 0 \le x \le W \tag{1.31}$$

This is clearly a much simpler expression than eq. (1.12), and when integrated a second time it gives the potential variation as

$$\phi(x) = qN_B(W - x)^2/2K_s\varepsilon_0 \quad \text{for } 0 \le x \le W \tag{1.32}$$

The surface potential is the potential at $x = 0$—i.e.,

$$\phi_s = qN_B W^2/2K_s\varepsilon_0 \tag{1.33}$$

A simple rearrangement of eq. (1.33) gives the scr width as a function of the surface potential:

$$W = (2K_s\varepsilon_0\phi_s/qN_B)^{1/2} \tag{1.34}$$

As mentioned earlier, the point of strong inversion is defined as $\phi_s = 2\phi_F$. When substituted into eq. (1.34), the corresponding scr width W_T is

$$W_T = (4K_s\varepsilon_0\phi_F/qN_B)^{1/2} \tag{1.35}$$

It is quite obvious that the delta-depletion approximation is a simplified description of the exact solution. For the equilibrium device it offers an easier calculation of the charge and capacitance. But there are exact solutions available that are not difficult to use. They are only a little more complex. It is for the deep-depletion device that the delta-depletion approximation becomes important, because the exact solution can be obtained only through computer analyses. The reason for this is the splitting of the Fermi level into quasi-Fermi levels, so that n and p are no longer well defined. It is then that a simplified approach is very welcome, especially if that simplified approach agrees quite well with the exact solution. We will see that the delta-depletion approximation does just that.

1.1.4.5 The Delta-Depletion Solution–Deep Depletion

The approach in this section is different from that in Section 1.1.4.4, but follows closely that used in most treatises on charge-coupled devices. However, the concept is still that of the delta-depletion approximation. From Section 1.1.4.3 we have

$$V_G' = \phi_s + V_{ox} = \phi_s - Q_s/C_o \qquad (1.36)$$

In deep depletion, the semiconductor charge is either scr bulk charge ($Q_B = -qN_B W$), or bulk charge Q_B plus inversion charge Q_N. In general, then, we have

$$Q_s = (Q_N + Q_B) = (Q_N - qN_B W) \qquad (1.37)$$

Q_N and Q_B are both negative quantities for a p-type substrate, but $qN_B W$, as we defined it above, is a positive quantity.

Eq. (1.36) can then be written as

$$V_G' = \phi_s - (Q_N - qN_B W)/C_o \qquad (1.38)$$

A very important relationship is the dependence of the surface potential on the gate voltage and inversion charge. We can derive this relationship by using W from eq. (1.34) and substituting it into eq. (1.38). Then we solve for the surface potential in terms of the gate voltage and inversion charge. This is one of the key CCD equations:

$$\boxed{\phi_s = V_G' + Q_N/C_o - V_0\{[1 + 2(V_G' + Q_N/C_o)/V_0]^{1/2} - 1\}} \qquad (1.39)$$

where $V_0 = qK_s\varepsilon_0 N_B/C_o^2$.

Eq. (1.39) is a general equation expressing the dependence of the surface potential on inversion charge and gate voltage. As it was derived in the delta-depletion approximation, it is of course valid only for surface potentials between total deep depletion, when there is no inversion layer, and complete inversion when $\phi_s = 2\phi_F$. In other words, it holds for the path (f) to (e) in Fig. 1.3. Knowing the surface potential allows us to calculate the scr width W with ϕ_s substituted into the expression $W = (2K_s\varepsilon_0\phi_s/qN_B)^{1/2}$ as

$$W = (K_sx_o/K_o)\{[1 + 2(V_G' + Q_N/C_o)/V_0]^{1/2} - 1\} \qquad (1.40)$$

For total deep depletion, $Q_N = 0$ and the surface potential takes its maximum value:

$$\phi_s(Q_N = 0) = V_G' - V_0\{[1 + 2V_G'/V_0]^{1/2} - 1\} \qquad (1.41)$$

For p-type substrates, V_G', ϕ_s, N_B, and V_0 are positive quantities, and Q_N is negative. For n-type substrates, all signs are reversed.

1.1.5 Charge-Voltage Characteristics

The semiconductor charge in the equilibrium MOS-C is uniquely defined for a given gate voltage. This is no longer true for the deep-depletion MOS-C, because the inversion charge can vary from zero to maximum inversion charge. When the deep-depletion MOS-C is used as a test structure to measure the generation parameters, the important device parameter is its **capacitance**. (This is discussed in the next chapter.) When the device is used in the charge-coupled device, the **charge** is the important quantity and it is therefore important to understand it. We will, in this chapter, treat both the equilibrium and deep-depletion conditions, because they bound the nonequilibrium device.

The semiconductor charge of the equilibrium MOS-C is given in eq. (1.16) as

$$Q_s = -K_s\varepsilon_0\mathscr{E}_s \qquad (1.42)$$

where the electric field is given by eq. (1.12). The charge Q_s is easily calculated as a function of surface potential from these two equations. The surface potential is then converted to gate voltage using eq. (1.29). Such a plot of charge as a function of gate voltage is shown in Fig. 1.8 by the solid lines. We show the charge only for the positive gate voltages applicable to deep-depletion devices.

There are two distinct regions in the plot. The charge increases slowly with gate voltage in the depletion regime up to $V_G' \approx 1$ V and then rises rapidly beyond that voltage when the surface inverts. We show normalized surface-potential values, and it is quite clear that beyond $U_s = 2U_F$ the curve rises sharply. The other thing to notice is that, beyond the point of strong inversion, rather large changes in gate voltage are produced by unit increments of normalized surface potential. Remember, each unity U_s increment corresponds to a surface-potential increase of $kT/q \approx 25$ mV. In other words, once the MOS-C is inverted, large gate-voltage changes produce only small surface-potential changes.

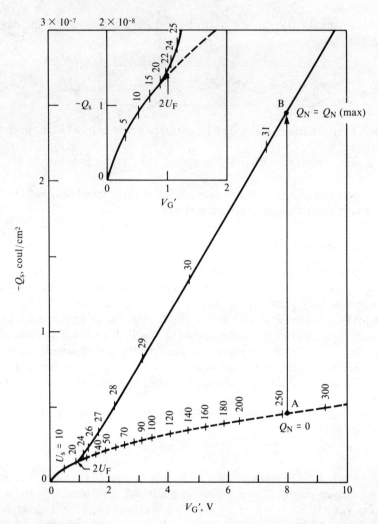

Fig. 1.8 Semiconductor charge as a function of gate voltage for equilibrium (solid curves) and deep-depletion (dashed curves) MOS-C's. The low-voltage range is shown enlarged in the inset. $N_A = 10^{15}$ cm^{-3}, $T = 300$ K, $U_F = 11.18$, $x_o = 0.1$ μm.

In the deep-depletion case with zero inversion charge, we find the semiconductor charge given by the bulk charge:

$$Q_s = Q_B = -qN_B W \qquad (1.43)$$

and using the relationship between surface potential and scr width given by eq. (1.34), we have

$$Q_s = -(2qK_s\varepsilon_0\phi_s N_B)^{1/2} \tag{1.44}$$

The conversion from surface potential to gate voltage is obtained from

$$V_G' = \phi_s + V_{ox} = \phi_s - Q_s/C_o \tag{1.45}$$

which, of course, is also the basis for eq. (1.29). The $-Q_s$ vs. V_G' plot for this case is shown by the dashed curve in Fig. 1.8. Note the good agreement with the exact equilibrium solution for voltages below 1 V, corresponding to surface potentials below $2U_F$. A very obvious difference between the two curves is the very different relationship between the surface potential and the gate voltage. In deep depletion, the surface potential assumes very high values, because of the relatively small semiconductor bulk charge that is induced by the gate voltage under depletion conditions. Pictorially, the band diagrams in Fig. 1.5 represent these very different surface potentials at a constant gate voltage. The capacitance range from (f) to (e) in Fig. 1.3 corresponds to the charge range from A to B in Fig. 1.8. The deep-depletion MOS-C can have inversion charges anywhere along the line A-B.

An interesting observation in Fig. 1.8 is a comparison of the inversion charge and the bulk charge at $U_s = 2U_F$, which is the surface potential traditionally considered to be the onset of strong inversion. Note that the inversion charge accounts for only a very small fraction of the total semiconductor charge, typically 2 to 3%. By far the largest contribution is the bulk charge. This situation changes very quickly, however, with increasing surface potential. The bulk charge increases only as the square root of surface potential, while the inversion charge increases exponentially with surface potential.

An important quantity is the maximum inversion charge that can be held in the MOS-C. An expression for this is obtained by solving eq. (1.39) for Q_N:

$$Q_N = -[V_G' - \phi_s - (2V_0\phi_s)^{1/2}]C_o \tag{1.46}$$

Traditionally one substitutes here $\phi_s = 2\phi_F$. Now we know from Fig. 1.8 that for strong inversion, $\phi_s > 2\phi_F$. Let us look at this quantitatively. For a bulk doping of 10^{15} cm^{-3}, $2\phi_F \approx 0.58$ V. From Fig. 1.8, heavy inversion exists for $2\phi_F$ + few kT/q, say 5 to $10kT/q = 0.12$ to 0.25 V. So we should really use $\phi_s \approx 0.7$ to 0.8 V in eq. (1.46). Actually, compared to typical gate voltages of 5 to 10 V, it really does not matter whether $\phi_s = 2\phi_F$ or $\phi_s = 2\phi_F + 10kT/q$ is used. Either one is quite small compared to V_G'. It is for this reason that the $2\phi_F$ condition is generally used.

For $\phi_s = 2\phi_F$, we get

$$Q_N \approx -[V_G' - 2\phi_F - (4V_0\phi_F)^{1/2}]C_o \tag{1.47}$$

For our example with $N_B = 10^{15}$ cm^{-3}, we find $V_0 = 1.4 \times 10^9 x_o^2$. For the oxide thickness of 0.1 μm used in Fig. 1.8, we find $V_0 = 0.14$ V, and the square-root term in eq. (1.47) has a value of 0.57 V, again small compared with V_G'. Incidentally, the square-root term represents the bulk charge, and as we can see from Fig. 1.8 it is indeed negligibly small compared with the inversion charge once the device is in strong inversion. It is for this reason that Q_N is often approximated as

$$Q_N \approx -(V_G' - 2\phi_F)C_o \tag{1.48}$$

We return to this expression in the charge-coupled-device section dealing with charge-handling capability.

1.1.6 Capacitance-Voltage Characteristics

We saw in Section 1.1.4 that the delta-depletion analysis is the most reasonable one for the deep-depletion MOS-C, because it lends itself most readily to charge and voltage calculations without having to resort to computers. It is our belief that expressions that lend themselves to simple calculations are most useful, as long as the results agree reasonably closely with the exact ones. Generally, the fact that the results are approximate is balanced by the simplicity of the approach. As an example, consider the two plots of Fig. 1.8. Below $2U_F$, the curves are for practical purposes identical. But two quite different expressions were used. The simpler one is easily calculated with a hand calculator, while the exact one requires more elaborate calculations.

It has been our experience that the simpler solutions are much more frequently used. Full-scale computer solutions are the exception. Of course, there are times when nothing but a detailed computer solution is necessary. For exact device simulations, two- and sometimes three-dimensional solutions are required. And at times, these solutions uncover details of device operation that intuition and first-order calculations cannot. Most new devices, however, have been proposed on the basis of simple, first-order calculations.

For the capacitance calculations in this section, we limit ourselves to the delta-depletion approach. As before, we refer the interested reader to Volume IV, where an excellent discussion of the equilibrium MOS-C can be found. It explains not only the relevant equations, but also the mechanism of capacitance measurement.

The capacitance of a semiconductor device, with its nonlinear charge-voltage relationship, is defined by

$$C = dQ/dV \tag{1.49}$$

Viewed from the gate, the MOS capacitance becomes

$$C = dQ_G/dV_G' = dQ_G/dV_G \quad \text{(assuming } dV_{FB} = 0) \tag{1.50}$$

The gate voltage is the sum of oxide and semiconductor voltages, leading to

$$C = dQ_G/(dV_{ox} + d\phi_s) = 1/[1/(dQ_G/dV_{ox}) + 1/(dQ_G/d\phi_s)] \tag{1.51}$$

Recall that the semiconductor voltage, being the potential drop across the semiconductor, is equivalent to the surface potential. The first term, dQ_G/dV_{ox}, is the oxide capacitance C_o. In the second term, we use $Q_G = -Q_s = -(Q_N + Q_B)$ to give

$$C = 1/[(1/C_o) + 1/(C_N + C_B)] \tag{1.52}$$

C_N is the inversion-layer capacitance, and C_B is the bulk scr capacitance due to an scr charge change with surface potential derived from the bulk charge in eqs. (1.43) and (1.44). Since a higher positive surface potential results in a higher **negative** bulk charge, we use $C_B = -dQ_B/d\phi_s$ to give

$$C_B = (qK_s\varepsilon_0 N_B/2\phi_s)^{1/2} = K_s\varepsilon_0/W \tag{1.53}$$

The equivalent circuit representing eq. (1.52) is shown in Fig. 1.9. It consists of the oxide capacitance in series with the inversion/bulk capacitance parallel combina-

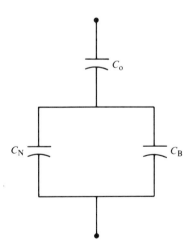

Fig. 1.9 MOS-C capacitance equivalent circuit for inversion and deep depletion.

tion. Since our main interest lies in the depletion/inversion part of the device operation, we have not included the accumulation capacitance. To include it would only require a minor change. One merely adds the accumulation charge to the semiconductor charge in the term leading to eq. (1.52), and the result would be the oxide capacitance in series with the inversion/bulk/accumulation parallel combination.

Let us now discuss the equivalent circuit of Fig. 1.9 with reference to the C-V_G' curves of Fig. 1.10. When the device is driven from accumulation into depletion, shown by (a) to (b) in Fig. 1.10, the inversion-layer charge is negligible compared with the bulk charge. As a result, $C_N \approx 0$. This is equivalent to an open circuit, and C is merely C_o in series with C_B. As the voltage continues to increase beyond point (b), the surface becomes strongly inverted **if** the voltage is swept slowly enough to allow generation of the minority carriers required for formation of this inversion layer. If the ac probing voltage used in the capacitance measurement is of sufficiently low frequency that the inversion charge is able to follow the ac probing voltage **and** the dc sweeping voltage, then the low-frequency (LF) curve is obtained. If the ac voltage frequency is too high, but the dc sweep voltage rate is sufficiently low, then the high-frequency (HF) curve is measured. If the sweep voltage rate is too high and there is not enough time for the inversion charge to be thermally generated, then the deep-depletion (DD) curve is obtained regardless of the frequency of the ac probing voltage.

Let us explain in more detail what we mean by these statements. The role of the dc sweep voltage is explained in Section 1.1.3. The true deep-depletion curve can be obtained only by sweeping the gate voltage very rapidly. The easiest way to do this is to apply a voltage step. Then the gate voltage changes essentially instantly. Alternatively, a fast voltage ramp can be employed.

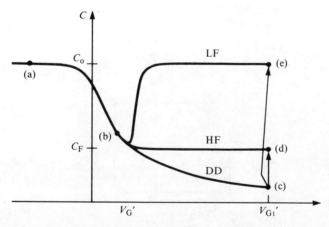

Fig. 1.10 Low-frequency (LF), high-frequency (HF), and deep-depletion (DD) capacitance-voltage curves.

The ac probing signal also plays an important role. Eq. (1.49) states that a time-varying voltage must be applied to a semiconductor device to measure its capacitance. What takes place in an MOS-C biased into inversion? The device is biased at some positive dc voltage. On its positive voltage swing, the ac voltage adds to the dc voltage, attempting to drive the device into stronger inversion. This, however, can happen only if the thermal generation rate is sufficiently high to generate the necessary minority carriers required for the additional inversion charge. There are two situations that allow this to happen. Either the probing frequency is so low that the generation rate has no problem keeping up with it, or the generation rate is so high that all the necessary carriers can be generated. The time-varying inversion charge compensates the time-varying gate charge in either case, and the MOS-C behaves like a parallel plate capacitor with the gate charge on one "plate" and the inversion charge on the other "plate." The "plates" are spaced by the oxide thickness, and the resulting capacitance is the oxide capacitance shown as "LF" in Fig. 1.10.

During the negative voltage swing, the ac voltage subtracts from the dc voltage, and now a smaller inversion charge suffices. This simply means that that portion of the inversion charge not required is injected into the substrate as minority carriers to re-combine there with majority carriers. So we see the critical process in the low-frequency curve to be the inversion charge **generation** during the positive swings of the ac probing voltage.

If the probing frequency is too high or the generation rate too low for the inversion charge to respond, then the inversion charge cannot contribute to the capacitance. In other words, if $dQ_N = 0$ for any $d\phi_s$, then $C_N = -dQ_N/d\phi_s = 0$. Now, the time-varying gate charge is compensated, not by a time-varying inversion charge, but instead by a time-varying bulk charge. Physically, **majority** carriers flow in and out of the scr at its $x = W$ edge, exposing less or more ionized acceptor charge. This is discussed in more detail in Chapter 2. Majority carriers respond extremely fast to the ac signal since their response is governed by the dielectric relaxation time, which is typically 10^{-12} to 10^{-10} s. Typical ac voltage frequencies of 1 MHz pose no device response problems. Our parallel plate capacitor now has the gate as one "plate" and the edge of the scr at $x = W$ as the other "plate," giving the "HF" curve of Fig. 1.10. Note that while the inversion charge does not respond to the ac probing voltage, it nevertheless exists and shields the device interior from the dc voltage, causing the capacitance to saturate, as discussed in Section 1.1.2.

A voltage step V_{G1}' initially drives the device into deep depletion, as shown by point (c) in Fig. 1.10. The capacitance will subsequently increase to point (d) for high-frequency measurements and to point (e) for low-frequency probing signals. The mechanism within the device is identical for the two cases, and the time to go from (c) to (d) is identical to that from (c) to (e). It is only a question of which charge response is measured by the capacitance meter—the bulk charge in the former or the inversion charge in the latter. The minority-carrier generation mechanism is the same. It is practically easier to measure the high-frequency curve than the low-frequency one, and so it is the HF response that is almost always measured. For high-quality silicon devices, the low-frequency curve requires probing frequencies of 1 Hz or less, and these are difficult to measure. When a low-frequency curve is required, it is generally determined by the quasistatic current-voltage technique,[3] in which a slowly varying gate voltage ramp is applied to the gate and the resulting current flow through the device is measured.

The "HF" and "LF" curves of Fig. 1.10 correspond to maximum inversion, and the "DD" curve is for zero inversion layer. For intermediate inversion-layer charge lying somewhere between these two extremes, we substitute eq. (1.40) into eq. (1.53) and find the MOS capacitance to be

$$ C = C_o/[1 + 2(V_G' + Q_N/C_o)/V_0]^{1/2} \qquad (1.54) $$

This expression is valid only in the deep-depletion regime of the device and can be used to predict the C-V_G' curve for known inversion charge Q_N. Recall that "deep-depletion" refers not only to curve DD in Fig. 1.10, but also to the entire shaded region in Fig. 1.3. For a step gate voltage, however, curve DD in Fig. 1.10 results.

1.2   GENERATION-RECOMBINATION STATISTICS

1.2.1   Introduction

The deep-depletion MOS-C is a nonequilibrium device. The very name "nonequilibrium" implies that a system in such a state, if given enough time, will return to equilibrium. A current always flows in nonequilibrium devices. It should be clear from the previous chapter that a deep-depletion MOS-C is under **reverse** bias and that **generation** processes dominate. In this chapter we review the relevant generation/recombination theory with emphasis on generation. A more thorough discussion is given in Ref. [2].

1.2.2   A Pictorial View

The band diagram of a perfect single-crystal semiconductor consists of a valence band and a conduction band, the two being separated by the band gap or the energy gap. When the periodicity of the single crystal is perturbed by foreign atoms or crystal defects, discrete energy levels are introduced into the band gap, as shown by the "E_T" lines in Fig. 1.11. Each line represents one such defect with energy E_T. It is commonly called a generation-recombination (G-R) center. G-R centers lie deep in the band gap and are known as deep-energy-level impurities, or simply *deep levels*. They act as recombination centers when there are excess carriers in the semiconductor and as gen-

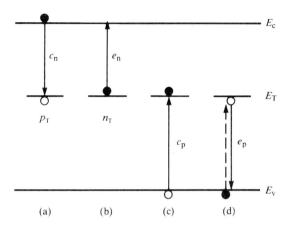

Fig. 1.11 Electron energy-band diagram for a semiconductor with deep-level impurities. The various capture and emission processes are described in the text.

eration centers when the carrier density is below its equilibrium value. The latter is the case in the reverse-biased scr of a *pn* junction or MOS-C, for example.

For the common semiconductors — silicon, germanium, and gallium arsenide — the deep levels are commonly metallic impurities such as iron, gold, and copper. But sometimes they are the result of crystal imperfections, such as dislocations, precipitates, vacancies, or interstitials. There are always some of these deep-level impurities in every semiconductor. For the most part they are undesirable. Occasionally, however, they are deliberately introduced to alter a device characteristic. Most frequently it is the switching time of a device that is reduced by the introduction of controlled densities of deep-level impurities.

Other impurities that also introduce energy levels into the band gap are the common donor and acceptor doping atoms that are found in every semiconductor. They introduce levels near the conduction or valence band, called *shallow levels,* in contrast to deep levels that lie near the middle of the band gap.

Let us consider one such deep-level impurity, shown in Fig. 1.11. It has an energy E_T and consists of N_T impurities/cm^3 uniformly distributed throughout the semiconductor wafer. The semiconductor has mobile electrons and holes that are introduced by shallow-level dopants, not shown in the figure. To follow the various capture and emission processes, let the G-R center first capture an electron from the conduction band, shown in Fig. 1.11a. The conduction band has n electrons/cm^3, and the valence band has p holes/cm^3. After electron capture, one of two events takes place. The center can either emit the electron back to the conduction band from which it came, called electron emission* and shown by (b) in Fig. 1.11, or it can capture a hole from the valence band, shown by (c). After either of these events, the G-R center is occupied by a hole and again has two choices. It either emits the hole back to the valence band (d) or captures an electron (a). These are the only four possible events between the conduction band, the impurity, and the valence band.

A **recombination** event is (a) followed by (c) in Fig. 1.11, and a **generation** event is (b) followed by (d). A third event, which is neither recombination nor generation, is the **trapping** event. Electron trapping is (a) followed by (b); hole trapping is (c) followed by (d). In either of these trapping events, a carrier is captured and subsequently emitted back to the band from which it came, and only one of the two bands and the center participate. In contrast, for both recombination and generation, the G-R center and **both** the conduction and valence bands participate.

Whether an impurity acts as a trap or a G-R center depends on the location of the Fermi level in the band gap, the temperature, and the capture cross section of the impurity. Generally, those impurities whose energies lie near the middle of the band gap behave as G-R centers, while those near the band edges act as traps.

1.2.3   A Mathematical Description–Bulk States

The G-R centers can be in one of two charge states. If they are occupied by electrons, they are in the n_T state, and if they are occupied by holes, they are in the p_T state, both of which are shown in Fig. 1.11. When electrons and holes recombine or are generated, the electron concentration in the conduction band, n, the hole concentration in the valence band, p, and the charge state of the centers, n_T or p_T, are all functions of time. For that reason, we will first address the question "what is the time rate of change of n and p?" We develop the appropriate equations for electrons in detail and then merely state the equations for holes. The equations for holes are exactly analogous, and their derivation proceeds along the same lines.

The electron concentration in the conduction band, n, is diminished by electron capture [process (a) in Fig. 1.11] and increased by electron emission [process (b) in Fig. 1.11]. The time rate of change of the electrons in the conduction band due to G-R mechanisms is given by

$$dn/dt|_{G\text{-}R} = (b) - (a) \qquad (1.55)$$

Electron emission depends on the density of G-R centers occupied by electrons, n_T, and the emission rate, e_n, through the relation: process (b) = $e_n n_T$. This relationship does not contain n because it is not necessary for there to be electrons in the conduction band during the emission process. But there must be G-R centers that are occupied by electrons. After all, if there are no electrons on the centers, none can be emitted.

The capture process is slightly more complicated, because it depends on n, p_T, and the capture coefficient c_n through the relation: process (a) = $c_n n p_T$. Notice that the electron concentration n is involved here. For electrons to be captured, there must be electrons in the conduction band.

The density of G-R centers occupied by electrons and holes must equal the total density N_T:

$$N_T = n_T + p_T \tag{1.56}$$

In other words, a center is occupied either by an electron or by a hole.

Eq. (1.55) becomes

$$dn/dt \big|_{\text{G-R}} = e_n n_T - c_n n p_T \tag{1.57}$$

and for holes we find the parallel expression

$$dp/dt \big|_{\text{G-R}} = e_p p_T - c_p p n_T \tag{1.58}$$

The emission rate e_n represents the density of electrons emitted per second from electron-occupied G-R centers to the conduction band. The capture rate $c_n n$ is the density of electrons captured per second from the conduction band by the G-R centers. The reader may wonder how there can be more than one electron emitted from a G-R center. What happens is that once an electron has been emitted, the center finds itself in the p_T state and subsequently emits a hole, returning it to the n_T state. The cycle then repeats.

Where do the electrons and holes come from for this cycle to continue? Surely they cannot come from the center itself. To answer this question, it may be helpful to view the hole emission process as one of electron emission from the valence band to the G-R center, indicated by the dashed line in Fig. 1.11d. In this picture, the electron-hole emission process is nothing more than an electron jumping from the valence band to the conduction band with an intermediate stop at the E_T level. However, it is easier to deal with the equations if we consider hole and electron emission as shown by the solid lines in Fig. 1.11.

The capture coefficient is a little more complicated than the emission rate. It is defined by

$$c_n = v_{\text{th}} \sigma_n \tag{1.59}$$

where v_{th} is the thermal velocity of the electrons and σ_n is the electron capture cross section of the G-R center. A physical explanation of c_n can be gleaned from eq. (1.59). We know that electrons move randomly at their thermal velocity and that the G-R centers remain immobile in the lattice. Nevertheless it is helpful to change the frame of reference by letting the electrons be immobile and the G-R centers move at velocity v_{th}. The centers then sweep out a volume per unit time given by $\sigma_n v_{\text{th}}$, and those electrons that find themselves in that volume have a very high probability of being captured. Capture cross section values vary widely depending on whether the center is neutral, negatively charged, or positively charged. A center with a negative or repulsive charge has a smaller cross section than one that is neutral or attractively charged. Neutral capture cross sections are on the order of 10^{-15} cm^2 — roughly the physical size of the atom.

Let us extend this physical picture a little further. Imagine sitting in a car driving along the highway at $v = 100$ km/h. The windshield of area σ_w sweeps out the volume/time $c_w = v\sigma_w$. For $\sigma_w = 0.5$ m^2, we find that the windshield sweeps out $c_w \approx 14$ m^3/s. All insects that are within this volume will be "captured" by the windshield. This is a fairly close analogy, except, of course, that in the semiconductor the "car" (G-R center) stands still and the "insects" (electrons) fly into the "windshield" (capture cross section). If the car has a wind deflector on the hood, some of the insects are deflected away from the windshield to escape capture. The windshield appears to have a repulsive potential to the insects, much as a negatively charged G-R center has a repulsive potential to electrons. The capture cross section is reduced, and the insect lifetime is extended.

Every time an electron or hole is captured or emitted, the center occupancy changes, and that rate of change is given by

$$dn_T/dt\big|_{\text{G-R}} = dp/dt - dn/dt \tag{1.60}$$

With eqs. (1.57) and (1.58), it is, in principle, possible to solve eq. (1.60). In practice, however, it is quite difficult, because n and p are generally not known. Significant simplifications are obtained under steady-state conditions, where there is no net change in G-R center occupancy. This corresponds to $dn_T/dt = 0$. Remember, steady state is not equilibrium. In steady state there can be current flow but no time-varying transients. Equilibrium implies zero current. From eq. (1.60), we define a **steady-state electron-hole pair generation rate**, G, as

$$G = dp/dt = dn/dt \tag{1.61}$$

G is positive when p or n increases as a function of time and negative when they decrease. G is the quantity that determines the junction leakage current in a reverse-biased pn junction or deep-depletion MOS-C. Strictly speaking, it is improper to use the steady-state eq. (1.61) for the MOS-C capacitance-time transient. But the transient time is generally sufficiently long for the steady-state treatment to give very acceptable results.

Using eqs. (1.57) to (1.61), we arrive at

$$G = [(e_n e_p/c_n c_p) - pn]c_n c_p N_T/[c_n(n + e_n/c_n) + c_p(p + e_p/c_p)] \tag{1.62}$$

which is the well-known Shockley-Read-Hall generation rate expression.[4]

In order to cast this equation into a more useful form, it is necessary to eliminate the emission- and capture-rate constants. This is usually done by simplifying the steady-state conditions further and invoking equilibrium concepts. It should be kept in mind, however, that it is only an approximation of the real device. In particular, it assumes the electric field to be sufficiently small to have little effect on carrier capture and emission. This can be a limitation in the reverse-biased MOS-C scr, where fairly high electric fields exist. It is nevertheless very useful because it results in simple expressions and is frequently used.

We will not present the details of the derivation. They are given in Volume VI.[2] The generation rate becomes

$$G = (n_i^2 - pn)c_n c_p N_T / [c_n(n + n_1) + c_p(p + p_1)] \qquad (1.63)$$

where

$$n_1 = n_i \exp[(E_T - E_i)/kT] \qquad (1.64a)$$

$$p_1 = n_i \exp[-(E_T - E_i)/kT] \qquad (1.64b)$$

These concentrations were so defined in Ref. [4]. Most of the active G-R centers have their energy levels near the middle of band gap. Hence, to first order, both n_1 and p_1 are on the order of n_i. As shown in Ref. [2], E_T should actually contain the degeneracy factor of the G-R center. We assume here that it is already contained within E_T.

Defining $\tau_n = 1/c_n N_T$ and $\tau_p = 1/c_p N_T$ allows eq. (1.63) to be written as

$$\boxed{G = (n_i^2 - pn)/[\tau_p(n + n_1) + \tau_n(p + p_1)] \qquad (1.65)}$$

For a reverse-biased device we assume the electron and hole concentrations to be very small. If they are negligibly small compared to n_1 and p_1, the generation rate becomes

$$G = n_i/\{\tau_p \exp[(E_T - E_i)/kT] + \tau_n \exp[-(E_T - E_i)/kT]\} \qquad (1.66)$$

This expression gives the generation rate in a depleted scr in which the electron and hole concentrations are negligibly small. We now define a *generation lifetime* by

$$\boxed{\begin{aligned} \tau_g &= \tau_p \exp[(E_T - E_i)/kT] + \tau_n \exp[-(E_T - E_i)/kT] \\ &= 2(\tau_p \tau_n)^{1/2} \cosh[(E_T - E_i)/kT + 0.5 \ln(\tau_p/\tau_n)] \end{aligned}} \qquad (1.67)$$

allowing the generation rate to be written as

$$G = n_i/\tau_g \qquad (1.68)$$

The generation lifetime, τ_g, represents the time required to **generate** one ehp. It describes the generation properties in the scr of reverse-biased devices where there are very few electrons or holes. For deep-depletion MOS capacitors we are mainly concerned with generation. However, for completeness we will briefly discuss recombination. In forward-biased devices there are excess carriers, and they recombine. The time for one ehp to recombine is the *recombination lifetime*, τ_r. Actually, one should not speak of one ehp, but instead should consider average concentrations of electron-hole pairs.

Let us now see how generation and recombination lifetimes compare to each other. Under recombination conditions, there are excess carriers in the device, and $pn > n_i^2$. The generation rate G in eq. (1.65) becomes the recombination rate, R, where $R = -G$:

$$R = (pn - n_i^2)/[\tau_p(n + n_1) + \tau_n(p + p_1)] \qquad (1.69)$$

The carrier concentrations are given by

$$n = n_0 + \Delta n; \qquad p = p_0 + \Delta p \qquad (1.70)$$

where n_0 and p_0 are the equilibrium concentrations and Δn and Δp are the excess concentrations. We define the recombination lifetime by

$$\tau_r = \Delta n/R \qquad (1.71)$$

From eq. (1.69), this results in

$$\tau_r = [\tau_p(n + n_1) + \tau_n(p + p_1)]/(p + n_0) \qquad (1.72)$$

where we use $\Delta n = \Delta p$ and $p_0 n_0 = n_i^2$.

For a p-type substrate, where $n_0 \ll p$, eq. (1.72) reduces to

$$\tau_r = \tau_p(n + n_1)/p + \tau_n(1 + p_1/p) \qquad (1.73)$$

Let us make some additional simplifications. We assume that the material is moderately doped with $p \geq 10^{14}$ cm^{-3}. The most active G-R centers are generally found to have energy levels near the middle of the band gap. For $E_T \approx E_i$ we find $p_1 \approx n_1 \approx n_i$. Even if p_1 and n_1 are different from n_i, as long as $p_1 \ll p$ and $n_1 \ll p$ eq. (1.73) becomes

$$\tau_r = \tau_p(n/p) + \tau_n \qquad (1.74)$$

Two cases are of interest: (i) low-level injection (ll), for which $n \ll p$ and

$$\tau_r(ll) = \tau_n \tag{1.75}$$

and (ii) high-level injection (hl), for which $n \approx p$ and

$$\tau_r(hl) = \tau_p + \tau_n \tag{1.76}$$

Eq. (1.75) shows τ_n to be the low-level injection electron recombination lifetime or the minority-carrier lifetime. Similarly, τ_p is the low-level injection minority-carrier lifetime in an n-type substrate.

The mechanisms governing recombination and generation are quite different. This should be obvious from the discussions above. It is therefore important to be cognizant of what is measured in a given lifetime measurement technique. The magnitude of the recombination lifetime is likely to be quite different from the generation lifetime for a given device. For low-level injection, the ratio of generation to recombination lifetime is

$$\tau_g/\tau_r = 2(\tau_p/\tau_n)^{1/2} \cosh[(E_T - E_i)/kT + 0.5 \ln(\tau_p/\tau_n)] \tag{1.77}$$

This ratio can be calculated only if the capture cross sections of the G-R center are known. Unless a specific center is identified, they are not known. We do know, however, that the lifetime ratio τ_p/τ_n, which is also equal to the capture cross section ratio σ_n/σ_p, lies typically between 0.01 and 100. To first order, we assume it to be around unity. This gives

$$\tau_g/\tau_r \approx 2 \cosh[(E_T - E_i)/kT] \tag{1.78}$$

In other words, for centers with $E_T \neq E_i$, the generation lifetime can be much larger than the recombination lifetime. This has been experimentally confirmed.[5] Ratios of $\tau_g/\tau_r \approx 100-1000$ are frequently observed.

We have so far discussed the effect of bulk G-R centers on the generation and recombination lifetimes. Surface G-R centers, better known as *interface states*, play a similar role. They are best characterized by the surface-recombination and surface-generation velocity. We consider them next.

1.2.4   A Mathematical Description–Interface States

The SiO_2/Si interface is an integral part of the MOS-C. It is an interface between a single-crystal substrate and an amorphous oxide. In the single-crystal substrate, covalent bonds represent a sharing of valence electrons between atoms. At the surface, the sharing is incomplete because a host atom is missing. Consequently, the perfect periodicity of the substrate is interrupted. Some of the bridging bonds between the bulk atoms no longer have partners, and they become interface states. Because they are not the result of foreign impurities, but instead are due to a disruption of the periodicity of the crystal lattice, they do not have well-defined energy levels. Their levels are closely spaced and distributed throughout the entire band gap. They are electrically active and act as G-R centers, much as discrete bulk centers do.

Most of the bulk-state theory in the previous section also applies to interface states, with two modifications: (i) interface states exist along a two-dimensional surface instead of a three-dimensional volume, and (ii) their energy levels are continuously distributed throughout the band gap. This latter point complicates the mathematics somewhat but leaves the concepts unchanged.

The generation rate expression, analogous to the volume generation rate in eq. (1.63), becomes

$$G_s = \int_{E_v}^{E_c} \{(n_i^2 - p_s n_s)c_{ns}c_{ps}D_{it}/[c_{ns}(n_s + n_{1s}) + c_{ps}(p_s + p_{1s})]\}\,dE \qquad (1.79)$$

The integral sign accounts for the distributed nature of the interface states, whose density D_{it} interface states/cm^2 eV must be integrated over the band gap. Further, note the subscript "s." It refers to the surface. For example, n_s is the volume concentration of electrons at the semiconductor surface.

The generation-recombination behavior of interface states is shown in Fig. 1.12. The solid circles represent interface states occupied by electrons. For an excess ehp injected into the semiconductor near the interface, the capture process might be (i) to

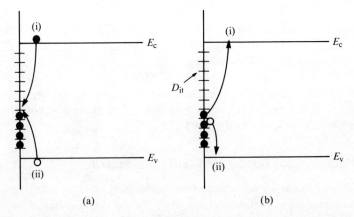

Fig. 1.12 Band diagram of an oxide/semiconductor interface. The short horizontal lines represent the interface states. The recombination process is shown in (a), and the generation process in (b).

(ii) in Fig. 1.12a. First the electron is captured by an empty state, thereby filling it, and subsequently the hole is captured by the occupied state. The empty states are indicated by the short horizontal lines. As in Fig. 1.11, they should have holes on them, which, for clarity, are not shown.

The emission processes are shown in Fig. 1.12b. First an electron is emitted, leaving a hole behind. Then the hole is emitted and the process repeats. Those states with energies near the Fermi level are the most active recombination centers. Those much above or below E_F are relatively inactive. For generation, it is the interface states near the middle of the band gap that are most active.

Eq. (1.79) is a rather complicated expression and is not very useful as it stands. To simplify it, we will assume that both the capture-rate constants and the interface-state density are independent of energy. From experiments this is known not to be strictly true, as shown in Ref. [2]. For the most part we are concerned with those states whose energies lie near the middle of the band gap. For those states it is reasonable to assume D_{it}, c_{ns}, and c_{ps} to be reasonably constant. In addition, under reverse-bias conditions we neglect n_s and p_s. We leave it as a problem to show that eq. (1.79) becomes

$$G_s = (\pi/2)(c_{ns}c_{ps})^{1/2}kTD_{it}n_i \qquad (1.80)$$

Similar to the transition from eq. (1.65) to eq. (1.68), we rewrite eq. (1.80) as

$$\boxed{G_s = s_0 n_i} \qquad (1.81)$$

Just as τ_g is the bulk scr generation lifetime, so s_0 is the surface scr *generation velocity* under the conditions of zero electron and hole surface concentrations.[†]

When the surface is not totally depleted of electrons and holes, and n_s and p_s are not negligible, then the surface generation rate is expressed as

$$G_s = sn_i \qquad (1.82)$$

where s is the surface scr generation velocity of a surface not totally depleted. We see from eq. (1.79) a maximum generation rate for $p_s n_s = 0$. When this is no longer true, because either n_s or p_s becomes large, their product is no longer zero and the surface generation rate decreases. This occurs when the surface is accumulated and p_s is high,

---

[†]We point out that A. S. Grove[6] introduced τ_0 as the bulk generation parameter and s_0 as the surface generation parameter. We have departed slightly from his original definitions. In his derivation of the bulk generation rate, he assumes $\sigma_n = \sigma_p$ and $E_T = E_i$. For that case we find from eq. (1.66) that $\tau_n = \tau_p = \tau_0$ and $G = n_i/2\tau_0$. This places undue restrictions on τ_0, and we prefer the more general definition $G = n_i/\tau_g$. This requires no assumptions regarding τ_g. By similar arguments, Grove defines the surface generation rate as $G_s = n_i(s_0/2)$. We prefer the more general definition $G_s = n_i s_0$, with no such restrictions on s_0.

or when the surface is inverted and n_s is high. When the $p_s n_s$ product approaches n_i^2, generation ceases altogether. For that reason we find $s < s_0$.

Both bulk and surface or interface-state generation are active in the pulsed MOS-C. Both are maximum at the time the device is driven into deep depletion. The scr bulk generation rate remains approximately constant, but the generation volume decreases. The surface generation area remains constant, but the surface generation rate decreases. Hence, the actual number of generated electron-hole pairs decreases, and when equilibrium is finally reached, both generation components become zero.

1.3 SUMMARY

We have reviewed the fundamentals of the MOS capacitor and the generation-recombination statistics in this chapter. In the first part we derived the exact electrostatic equations and then simplified them through use of the delta-depletion approximation. This approximation is shown to give very good agreement when compared with the accurate solution, and we use it subsequently to derive the surface potential, the charge-voltage, and the capacitance-voltage relationships. G-R statistics were used to derive expressions for bulk and surface generation characterized by the generation lifetime and the surface generation velocity.

The key equations from the first part of this chapter are the surface potential

$$\phi_s = V_G' + Q_N/C_o - V_0\{[1 + 2(V_G' + Q_N/C_o)/V_0]^{1/2} - 1\}$$

the space-charge region width

$$W = (K_s x_o/K_o)\{[1 + 2(V_G' + Q_N/C_o)/V_0]^{1/2} - 1\}$$

the inversion-charge density

$$Q_N = -[V_G' - \phi_s - (2V_0\phi_s)^{1/2}]C_o$$

and the capacitance expression

$$C = C_o/[1 + 2(V_G' + Q_N/C_o)/V_0]^{1/2}$$

From the generation portion of the chapter, the key equations are the bulk generation rate

$$G = n_i/\tau_g$$

with the bulk generation lifetime defined by

$$\tau_g = \tau_p \exp[(E_T - E_i)/kT] + \tau_n \exp[-(E_T - E_i)/kT]$$

and the surface generation rate

$$G_s = s_0 n_i$$

with the surface generation velocity given by

$$s_0 = (\pi/2)(c_{ns}c_{ps})^{1/2}kTD_{it}$$

REFERENCES

[1] R. F. Pierret, *Field Effect Devices*, Vol. IV in *Modular Series on Solid State Devices*, Addison-Wesley Publ. Co., Reading, MA, 1983.

[2] R. F. Pierret, *Advanced Semiconductor Fundamentals*, Vol. VI in *Modular Series on Solid State Devices*, Addison-Wesley Publ. Co., Reading, MA, 1986.

[3] M. Kuhn, "A Quasi-Static Technique for MOS C-V and Surface State Measurements," Solid-State Electr., *13*, 873-885, June, 1970.

[4] W. Shockley and W. T. Read, "Statistics of the Recombination of Holes and Electrons," Phys. Rev., *87*, 835-842, Sept., 1952; R. N. Hall, "Electron-Hole Recombination in Germanium," Phys. Rev., *87*, 387, July, 1952.

[5] D. K. Schroder, "The Concept of Generation and Recombination Lifetime in Semiconductors," IEEE Trans. Electr. Dev., *ED-29*, 1336-1338, Aug., 1982.

[6] A. S. Grove, *Physics and Technology of Semiconductor Devices*, J. Wiley & Sons, New York, 1967.

PROBLEMS

1.1 Switch S in Fig. P1.1 is briefly closed and then opened for a time sufficiently long for the MOS-C to reach equilibrium. The sequence is then repeated one more time. The time of closure is infinitesimally short in this problem. $V_{FB} = 0$.

Draw the resulting $-Q_s$ vs. V_G and C vs. V_G curves.

1.2 Plot the C/C_o vs. V_G curve for each of the two MOS-C's in Fig. P1.2a and b. The dc gate voltage is swept sufficiently slowly from $-V_G$ to $+V_G$ that the devices can be considered to be in equilibrium. The ac frequency is the conventional 1 MHz.

For the metal-oxide-n^+p device in (b), consider two cases:

(i) the n^+ island is so heavily doped that it cannot be inverted;

(ii) the n^+ island is less heavily doped so that it can be inverted.

1.3 Plot the high-frequency C vs. V_G curves for the three structures in Fig. P1.3 when the dc gate voltage is swept very slowly. Plot all three curves on the same figure.

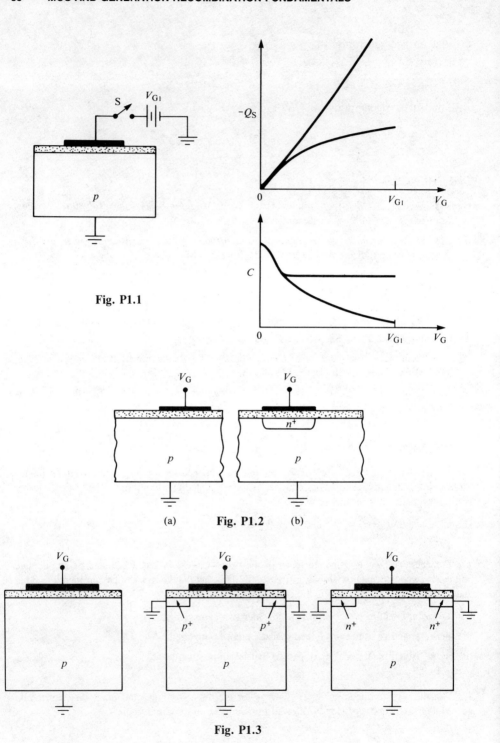

Fig. P1.1

Fig. P1.2

(a)   (b)

Fig. P1.3

1.4 The MOS-C in Fig. P1.4 is biased at $V_G = V_{G1}$ for a time sufficiently long for the device to be in equilibrium. At $t = 0$, the bias voltage is briefly pulsed to zero and then back to V_{G1}. The pulse width time t_p is longer than the recombination lifetime. Show the C-V_{G1} point at time $t = t_1$—i.e., immediately after the pulse returns to V_{G1}. The time, t_1, is sufficiently long for any circuit transients to have decayed but sufficiently short that essentially no electron-hole pairs have been generated.

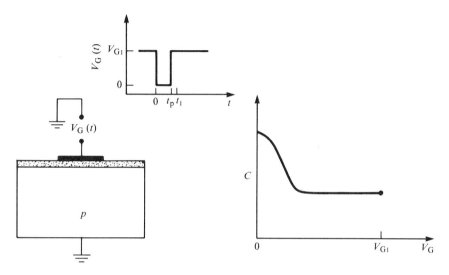

Fig. P1.4

1.5 Draw the C vs. V curve for the pn junction in series with a capacitor consisting of two metal plates shown in Fig. P1.5 for positive and negative V. $C(pn$ junction at zero bias) $= C$(metal capacitor).

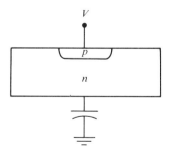

Fig. P1.5

1.6 Derive eq. (1.62).

1.7 The surface generation rate is given by eq. (1.79). For c_{ns}, c_{ps}, and D_{it} constant—i.e., not a function of energy—show that

(a) for $p_s\sqrt{\beta} + n_s/\sqrt{\beta} < 2n_i$

$$G_s = \sqrt{\alpha}kTD_{it}(n_i^2 - p_sn_s)\left\{\frac{\text{arcos}[(p_s\sqrt{\beta} + n_s/\sqrt{\beta})/2n_i]}{n_i\sqrt{1 - [(p_s\sqrt{\beta} + n_s/\sqrt{\beta})/2n_i]^2}}\right\}$$

(b) for $p_s\sqrt{\beta} + n_s/\sqrt{\beta} \geq 2n_i$

$$G_s = \sqrt{\alpha}kTD_{it}(n_i^2 - p_sn_s)\left\{\frac{\text{arcosh}[(p_s\sqrt{\beta} + n_s/\sqrt{\beta})/2n_i]}{n_i\sqrt{[(p_s\sqrt{\beta} + n_s/\sqrt{\beta})/2n_i]^2 - 1}}\right\}$$

where $\alpha = c_{ps}c_{ns}$ and $\beta = c_{ps}/c_{ns}$.
Then show that for $p_s = n_s = 0$

$$G_s = (\pi/2)\sqrt{c_{ps}c_{ns}}kTD_{it}n_i$$

1.8 The reverse-bias current of an n^+p junction is given by $I_r = qn_iAW/\tau_g$, and the capacitance is given by $C = K_s\varepsilon_0 A/W$, where $W = [2K_s\varepsilon_0(V_{bi} + V)/qN_A]^{1/2}$ assuming that the space-charge region stretches only into the lowly doped p-side.
The diode in Fig. P1.8 is reverse-biased to voltage V_1 and then open-circuited. Find the time constant, τ, that determines the diode voltage relaxing from V_1 to zero volts. Express the results in the form $V(t) = V_1 \exp(-t/\tau)$ and use $W = [2K_s\varepsilon_0 V/qN_A]^{1/2}$ for simplicity. Hint: $I_r = -C \, dV/dt$.

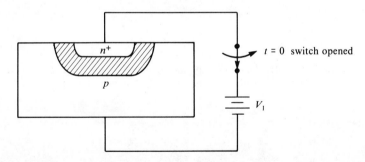

Fig. P1.8

2 / Material and Device Characterization

2.1 LIFETIME CHARACTERIZATION

2.1.1 Introduction

The MOS capacitor is an exceedingly useful device for characterizing the oxide, the semiconductor, and the fabrication process. It was shown in Volume IV[1] how the oxide thickness, the oxide charge, the interface-state density, and, to some extent, the doping concentration can be measured with the **equilibrium** device. It is for this reason that MOS-C's are found on many test structures. These can be either "stand-alone" test structures, where in the extreme an entire wafer is covered with nothing but test structures, or "drop-in" test structures in regular production wafers, where they take the place of a regular integrated circuit or more frequently are placed within the scribe lines between the circuits.

The **nonequilibrium** or **deep-depletion** MOS-C is also used as a test device to measure nonequilibrium properties, such as the generation and recombination lifetime as well as the surface generation and recombination velocity.

In the first part of this chapter, we discuss several methods of extracting generation-recombination parameters. One important reason for devoting so much space to this device is that, in contrast to almost all other semiconductor devices, which are characterized by their current-voltage behavior, deep-depletion MOS devices are characterized by their charge-voltage or charge-time behavior. This brings up some interesting concepts that are not covered by the more conventional device theories. These should be part of a general semiconductor education, because they can lead to new insights and new discoveries.

We give a qualitative discussion of the capacitance-time (C-t) transient response and then develop the appropriate equations for the pulsed gate voltage transient capacitance technique. This is the most popular generation lifetime extraction method in use today. Next we treat the linear-sweep method. Then we introduce the gate-controlled diode and its use as a test structure for measuring the generation lifetime and the surface generation velocity. The chapter is concluded by a discussion of doping concentration profile measurements using *pn* junction and MOS capacitor capacitance-voltage data.

2.1.2 The Pulsed Gate Voltage Technique

In the **pulsed** gate voltage technique, a voltage pulse is applied to the MOS-C to drive it into deep depletion. It may originally be biased in accumulation, depletion, or even inversion. We assume that prior to the depleting gate voltage application the device is in equilibrium. We illustrate the technique in Fig. 2.1. Here the MOS-C is biased in accumulation and then a depleting voltage step is applied, driving it from point A to B. Thermal generation will return it to equilibrium, shown by the path B to C. On the C-V_G' figure, where the gate voltage is constant, this takes place along a vertical line. On the C-t diagram, the return to equilibrium is typically as shown in Fig. 2.1b. The various capacitances are determined by oxide thickness, semiconductor doping, and gate voltage. The recovery time, t_F, is determined by the thermal ehp generation properties of the bulk semiconductor and by the oxide/semiconductor interface.

2.1.2.1 The Generation Sources

When the depleting voltage step or pulse is applied, the majority carriers are repelled over the depth of the depleted scr. This occurs instantaneously on the time scale of typical C-t responses, which last on the order of seconds or minutes. We showed earlier that times on the order of 10^{-10} s are typical. Consequently, the capacitance decreases very quickly. In fact, it is the measurement instrument—typically a capacitance meter—that is the time-limiting element during the capacitance decrease.

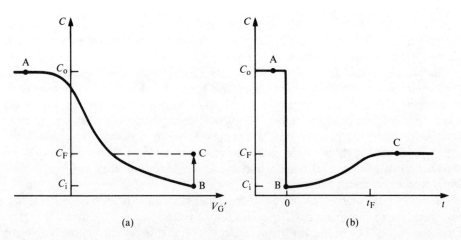

Fig. 2.1 Deep-depletion MOS-C characteristics: (a) the C-V_G' curve; (b) the C-t transient. The device is pulsed from A to B and then relaxes to C through thermal generation of electron-hole pairs.

Once the device is in deep depletion, it will attempt to revert to the equilibrium state through the thermal generation of ehp. It is important that there be no other sources of minority carriers during the measurement. There should not be any *pn* junctions nearby capable of injecting minority carriers into the MOS-C. For example, if the measurement is made on a MOSFET with source and drain connected to the substrate, then both the source and drain inject minority carriers and the *C-t* decay time will be very short. It becomes a measure of the injection efficiency of the source and drain, but not of the generation parameters of the device. By similar arguments, it should be evident that the measurement must be performed in the dark. Otherwise, photon-generated ehp will contribute to the capacitor discharge and again an erroneous reading will be obtained.

The thermal generation components that participate in the capacitance discharge are shown in Fig. 2.2: component (1) is the bulk scr generation, characterized by the generation lifetime τ_g; component (2) is the lateral surface scr generation, characterized by the surface generation velocity s_0; component (3) is the scr surface generation under the gate, characterized by s; component (4) is the quasineutral bulk generation component, characterized by the minority-carrier diffusion length L_n; and component (5) is the surface generation component at the back of the substrate, described by yet another surface generation velocity s_1.

The semiconductor/oxide interface ehp generation is divided into the two components (2) and (3) in Fig. 2.2. The lateral portion of the surface scr beyond the inversion layer is always depleted of minority carriers. In contrast, the area under the gate is depleted only at the beginning of the capacitance-time transient. For $t > 0$, the inversion layer forms. As shown in Section 1.2.4, ehp generation is maximum for a depleted surface and diminishes as an inversion layer forms. Surface generation is identical for the two areas at $t = 0$. When the inversion layer forms in the gate area for $t > 0$, surface generation decreases under the gate, and $s < s_0$.

The considerations for surface generation hold when the MOS-C is pulsed from accumulation into deep depletion. The area under the gate is already inverted at $t = 0$ when the device is initially biased in inversion and then pulsed into deep depletion. The two generation components are never equal in that case, even at $t = 0$. Pulsing from inversion instead of from accumulation is commonly used when surface generation is to be reduced as much as possible.

Generation components (4) and (5) need some explanation. The delta-depletion approximation assumes the scr to end abruptly at $x = W$, where both majority- and minority-carrier concentrations rise abruptly from zero to their equilibrium values. That, of course, cannot be the case in reality, where both concentrations rise somewhat gradually, and the minority concentration rises from essentially zero in the scr to its equilibrium value over a distance determined by the diffusion length. This was discussed in Volume II,[2] where for forward-biased *pn* junctions, the excess minority carriers decay to their equilibrium value over a distance of the minority-carrier diffusion length. Under reverse-bias conditions, they rise to their equilibrium value over the same distance.

The minority carriers in a deep-depletion MOS-C will behave in exactly the same way, because they are indifferent to the manner in which the scr is formed. For a

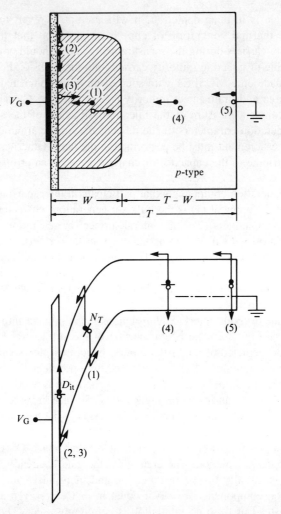

Fig. 2.2 Space-charge region (scr) and quasineutral region generation components of a deep-depletion MOS-C.

quasineutral bulk width, T-W, less than the minority-carrier diffusion length, the non-equilibrium state will persist all the way to the back contact, and surface generation at that contact will also contribute thermally generated ehp. This component is characterized by the surface generation velocity s_1. Its magnitude can be varied by device design. If the back contact is a p-semiconductor/metal contact, its surface generation velocity will be very high. If, however, a p-p^+ semiconductor/metal contact is formed, it has low s_1, because the low-high p-p^+ contact represents a barrier for minority carriers. It should be mentioned that while the back ohmic contact can contribute ehp by virtue of surface generation, it cannot inject minority carriers. Minority-carrier injection can be done only by a *pn* junction, not by an ohmic contact.

2.1.2.2 The Capacitance-Time Transient

The expression for the deep-depletion MOS-C was developed in Section 1.1.6. The relevant expression for the capacitance as a function of gate voltage and inversion charge is eq. (1.54), repeated here as

$$C = C_o/[1 + 2(V_G' + Q_N/C_o)/V_0]^{1/2} \tag{2.1}$$

Solving eq. (2.1) for V_G' and differentiating with respect to time gives

$$\boxed{dV_G/dt = -(1/C_o)\,dQ_N/dt - (qK_s\varepsilon_0 N_B/C^3)\,dC/dt} \tag{2.2}$$

where we let $dV_{FB}/dt = 0$.

Eq. (2.2) is an important equation relating gate voltage rate of change with time to inversion charge and capacitance rate of change with time.

For the **pulsed** capacitor case, V_G is constant after it is applied, or $dV_G/dt = 0$, and eq. (2.2) solved for dQ_N/dt becomes

$$dQ_N/dt = -(qK_s\varepsilon_0 C_o N_B/C^3)\,dC/dt \tag{2.3}$$

Here, dQ_N/dt stands for the thermal generation components in Fig. 2.2, which can be written as

$$dQ_N/dt = -q\int_0^W G_{scr}\,dx - q\int_W^{T-W} G_{qn}\,dx \tag{2.4}$$

Eq. (2.4) includes all five generation components, and a complete solution requires a numerical analysis. However, very reasonable approximations retain physical insight and allow the experimental C-t data to be used to extract device and material parameters.

For simplicity we will first develop the pulsed MOS-C theory by considering bulk scr generation only. This will demonstrate the main concepts but keep the analysis simple. Later we will add the other components. Eq. (2.4) becomes

$$dQ_N/dt(\text{bulk scr}) = -q\int_{W_F}^W G_{scr}\,dx = -q\int_{W_F}^W (n_i/\tau_g)\,dx \tag{2.5}$$

for scr bulk generation only. Note the change in the integration limits. The upper limit is the initial deep-depletion scr width W, and the lower limit is the final width W_F. W_F is used because at the end of the C-t transient the scr width is W_F, not zero. Eq. (2.5) is an approximation. A more exact analysis should substitute eq. (1.63) instead of (n_i/τ_g) for the generation rate. That would make the problem a computer problem, because p and n are not known as functions of time.

Integration of eq. (2.5) gives

$$dQ_N/dt\,(\text{bulk scr}) = -qn_i(W - W_F)/\tau_g \tag{2.6}$$

This expression was first proposed by Zerbst.[3] It is correct in the limit of $W \to W_F$ where $dQ_n/dt \to 0$. However, at the onset of deep depletion it assumes the generation width to be only $W - W_F$, not W as might at first seem appropriate. This may seem somewhat arbitrary but is actually quite realistic. Let us examine it a little more closely.

The band diagram of a deep-depletion MOS-C is shown in Fig. 2.3a. The bulk scr generation rate with the generation width of W is represented by the box-shaped generation function in Fig. 2.3b. Now we know that even at $t = 0^+$, immediately after the depleting voltage pulse is applied, the scr is not entirely depleted of mobile carriers. Towards the edge of the scr at $x = W$, the carriers have a smeared-out tail, causing the active generation width to be less than W. Furthermore, as the inversion layer forms, the scr region near the surface becomes inverted, and generation in that part of the scr diminishes too. Hence, the actual generation width is less than W and has roughly the shape shown in Fig. 2.3c. The exact shape of the generation width is difficult to determine, but by using $(W - W_F)$ instead of W, a more realistic generation width ensues and simple solutions are obtained that agree well with experiment.

The scr width is related to the MOS-C capacitance through

$$W = K_s\varepsilon_0(C_o - C)/C_o C \tag{2.7}$$

The expression relating the generation rate and the capacitance transient is obtained by combining eqs. (2.3), (2.6), and (2.7) into

$$n_i(C_F/C - 1)/C_F\tau_g = (C_o N_B/C^3)\,dC/dt \tag{2.8}$$

This is the chief equation that relates the capacitance to the bulk scr generation rate. To bring this equation into a form that relates C and t directly, it is necessary to integrate it. The lower integration limits are $t = 0$ and $C = C_i$, the initial capacitance at $t = 0$, immediately after the voltage pulse is applied. The upper limits are t and C. Performing the integration gives the equation

$$\ln\frac{(C_F/C_i - 1)}{(C_F/C - 1)} + \frac{C_F}{C_i} - \frac{C_F}{C} = \frac{C_F n_i t}{C_o N_B \tau_g} \tag{2.9}$$

Eq. (2.9) is **the** equation used to calculate the transient C-t response.

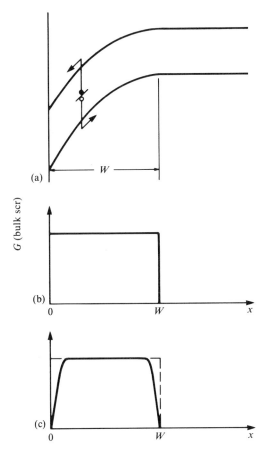

Fig. 2.3 The scr bulk generation is to first order the box-shaped distribution shown in (b), representing the scr width (W) shown in (a). The more realistic distribution shown in (c) allows for the inversion-layer thickness and the majority-carrier transition at the edge of the scr.

A discrepancy is always observed when the C-t transient described by eq. (2.9) is compared with experimental data. This discrepancy is the result of neglecting the surface and quasineutral bulk generation components. The two surface generation rates are

$$G_{scr}(2) = n_i s_0 A_s / A_G \qquad (2.10a)$$

$$G_{scr}(3) = n_i s \qquad (2.10b)$$

The surface term (2) is modified to account for the fact that it is active only over the surface area of the lateral part of the scr, A_s, normalized by the gate area A_G.

If we assume a symmetrical scr, in the sense that its lateral width is identical to its depth into the substrate, then we find the area of the lateral scr to be $A_s = 2\pi r(W - W_F)$ and the ratio $A_s/A_G = 2(W - W_F)/r$, where the gate area is taken as $A_G = \pi r^2$, with r being the radius of the circular gate. The total scr generation rate becomes

$$dQ_N/dt(\text{scr}) = -qn_i(W - W_F)(1/\tau_g + 2s_0/r) - qn_is$$

$$= -qn_i(W - W_F)/\tau_g' - qn_is \tag{2.11}$$

where $\tau_g' = \tau_g/(1 + 2s_0\tau_g/r)$ is an effective generation lifetime incorporating both scr bulk and lateral scr surface generation.

The quasineutral bulk generation rate is a rather complicated expression, when both the quasineutral bulk and the back surface generation components are considered. Both are to first order independent of W. For that reason we will simplify the analysis here by not including the detailed expressions. Instead we will include both components in the second term in eq. (2.11), which is also independent of W. This allows us to write the dQ_N/dt expressions as the two simple terms

$$\boxed{dQ_N/dt = -qn_i(W - W_F)/\tau_g' - qn_is'} \tag{2.12}$$

The first term includes all W-dependent generation components, and the second term accounts for all W-independent ones. The effective surface generation velocity s' includes, then, the surface generation under the gate as well as both quasineutral bulk generation components. It is definitely not the surface generation velocity alone as is frequently stated in the published literature. For a more detailed discussion, with all equations shown in their full glory, the reader is referred to Ref. [4].

With eq. (2.12) instead of eq. (2.6) substituted into eq. (2.3), we find eq. (2.8) replaced by

$$n_i(C_F/C - 1)/C_F\tau_g' + n_is'/K_s\varepsilon_0 = (C_oN_B/C^3)\,dC/dt \tag{2.13}$$

and eq. (2.9) becomes

$$\boxed{(1 - \gamma)\ln\frac{(C_F/C_i - 1 + \gamma)}{(C_F/C - 1 + \gamma)} + \frac{C_F}{C_i} - \frac{C_F}{C} = \frac{C_Fn_it}{C_oN_B\tau_g'}} \tag{2.14}$$

where $\gamma = C_Fs'\tau_g'/K_s\varepsilon_0$. Eq. (2.14) has been shown to be in excellent agreement with experimental data, as shown in Fig. 2.4.

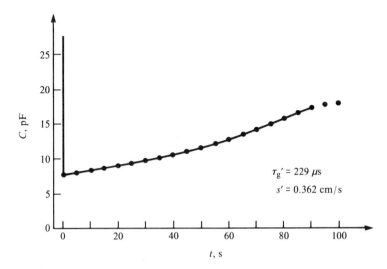

Fig. 2.4 Experimental C-t curve (shown by data points). The solid line is calculated from eq. (2.14), with $N_A = 4.8 \times 10^{14}$ cm^{-3}, $x_o = 1020$ Å, $A = 3.42 \times 10^{-3}$ cm^2, and $T = 300$ K. Reprinted after Ref. [4] with permission.

    The MOS pulsed C-t technique has found wide acceptance because it is easily implemented with commercially available capacitance meters, a dc power supply, a microswitch or very-low-frequency function generator, and an X-Y recorder. No fast-response circuitry is required. For short C-t response times, the output is displayed on an oscilloscope instead of an X-Y recorder.

    The measured C-t transient times are usually quite long, with times of tens of seconds to minutes being common. The reason for these relatively long times can be found from eq. (2.14). We know that as $t \rightarrow t_F$ the capacitance $C \rightarrow C_F$. Letting $C = C_F$ in eq. (2.14) and using typical values of $C_F/C_i \approx 2.5$ and $\gamma \approx 3$, we find

$$t_F \approx (N_B/n_i)\,(C_o/C_F)\tau_g' \tag{2.15}$$

This equation brings out a very important feature of the pulsed MOS-C. This is the magnification factor built into the measurement. First, there is the ratio of doping concentration to intrinsic carrier concentration, N_B/n_i. This is generally in the 10^4 to 10^6 range. Then, there is the additional capacitance ratio C_o/C_F. This is much smaller, with 2 to 5 being typical. All of this leads to

$$t_F \approx (10^4 - 10^6)\tau_g' \tag{2.16}$$

Values of τ_g' range over many orders of magnitude, but representative values for high-quality silicon devices lie in the range of 10^{-5} to 10^{-3} s. Eq. (2.16) predicts the actual

C-t transient time as 1 to 1000 s. These long times point out the great virtue of the pulsed MOS-C lifetime measurement technique. To measure lifetimes in the microsecond range, it is only necessary to measure capacitance transient or recovery times on the order of seconds. The circuit implementation needed to do this is very simple, which accounts for the method's popularity.

2.1.2.3 Lifetime Extraction

Now that we have developed the appropriate expressions for the *C-t* response, we will discuss a method for interpreting the experimental *C-t* data and extracting generation parameters. Using the identity $(1/C^3)\,dC/dt = -[d(1/C)^2/dt]/2$ allows eq. (2.13) to be written as

$$-d(C_o/C)^2/dt = (2n_i C_o/N_B C_F \tau_g')(C_F/C - 1) + 2n_i C_o s'/K_s \varepsilon_0 N_B \qquad (2.17)$$

This equation is the basis of the well-known *Zerbst Plot*, shown in Fig. 2.5, named after M. Zerbst, who first proposed it.[3] It is a plot of $-d(C_o/C)^2/dt$ vs. $(C_F/C - 1)$. The slope of such a plot is given by $2n_i C_o/N_B C_F \tau_g'$, and its intercept on the vertical axis is $2n_i C_o s'/K_s \varepsilon_0 N_B$. Clearly the slope is a measure of the scr generation parameters

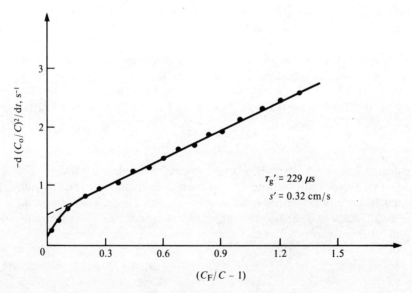

Fig. 2.5 *Zerbst Plot* of the *C-t* transient of Fig. 2.4. From the slope, $\tau_g' = 2n_i C_o/[N_B C_F \times$ slope], and from the intercept, $s' = (K_s \varepsilon_0 N_B \times$ intercept$)/2n_i C_o$.

τ_g and s_0, while the intercept is related to the scr width-independent generation parameters s, L_n, and s_1. We like to point out that s' obtained from the intercept should not be interpreted as **the** surface generation velocity as is sometimes done. First of all, it includes the quasineutral bulk generation parameters. Secondly, a more detailed analysis of the C-t response shows that the inherent inaccuracy of the $W - W_\mathrm{F}$ approximation for the generation width can lead to a nonzero Zerbst plot intercept even if $s' = 0$.[5]

It is instructive to examine the two axes of the *Zerbst Plot* in more detail for a better insight into the physical meaning of such a plot. If we use the identity that leads to eq. (2.17), we find from eq. (2.3)

$$-\mathrm{d}(C_\mathrm{o}/C)^2/\mathrm{d}t \sim \mathrm{d}Q_\mathrm{N}/\mathrm{d}t \tag{2.18}$$

The *Zerbst Plot* vertical axis is proportional to the total ehp carrier generation rate or the generation current.

From eq. (2.7) we find

$$(C_\mathrm{F}/C - 1) \sim (W - W_\mathrm{F}) \tag{2.19}$$

i.e., the horizontal axis is proportional to the scr generation width. So we find the rather complicated *Zerbst Plot* to be nothing more than a plot of generation current vs. scr generation width. The current can, of course, be measured directly. The generation width cannot be measured directly and is most easily extracted from capacitance data. Recent implementations of this generation lifetime measuring technique have utilized computers to extract the relevant data from the experimental C-t curve directly.

There is a variation on the "Zerbst" technique in which the current and capacitance are measured directly and plotted against one another.[6] No differentiation of the experimental data is required, but one must measure both current and capacitance. It is one of many variations that have been developed over the years. For a detailed review of the many lifetime extraction methods based in one form or another on the deep-depletion MOS-C, the reader is referred to Ref. [4].

2.1.3 The Linear-Sweep Technique

2.1.3.1 Introduction

The two most popular techniques for generation parameter measurement are the pulsed MOS-C method, discussed in Section 2.1.2, and the linear-sweep method.[7] The pulsed method was historically the first, which accounts for some of its popularity. Another reason is the availability of commercial instruments and software. The availability of test equipment is a very important factor in the use of characterization techniques. A method based on someone's home-built equipment finds use in some selected research laboratories, but is never fully accepted until commercial equipment is widely available for its use.

The linear-sweep technique can be implemented with conventional capacitance meters and has some advantages over the pulsed method. For example, for a complete characterization of the C-t transient in the pulsed method, it is necessary to wait for the entire response. For high-quality devices, that may be many minutes. In fact, extremely long decay times approach one hour. Some relief can be found by making the measurement at elevated temperatures. But care must be taken, because the quasineutral bulk generation components become dominant at temperatures of around 60 to 80 °C. However, temperatures around 40 °C are suitable and decrease the measurement time appreciably. The linear-sweep technique has the potential of reduced measurement time — a decided plus, when many devices need to be characterized.

2.1.3.2 The Capacitance-Voltage Transient

Consider a linearly varying voltage applied to the gate of an MOS-C of a polarity to drive the device into depletion. We know from Volume IV[1] and earlier discussions of the equilibrium MOS-C that for sufficiently slow sweep rates, the equilibrium C-V_G curve is traced out. We also know that when the sweep rate is so high that it can be considered a voltage step, the pulsed MOS-C deep-depletion curve is obtained. For intermediate sweep rates, an intermediate trace is swept out, shown in Fig. 2.6. It lies between the "no inversion layer" deep depletion and the equilibrium curves.

The interesting point about this curve is its saturation characteristic. It comes about for the following reason. Assume that the voltage sweeps from point A in Fig. 2.6 to the right. For voltages more positive than V_B, the device enters deep depletion and the scr width widens beyond W_F, with the capacitance being driven below C_F. Electron-hole pair generation will attempt to re-establish equilibrium. However, the gate voltage

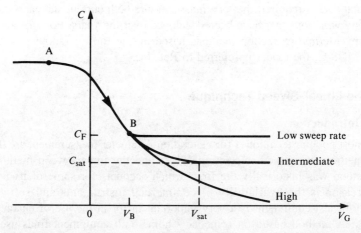

Fig. 2.6 Inversion, saturation, and deep-depletion curves for an MOS-C.

continues to drive the device into deep depletion, increasing W further. This, in turn, enhances the generation rate because it is proportional to W. At the voltage V_{sat}, the attempt by the linearly varying gate voltage to drive the device into deeper depletion will be exactly balanced by the generation rate holding it at that capacitance. The capacitance-voltage curve is now saturated at C_{sat} and will remain there as long as the linear sweep persists. For other sweep rates, the C-V_G curves will saturate at other C_{sat} values. There will always be saturation, unless the sweep rate is so high that the device will be driven along the "high sweep rate" true deep-depletion curve.

For $dV_G/dt = R$, a constant sweep rate, eq. (2.2) becomes

$$dQ_N/dt = -(qK_s\varepsilon_0 C_o N_B/C^3)\,dC/dt - C_o R \qquad (2.20)$$

Using the generation rate expression, eq. (2.12), leads to

$$-d(C_o/C)^2/dt = 2[qK_s\varepsilon_0 n_i(C_F/C - 1)/C_F C_o \tau_g{}' + qn_i s'/C_o - R]/V_0 \quad (2.21)$$

From Fig. 2.6 we see that when the device enters the saturation regime, the capacitance is given by C_{sat} and no longer changes with either voltage or time. Hence the left side of eq. (2.21) becomes zero. Solving for R gives

$$\boxed{R = qK_s\varepsilon_0 n_i(C_F/C_{sat} - 1)/C_F C_o \tau_g{}' + qn_i s'/C_o} \qquad (2.22)$$

2.1.3.3   Lifetime Extraction

Eq. (2.22) gives a direct relationship between the linear sweep rate, R, and the generation parameters $\tau_g{}'$ and s'. In the experiment, a series of C-V_G curves at different linear sweep rates are taken. The C_{sat} values are taken from these curves, and a plot of R vs. $(C_F/C_{sat} - 1)$ yields a straight line of slope $K_s\varepsilon_0 n_i/C_F C_o \tau_g{}'$ and intercept $qn_i s'/C_o$. Similar to the *Zerbst Plot*, the effective generation lifetime is obtained from the slope, and the effective surface generation velocity from the intercept.

It may appear from eq. (2.22) that a single value of R and $(C_F/C - 1)$ are sufficient to determine the two generation parameters. This is incorrect, because the R vs. $(C_F/C - 1)$ plot does not pass through the origin. Hence, a slope of that plot is not the same as the slope of a line from the origin to any one point on the line. This is important to keep in mind. It is generally more accurate to determine a device parameter from the slope of several data points than it is to use a single datum point. In many cases the answer is indeed very different, especially if the line containing the data points does not pass through the origin.

Experimental data for the linear-sweep method are shown in Fig. 2.7 for the device whose *Zerbst Plot* is shown in Fig. 2.5. Note the good agreement between the experimentally determined values for the effective generation lifetime and the effective

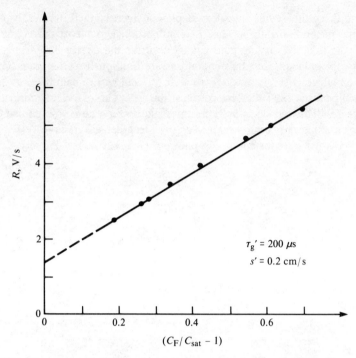

Fig. 2.7 Linear ramp plot for the device whose *Zerbst Plot* is shown in Fig. 2.5. From the slope, $\tau_g' = qK_s\varepsilon_0 n_i/(C_F C_o \times \text{slope})$, and from the intercept, $s' = (\text{intercept} \times C_o)/qn_i$.

surface generation velocity. Agreement within approximately 10% between different measurement techniques is considered to be good agreement.

2.1.3.4 A Comparison

A comparison between the pulsed and the linear-sweep methods is appropriate, since they are the two most commonly used techniques. The pulsed method was historically the first of the two and, as such, has found wide acceptance. Equipment is commercially available and a large body of literature has been published. It is easily implemented using standard laboratory components. Its two main disadvantages are (i) the long time that it takes to acquire the C-t curve for high-lifetime devices, and (ii) the differentiation that is required in the data analysis. The latter is no longer a problem for computer-equipped systems. The long data-acquisition time can be alleviated to some extent by making measurements at elevated temperatures. However, the temperature cannot be too high, or the quasineutral bulk generation components become dominant. A temperature around 40 °C is suitable. A further point to be considered is the necessity of measuring the doping concentration of the device. If that concentration is nonuniform, as in ion-implanted samples, for example, then the theory needs to be modified to take that into account. Such a modified theory is found in Ref. [8].

The linear-sweep technique does not require the acquisition of an entire C-t curve, nor the differentiation of the experimental data. It does, however, require multiple saturating C-V_G curves. For those devices with high lifetimes and consequent long C-t transients, it is found that very slow sweep rates are required with resultant long data-acquisition times. The use of a feedback circuit[9] reduces the data-acquisition time. The capacitance is preset to a certain value, and the linear sweep rate adjusts itself through feedback to maintain this preset capacitance value. Recently, a computer approach to the linear-sweep technique has been developed.[10]

Both of these methods, as well as that of Ref. [6], have found wide applications. The choice of a particular technique is largely determined by the experience and preference of the experimenter and the availability of commercial instrumentation. We will no doubt see further variations and automation of the methods. They are clearly among the more powerful measurement methods for device as well as process characterization. Frequently, a complete analysis of the experimental data is not necessary, and only the C-t data of devices made on different days or with different processes are compared. Significant variances are indicative of process problems.

2.1.4 The Gate-Controlled Diode

2.1.4.1 Introduction

The MOS-C is in deep depletion only when the gate voltage changes with time, and the more rapid the change, the more the deviation from equilibrium. The *gate-controlled diode* is in nonequilibrium at **steady-state** voltages. It can be viewed either as a diode with an adjacent gate or as an MOS capacitor with an adjacent diode. It is a very important device for several reasons. It links the MOS-C and the *pn*-junction diode. It is the building block of the MOSFET and can be thought of as a one-element charge-coupled device. But perhaps most important from an operational viewpoint is its use as a test device to extract several generation parameters.[11] We will first treat it as an MOS-C that can be in deep depletion for **dc** gate voltages. This state is impossible for a conventional MOS-C because the oxide allows no dc current flow.

The three-terminal gate-controlled diode structure is shown in Fig. 2.8. It consists of a p substrate, an n^+ region, a circular gate surrounding the n^+ region, and a circular guard ring surrounding the gate. In some designs the gate is located in the center with a circular n^+ region surrounding it. The n^+p junction and the gate make up the gate-controlled diode, and the gate should overlap the n^+ region slightly. There should be no gaps between them, because potential barriers can develop in such gaps. The guard ring is preferred, but is not always used. It should be close to the gate and biased to keep the semiconductor surface under it in accumulation in order to isolate the gate-controlled diode from the rest of the wafer. For example, moderately doped and oxidized p-type silicon substrates are easily inverted by the positive fixed oxide charge

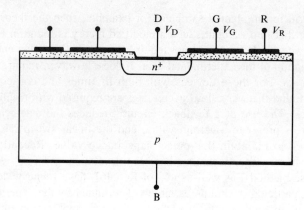

Fig. 2.8 Gate-controlled diode. D is the n^+p junction diode, G is the gate, R is the guard ring, and B is the substrate.

that is always present in thermally grown SiO_2. Such an inversion layer is capable of coupling adjacent devices. The guard ring prevents this. Devices can also be decoupled by doping the semiconductor between the devices more heavily.

2.1.4.2 Capacitance-Voltage Characteristics

A part of the symmetrical structure of Fig. 2.8, without the guard ring, is repeated in Fig. 2.9 together with its capacitance-voltage curves. We consider first the high-frequency capacitance behavior of the MOS-C with the diode zero biased. For negative gate voltages, the surface under the gate is accumulated and the capacitance is the oxide capacitance. For small positive gate voltages, the surface is driven into depletion. For gate voltages less than those necessary to cause inversion, the device is no different than a normal MOS-C without the diode.

When the gate voltage is increased from zero toward positive values, the surface enters inversion when $\phi_s = 2\phi_F$. Beyond that gate voltage, the surface potential increases only a small amount, but the inversion charge increases drastically, as discussed in Section 1.1.5. The zero-biased diode cannot alter the surface potential, but it does provide a source of, and sink for, minority electrons. What effect does this minority carrier sink and source have?

In an MOS-C, the inversion charge is unable to respond to the conventionally used 1-MHz ac probe signal, because minority carriers cannot be generated at such a high rate. The C-V_G' curve is referred to as the *high-frequency* (HF) curve. In the gate-controlled diode, the diode adjacent to the MOS-C is a source/sink of minority carriers. On the positive swing of the ac probe voltage during the capacitance measurement, the gate voltage demands an increased inversion charge. The diode supplies all the required minority electrons even at a 1-MHz frequency, and the *low-frequency* (LF) curve is measured, as shown in Fig. 2.9b. Just how this comes about needs an explanation.

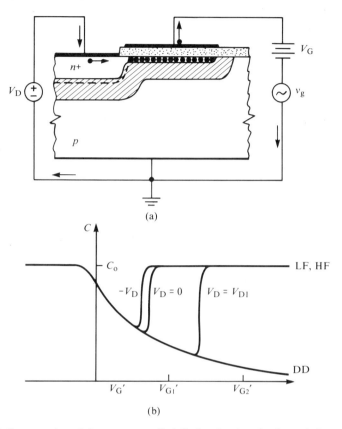

Fig. 2.9 (a) Cross section of the gate-controlled diode, showing the flow of electrons from the gate into the inversion layer; (b) C-V_G' curves for various diode voltages.

Let us look at the effect of the diode in some detail using Fig. 2.9a. The MOS-C is biased into inversion at the dc voltage V_G with a small ac voltage, v_g, superimposed. Now consider the situation when the ac voltage is zero and on its positive voltage swing. The total gate voltage increases from V_G to $V_G + v_g$. Clearly, charge considerations require the inversion charge to increase, as shown in Fig. 1.8. The electrons in the grounded n^+ region sense a slightly higher surface potential under the gate and flow in to furnish the necessary inversion charge. But how can electrons leave the n^+ region? As they leave they are replaced by electrons from the gate that flow through the power supplies and the ohmic contact. This is shown by the electron leaving the gate and by the arrows along the leads in Fig. 2.9. The end result is more electrons in the inversion layer, more positive charge on the gate, as required by charge-neutrality considerations, and no change in the electron concentration in the n^+ layer. Neither the positive gate charge nor the negative scr bulk charge is shown in Fig. 2.9. On the negative ac voltage swing, the process reverses and the electrons flow back onto the gate.

The n^+ region serves as a conduit in this process and always remains at zero bias. One can think of the n^+ region as a probe connecting the inversion layer to the outside world. This is exploited in a MOSFET, where the n^+ regions serve as the connecting link between the majority carriers in the source and drain and the minority carriers in the channel. Once the carriers are majority carriers, they can easily flow into and out of the semiconductor through its ohmic contact. In a conventional MOS-C, this link is missing, and an inversion layer can form only by thermal generation and disappear only by recombination because it is isolated from its surroundings.

The onset of inversion is delayed when the n^+p junction is reverse biased. When the diode is biased to $+V_D$ and the surface potential under the gate reaches $2\phi_F$, the minority carriers that formed an inversion layer for zero diode voltage now flow into the diode because $V_D > 0$. A higher gate voltage is now required for heavy inversion to set in. The surface potential must attain a value of $2\phi_F + V_D$. This is shown in Fig. 2.9b by the $V_D = V_{D1}$ curve. Note that the capacitance increases again very rapidly, as it did for the zero-bias case, but at a higher gate voltage.

Further diode-voltage increases extend the deep-depletion (DD) curve by delaying the onset of inversion. The DD curve here is a dc curve, obtained under slowly varying dc gate voltages or even under true dc gate-voltage conditions. This is in contrast to the MOS-C, where the deep-depletion curve can be obtained only by rapidly varying the gate voltage. For diode **forward** bias, the onset of inversion occurs at lower gate voltages than for zero bias, because now inversion sets in at $\phi_s = 2\phi_F - V_D$. We show this by the $-V_D$ curve in Fig. 2.9b.

For a quantitative description of these qualitative concepts, we must look at the band diagrams in Fig. 2.10. In Fig. 2.10a we show a part of the gate-controlled diode, and in Fig. 2.10b we show the band diagram **at the surface** for $V_D = V_G' = 0$. The Fermi level in the n^+ region depends on the doping concentration there, and is taken as coincident with the conduction band. The semiconductor under the gate is in flatband. For gate voltage V_{G1}', shown in Fig. 2.9, the band diagrams are shown in Fig. 2.10c and d. Case (c) is for zero diode voltage with the surface inverted. Raising the diode voltage to V_{D1}, but leaving the gate voltage unchanged, gives the band diagram in Fig. 2.10d, with the surface now definitely in deep depletion. The Fermi level has split into its two quasi-Fermi levels in both the diode and the gate regions.

In the diode we see the Fermi level splitting to be equal to V_{D1}. In the gate region it is not so obvious. Grove and Fitzgerald,[11] in their original paper on the gate-controlled diode, found a solution by making two crucial assumptions for the semiconductor region under the gate: (i) the majority-carrier quasi-Fermi level of the substrate does not vary with distance from the bulk to the surface, and (ii) the minority-carrier quasi-Fermi level of the substrate is separated from the majority-carrier quasi-Fermi level by the applied diode voltage—i.e., $F_N = F_P + V_{D1}$. This approximation is shown in Fig. 2.10d and e. Leaving the diode voltage at V_{D1}, but increasing the gate voltage to V_{G2}' shown in Fig. 2.9b gives the band diagram in Fig. 2.10e with the surface now clearly inverted again.

Figure 2.10d shows the electron concentration at the surface under the gate to be essentially zero. This is because the electron quasi-Fermi level lies so far below the in-

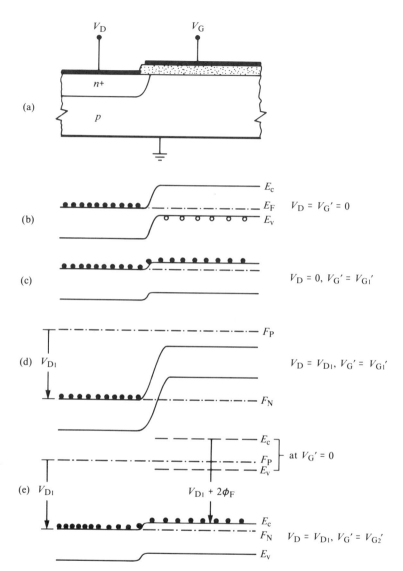

Fig. 2.10 (a) Partial cross section of the gate-controlled diode; (b) to (e) show the surface-band diagrams of the n^+p junction and the semiconductor under the gate for various diode and gate voltages.

trinsic level. According to eqs. (1.19) and (1.21), this results in a negligibly small n. We know, however, that a device in deep depletion will generate ehp. Some of those thermally generated electrons drift to the surface under the gate and subsequently flow into the n^+ region. So there must always be some electrons at the surface, and consequently F_N must lie higher than indicated in Fig. 2.10d. This has been addressed by Pierret.[12] For details, the interested reader is referred to that publication. We will see a little later how this influences interpretation of the gate-controlled diode current measurement.

As shown in Chapter 1, the semiconductor charge for the depletion/inversion regime is given by

$$Q_s = -\hat{U}_s(kT/q)K_s\varepsilon_0 F/L_D \qquad (2.23)$$

This equation still applies, but in light of the Grove-Fitzgerald assumptions the F-function simplifies to

$$F = \{\exp(U_F)[\exp(-U_s) + U_s - 1] + \exp[-(U_F + U_D)][\exp(U_s) - U_s - 1]\}^{1/2} \qquad (2.24)$$

using $U_{FP} = U_F$ and $U_{FN} = U_{FP} + U_D$, with $U_D = V_D/(kT/q)$. The capacitance is given by

$$C = C_o/[1 - C_o/(dQ_s/d\phi_s)] = C_o/[1 - (kT/q)C_o/(dQ_s/dU_s)] \qquad (2.25)$$

which is derived using eq. (1.51).

Although we are able to derive the capacitance expression, the C-$V_G{}'$ curves do not give much information and are not generally used. Being steady-state curves, they do not give generation or recombination parameters as the pulsed MOS-C does. They can, however, be used for carrier or doping concentration determination, as shown in Section 2.2. For now, we will turn to the current-voltage behavior of the gate-controlled diode, because it is more useful.

2.1.4.3   Current-Voltage Characteristics

The current-voltage characteristics of the gate-controlled diode have some unique properties, as far as extracting generation lifetimes and surface generation velocity are concerned. When the device is used for this purpose, it is better to treat it as a diode with a surrounding gate. The diode current is altered by the nearby gate. The function of the diode is to collect the current that is generated by the capacitor. The diode is biased at a constant voltage, and the gate voltage is varied. The main difference between the capacitance and the current measurements is the absence of the ac probing signal in the dc current measurements.

Let the diode be reverse-biased to V_{D1}. For negative gate voltage $-V_{G1}{}'$, the surface under the gate is accumulated and the junction scr is slightly pulled in at the surface, as shown in Fig. 2.11a. The measured current is the scr generated current, I_J, shown by the ehp in Fig. 2.11a and by point A in Fig. 2.11d. When the gate voltage is zero, the semiconductor is in flatband and the accumulation-induced scr width narrowing at the surface has disappeared. The scr width is now the same at the surface as in the bulk,

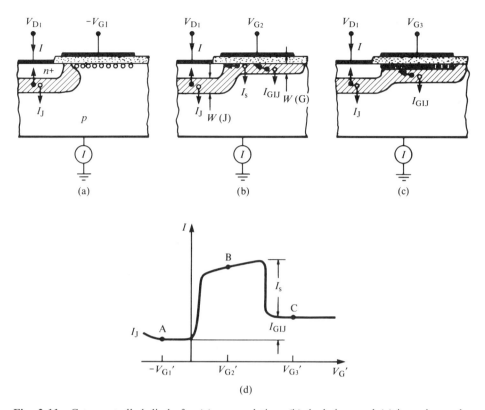

Fig. 2.11 Gate-controlled diode for (a) accumulation, (b) depletion, and (c) inversion under the gate; (d) shows the current, with points A, B, and C corresponding to (a), (b), and (c).

and the current is slightly increased as a result of the slightly larger generation volume. When the gate voltage is such that $\phi_s = V_{D1} + \phi_F$, the surface under the gate begins to deplete, and the current increases rapidly. This quite abrupt increase is due to surface generation current, I_s, and the gate-induced scr bulk current, I_{GIJ}, in Fig. 2.11b.

Once the surface is fully depleted, increasing the gate voltage leads initially to a more gradual current increase, because the scr width under the gate increases. Gate voltage V_{G2}' is characteristic of this part of the current-voltage curve. The surface potential lies in the range $V_{D1} + \phi_F \leq \phi_s < V_{D1} + 2\phi_F$. The generation regions are now shown in Fig. 2.11b to consist of three components: (i) the original diode scr, (ii) the gate-induced scr, and (iii) the depleted surface under the gate. The current is $I_J + I_s + I_{GIJ}$.

For a gate voltage where $\phi_s \geq V_{D1} + 2\phi_F$, the surface inverts and the gate-induced scr is pinned to its final value. Surface generation drops precipitously and generation component (iii) effectively disappears, as shown in Fig. 2.11c. Further gate-voltage increases beyond the inversion voltage, as for example V_{G3}' in Fig. 2.11c, give no fur-

ther current changes. This is also indicated in eq. (1.79), which shows surface generation to be at a maximum for small p_s and n_s values, as is the case for a depleted
surface. For the inverted surface, n_s is very high and the $p_s n_s$ product is no longer negligible. To first order, we assume that surface generation has become zero. The current
is now due to components (i) and (ii) and is shown by C in Fig. 2.11d and in cross section in Fig. 2.11c.

For a quantitative description, we make several assumptions. The first is a sufficiently high reverse bias for the mobile carriers to be negligibly small in the scr and at
the depleted surface. Then the bulk and surface generation rates are given by
eqs. (1.68) and (1.81):

$$G = n_i/\tau_g \quad \text{and} \quad G_s = n_i s_0 \tag{2.26}$$

The bulk scr generation current is $I_b = qG \times$ volume, and the surface component is
$I_s = qG_s \times$ area, where "volume" and "area" are the thermal generation volume and
area, respectively.

Using the same arguments leading to eq. (2.6), the three currents become

$$I_J = qn_i[W(J) - W_F(J)]A_J/\tau_g(J) \tag{2.27}$$

$$I_{GIJ} = qn_i[W(G) - W_F(G)]A_G/\tau_g(G) \tag{2.28}$$

$$I_s = qn_i s_0 A_G \tag{2.29}$$

where "J" and "G" stand for the n^+p junction and the gate, respectively. Note that, by
including the "W_F" term, the two scr currents approach zero as equilibrium is ap-
proached. No such term exists in the surface generation term. This is no particular
problem, since for the current measurements the device is always biased and current
must flow. This is in contrast to the pulsed MOS-C, for which the current decays
to zero during the C-t transient. In fact, for many measurements, the "W_F" terms are
neglected, and the currents are interpreted by

$$I_J = qn_i W(J)A_J/\tau_g(J) \quad \text{and} \quad I_{GIJ} = qn_i W(G)A_G/\tau_g(G) \tag{2.30}$$

To use the gate-controlled diode as a test structure, one must be able to measure or
calculate the various scr widths in order to extract the generation parameters. They can
be experimentally determined from capacitance measurements, but it is usually more
convenient to calculate them. From np junction theory, as discussed in Ref. [2], we
find for an n^+p junction, in which the n^+ region is much more heavily doped than the
p substrate,

$$W(J) = [2K_s\varepsilon_0(V_D + V_{bi})/qN_B]^{1/2} \tag{2.31a}$$

$$W_F(J) = [2K_s\varepsilon_0 V_{bi}/qN_B]^{1/2} \tag{2.31b}$$

with V_{bi} being the built-in or diffusion potential. For the gate-induced scr, we have for the deep-depletion case from eq. (1.40), with $Q_N = 0$:

$$W(G) = (K_s x_o/K_o)[(1 + 2V_G'/V_0)^{1/2} - 1] \qquad (2.32)$$

This condition applies to point B in Fig. 2.11d. For point C in heavy inversion, we use the arguments of Fig. 2.10e to write eq. (1.34) with $\phi_s = V_D + 2\phi_F$ as

$$W(G) = [2K_s\varepsilon_0(V_D + 2\phi_F)/qN_B]^{1/2} \qquad (2.33a)$$

$$W_F(G) = [2K_s\varepsilon_0 2\phi_F/qN_B]^{1/2} \qquad (2.33b)$$

Note the close relationship between eqs. (2.31) and (2.33). The only variation between them is the built-in voltage V_{bi} in the np junction and the Fermi potential $2\phi_F$ term in the gate-induced junction.

2.1.4.4   Lifetime Extraction

Figure 2.9 shows the C-V_G' behavior of a gate-controlled diode. It shows a rather gradual depletion followed by a quite abrupt inversion rise. When the surface depletes sufficiently for the majority-carrier concentration to drop below n_i, surface generation current should appear. This is indeed observed experimentally. There is a very sharp current rise followed by a more gentle increase as the scr under the gate widens. This is paralleled by a capacitance decrease in depletion. Then, as the inversion layer forms and the capacitance suddenly rises, the current drops quite abruptly as the surface generation diminishes.

The generation parameters are extracted from the current-voltage curve as

$$\tau_g(J) = qn_i[W(J) - W_F(J)]A_J/I_J \qquad (2.34)$$

$$\tau_g(G) = qn_i[W(G) - W_F(G)]A_G/I_{GIJ} \qquad (2.35)$$

$$s_0 = I_s/qn_i A_G \qquad (2.36)$$

The generation lifetimes under the diode and under the gate are determined separately, because they can be different. For example, it is possible that for an n^+p junction, the formation of the n^+ layer has some gettering properties. Gettering is a process whereby fast diffusing metallic impurities are removed from the substrate into a heavily doped region. If this process takes place, then $\tau_g(J) > \tau_g(G)$. On the other hand, it is also possible that the junction formation by ion implantation, for example, creates some damage in the junction region, in which case we would have $\tau_g(J) < \tau_g(G)$. It is for this reason that it is wise to calculate **both** generation lifetimes and not assume them to be identical.

The surface generation velocity calculated from eq. (2.36) lies typically in the 1 to 5 cm/s range for Si devices with well-annealed interfaces. Pierret[12] considered a nonconstant minority-carrier quasi-Fermi level along the surface under the gate. This corresponds to a weakly inverted surface, and s_0 so obtained is larger than that calculated from eq. (2.36). However, most of the published data have used eq. (2.36) without such corrections. Generation lifetimes for well-gettered Si devices lie in the 0.1 to 10 ms range.

For a measurement of the generation lifetime alone, it would appear that the pulsed MOS-C offers a simpler test structure. This is indeed the case, and the pulsed MOS-C is more frequently used. However, as shown by eq. (2.11), it does not allow for separation of bulk and surface scr generation. The gate-controlled diode does allow this separation. So whenever it is necessary to measure both surface and bulk generation parameters, the gate-controlled diode is the best device to use. It is frequently incorporated into test structures for this reason. The intercept of the pulsed MOS-C is sometimes used for a measure of the surface generation velocity. But, as we have pointed out, it does not give a valid surface generation velocity.

2.2 DOPING-CONCENTRATION PROFILING

2.2.1 Introduction

An examination of many semiconductor equations, including those of the pulsed MOS-C, shows the net doping concentration, N_B, playing an important role. Consequently it is essential to know N_B, especially for device-modeling purposes. N_B frequently varies with depth into the semiconductor, which rules out measurement of the doping concentration with a four-point probe, because the four-point probe gives an average value.

The final device frequently has a quite different doping concentration from that of the starting wafer. For example, repeated heat treatments during processing cause the dopant distribution to be nonuniform from the surface into the wafer. This can be caused by boron out-diffusion during oxidation cycles, leaving the surface with a concentration lower than that of the bulk. Other dopants, such as phosphorus, pile up at the surface during oxidation. In addition, ion implantation is used in many devices to control those device parameters that are dependent upon the doping concentration. The result of all these considerations is that the positional variation of N_B can be significant. The exact profile, however, is required to describe many MOS and bipolar characteristics accurately.

There are several techniques used for measuring doping profiles. In the spreading-resistance method,[13] the wafer is beveled by lapping it at a shallow angle. Two closely spaced probes are repeatedly stepped along the beveled surface, measuring the resistance between the probes. By employing standards of known resistivity, the spreading-resistance data are converted into doping-concentration profiles. An automated test system is commercially available, and the method is widely used for silicon devices. It does require a great deal of care, however, and a skilled operator. A related method is four-point probe/anodic oxidation measurement of the wafer. By repeatedly removing thin layers from the wafer by anodic oxidation and measuring the four-point probe resistivity each time, a doping-profile curve can be generated. Of course, the mobility of the semiconductor must be known. This technique is quite tedious, but has been successfully implemented by using anodic oxidation to remove well-controlled thin layers of the wafer.[14]

An entirely different method is secondary ion mass spectroscopy (SIMS). Here a small area of the wafer is sputtered away and the sputter-removed atoms are analyzed. By tuning the test system to a particular impurity such as boron, for example, the boron signal is monitored as a function of time. The sputtering time is proportional to depth into the wafer, assuming uniform sputtering rates. By measuring the depth of the sputtered hole and by using known doping-concentration standards, a concentration-depth profile is generated.[15] In contrast to the previous two methods, which rely on electrical measurements, in SIMS the total impurity concentration is measured, not just the electrically active concentration. The two may or may not be equal. All of the foregoing methods are destructive. The wafer needs to be beveled, etched, or have a hole sputtered into it.

Here we will discuss a fourth method — the capacitance-voltage method. The general principle of the C-V profiling technique is well understood[16] and has been implemented with pn junctions, Schottky barrier diodes, electrolyte-semiconductor junctions, MOS capacitors in the deep-depletion mode, and MOSFET's.

2.2.2   A Mathematical Description

The experimental arrangement is shown in Fig. 2.12. Although our derivation is for an MOS-C, very similar considerations apply to pn and Schottky barrier junction devices.

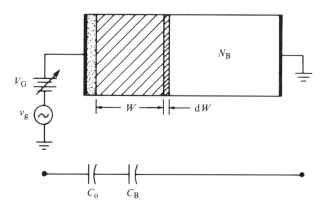

Fig. 2.12   Schematic of an MOS-C during capacitance measurements. The width W is determined by the dc voltage V_G, and the incremental width dW is determined by the ac voltage v_g. The equivalent circuit for the zero-inversion charge deep-depletion state is also shown.

A variable dc voltage, V_G, drives the MOS-C into deep depletion. A small signal ac voltage, v_g, superimposed on the dc voltage is used for the capacitance measurement. The requirement on V_G is that it must change sufficiently rapidly to drive the MOS-C into deep depletion without producing significant minority-carrier generation.

Following the concepts of Section 1.1.5, the capacitance is defined by

$$C = dQ_G/dV_G \tag{2.37}$$

The gate charge, Q_G, is balanced by the bulk semiconductor charge, Q_B, assuming zero inversion charge. This gives Q_G as

$$Q_G = -Q_B \tag{2.38}$$

where the semiconductor bulk charge is given by

$$Q_B = q \int_0^W [p - n + N_D(x) - N_A(x)] \, dx \tag{2.39}$$

In the delta-depletion approximation, we neglect the mobile carrier concentration in the depleted scr, resulting in

$$Q_B = -q \int_0^W [N_A(x) - N_D(x)] \, dx = -q \int_0^W N_B(x) \, dx \tag{2.40}$$

The capacitance is then

$$C = q d \left[\int_0^W N_B(x) \, dx \right] / dV_G = q N_B(W) \, dW/dV_G \tag{2.41}$$

where we have used the identity $d[\int_a^b f(x) \, dx]/dc = f(b)\partial b/\partial c - f(a)\partial a/\partial c$.

The dW/dV_G term is obtained from eq. (2.7) as

$$dW/dV_G = -(K_s\varepsilon_0/C^2) \, dC/dV_G \tag{2.42}$$

giving

$$C = -[qN_B(W)K_s\varepsilon_0/C^2] \, dC/dV_G \tag{2.43}$$

Solving for the doping concentration we find

$$N_B(W) = -[C^3/(qK_s\varepsilon_0)]/(dC/dV_G) \tag{2.44}$$

The capacitances in eq. (2.44) are in units of F/cm^2. However, measured capacitances are given in farads. Replacing C by the actual capacitance (CA_G), where A_G is the gate area, changes eq. (2.44) to

$$N_B(W) = -[(CA_G)^3/(qK_s\varepsilon_0 A_G^2)]/[d(CA_G)/dV_G] \qquad (2.45)$$

which can also be written as

$$N_B(W) = [2/(qK_s\varepsilon_0 A_G^2)]/\{d[1/(CA_G)^2]/dV_G\} \qquad (2.46)$$

Eqs. (2.45) and (2.46) are the key equations for interpreting C-V doping-profile measurements. They state that a measurement of device capacitance and its variation with gate voltage allows the doping concentration to be calculated. The equations are generally used with this interpretation. That is not strictly correct, however. Let us see why.

In the analysis we have used the delta-depletion approximation. It assumes the mobile carrier concentrations to be zero in the reverse-biased scr, with an abrupt rise to their equilibrium values at W, the edge of the scr. This is shown in Fig. 2.13. In Fig. 2.13a we show the doping concentration and majority hole concentration for a uniformly doped substrate at flatband in an MOS-C. $N_B(x) = p(x)$ if we neglect the small minority-carrier contribution. When the MOS-C is driven into deep depletion by gate voltage V_{G1}, we find that the majority-carrier concentration p is zero from $x = 0$ to $x = W$ in the delta-depletion approximation and, at $x = W$, rises sharply to its equilibrium concentration shown by $p_1(x)$ in Fig. 2.13b. The doping concentration is in its ionized state in the depleted scr.

Let us now consider the effect of the ac voltage. During that part of the ac voltage swing, when the ac voltage adds to the dc voltage, majority carriers are displaced from W to $W + dW$, shown by $p_2(x)$. They therefore expose additional ionized doping atoms over the incremental width dW. The majority-carrier density displaced by the ac voltage is shown by the cross-hatched area in Fig. 2.13b. It is given by

$$\Delta p(x) = p_2(x) - p_1(x) = N_B(x) \qquad (2.47)$$

Eq. (2.47) shows that the doping concentration at $x = W$ is determined in this measurement and that eqs. (2.45) and (2.46) are correct. If we consider the more realistic situation of a nonabrupt majority-carrier concentration transition at $x = W$, where $p(x)$ changes more gradually, the measured quantity is still $N_B(W)$.

Let us now consider the nonuniformly doped case of Fig. 2.14.[17] The semiconductor consists of a lowly doped epitaxial layer on a highly doped substrate. The transition doping-concentration gradient can be very steep, although it is usually not as abrupt as shown. For $x_2 < x < x_1$ we have, as before, $p(x) = N_B(x)$. However, the majority-carrier profile is now very different from the doping-concentration profile around the

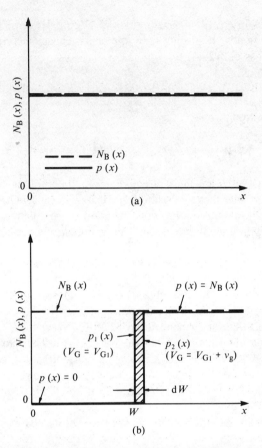

Fig. 2.13 Idealized doping and approximate majority-carrier concentrations for a uniformly doped substrate. (a) is for zero gate voltage; (b) is for a gate voltage sufficient to drive the MOS-C into deep depletion. $x = 0$ corresponds to the oxide/semiconductor interface.

transition region, x_t. Majority carriers diffuse from the more heavily into the more lightly doped side until an equilibrium is reached, as indicated by the solid curve in Fig. 2.14a. The carrier "smear-out" is determined by the extrinsic Debye length

$$L_D^* = \{kTK_s\varepsilon_0/[q^2(p + n)]\}^{1/2} \tag{2.48}$$

For gate voltages such that the scr edge $W < x_1$ and $W > x_2$, the arguments of the preceding discussion hold, and $N_B(W)$ is measured. However, for gate voltages corresponding to W near the transition region, $N_B(W)$ is no longer measured. $p(x)$ now lies in a region where, even in equilibrium, $p(x) \neq N_B(x)$. The majority-carrier distributions for gate voltages V_{G1} and $V_{G1} + v_g$ in Fig. 2.14b now show the increment

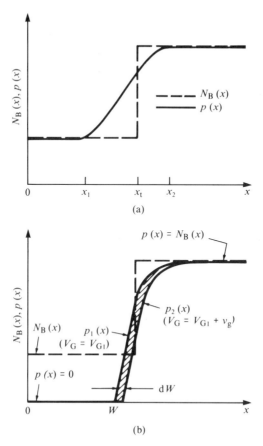

Fig. 2.14 Idealized doping and approximate majority-carrier concentrations for a nonuniformly doped substrate. (a) is for zero gate voltage; (b) is for a gate voltage sufficient to drive the MOS-C into deep depletion. $x = 0$ corresponds to the oxide/semiconductor interface.

$\Delta p(x) = p_2(x) - p_1(x)$ to lie partly in the lowly doped and partly in the highly doped region. Clearly,

$$p_2(x) - p_1(x) \neq N_B(x) \tag{2.49}$$

in this case, and eqs. (2.45) and (2.46) are incorrect.

These arguments show that in general it is incorrect to say that the C-V profiling technique measures the doping concentration. It has been shown that the concentration that is measured by C-V profiling is closer to the **majority**-carrier concentration profile than to the **doping**-concentration profile. Only in the special case of uniformly doped substrates are the two equal. When there are doping gradients, as in the example of

Fig. 2.14 or in diffused or ion-implanted layers, then to first order it is the majority-carrier profile that is measured. The more exact analysis in Ref. [17] shows the measured profile to be neither the majority nor the doping-concentration profile, but it is generally very close to the majority-carrier profile.

Eqs. (2.41), (2.45), and (2.46) should therefore be replaced by

$$C = qp(W)\,dW/dV_G \tag{2.50}$$

$$p(W) = -\frac{(CA_G)^3}{qK_s\varepsilon_0 A_G^2 d(CA_G)/dV_G} \tag{2.51}$$

$$p(W) = \frac{2}{qK_s\varepsilon_0 A_G^2 d[1/(CA_G)^2]/dV_G} \tag{2.52}$$

The scr width of an MOS-C can be written as

$$W = K_s\varepsilon_0\left(\frac{1}{C} - \frac{1}{C_o}\right) = K_s\varepsilon_0 A_G\left(\frac{1}{CA_G} - \frac{1}{C_o A_G}\right) \tag{2.53}$$

and for a *pn* or Schottky barrier junction it is

$$W = \frac{K_s\varepsilon_0 A_J}{CA_J} \tag{2.54}$$

A profile is generated by measuring the deep-depletion capacitance–gate voltage curve. From this curve, $p(W)$ is calculated using eq. (2.51) or (2.52). The depth W is obtained from eq. (2.53) for an MOS-C. The $p(W)$ calculation can use either $d(CA_G)/dV_G$ or $d[1/(CA_G)^2]/dV_G$. The second version is preferred if the calculation is done manually, because the $1/(CA_G)^2$ vs. V_G curve is more linear than the (CA_G) vs. V_G plot. If the doping concentration is uniform, then the former is truly linear. So merely by looking at a $1/(CA_G)^2$ vs. V_G curve, one gets a very good idea of how uniform the doping concentration is over the depth probed by the capacitance measurement.

There are several limitations to the capacitance-voltage profiling technique. Eq. (2.40) assumes that both the **majority**- and **minority**-carrier concentrations are negligible in the scr. While the gate voltage ensures that this is closely approximated by the majority carriers, the same is not necessarily true for the minority carriers. To ensure that a negligible density of minority carriers is thermally generated during the gate-voltage sweep, the gate voltage must be swept sufficiently fast. If an inversion layer is allowed to form, then the capacitance will be above its deep-depletion value, as shown in Fig. 1.3, and an artificially high carrier concentration will be obtained.

The frequency of the ac probing voltage should be sufficiently high that interface states at the oxide/semiconductor interface do not contribute a capacitance component. For well-annealed SiO_2/Si interfaces, this usually poses no problem at frequencies of 1 MHz. For a discussion of this aspect of profiling, see Ref. [18].

It is desirable to profile the wafer from the very surface of the wafer to a depth sufficient to measure that part of the wafer that is important for device operation. In practice it is not possible to profile all the way to the surface, because the depletion approximation, on which eq. (2.41) is based, fails as V_G approaches its flatband value. The majority-carrier concentration is no longer negligible there. The minimum distance from the surface to which a profile can conventionally be measured is given by[17]

$$W_{min} \approx 3L_D^*$$ (2.55)

However, a modified analysis taking the majority-carrier concentration near the surface into account has been developed. With this modified analysis, doping profiles up to the very surface can be obtained. We do not discuss this analysis here, because it is rather lengthy. The interested reader is referred to Ref. [19].

It should be mentioned that the MOS-C can be profiled closer to the wafer surface than either a Schottky barrier or pn junction diode. For Schottky diodes, the minimum depth from the surface is the zero-bias scr width, and for a pn junction it is the sum of junction depth and scr width. The extrinsic Debye length also places a limit on the spatial resolution of rapidly varying doping profiles. All C-V profiling techniques are insensitive to changes in profiles that occur over distances smaller than the extrinsic Debye length. Fortunately, L_D^* is generally small enough not to make this limitation significant.

In addition to the limit of generally not being able to profile all the way to the surface, there is also a limit on the profiled depth. This limit is set by avalanche-breakdown considerations. Obviously, W cannot be larger than the width corresponding to breakdown. The upper and lower depth profiling limits applicable for uniformly doped substrates are shown in Fig. 2.15.

2.3 SUMMARY

In this chapter we have used the concepts developed in Chapter 1 to show the use of MOS capacitors as test structures for the measurement of the generation lifetime and the doping-concentration profile. Both the deep-depletion MOS-C and the gate-controlled diode were discussed.

The key equation for the time-dependent capacitance dependence on gate voltage is

$$dV_G/dt = -(1/C_o)\, dQ_N/dt - (qK_s\varepsilon_0 N_B/C^3)\, dC/dt$$

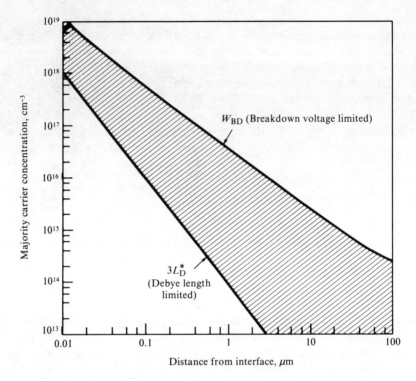

Fig. 2.15 Depth (shaded region) over which an MOS-C can be profiled by the capacitance-voltage technique. W_{BD} is limited by the breakdown voltage.[20]

From this equation one can extract the generation lifetime according to

$$-d(C_o/C)^2/dt = (2n_i C_o/N_B C_F \tau_g')(C_F/C - 1) + 2n_i C_o s'/K_s \varepsilon_0 N_B$$

using the pulsed MOS-C or "Zerbst" method. The generation lifetime can also be determined from the linear ramp technique by

$$R = qK_s \varepsilon_0 n_i (C_F/C_{sat} - 1)/C_F C_o \tau_g' + qn_i s'/C_o$$

Both generation lifetime and surface generation velocity can be obtained from the gate-controlled diode through the relations

$$\tau_g(J) = qn_i[W(J) - W_F(J)]A_J/I_J$$

$$\tau_g(G) = qn_i[W(G) - W_F(G)]A_G/I_{GU}$$

$$s_0 = I_s/qn_i A_G$$

The majority-carrier profile is determined during capacitance-voltage profiling from the equations

$$p(W) = -[(CA_G)^3/(qK_s\varepsilon_0 A_G^2)]/[d(CA_G)/dV_G]$$

$$p(W) = [2/(qK_s\varepsilon_0 A_G^2)]/\{d[1/(CA_G)^2]/dV_G\}$$

$$W = K_s\varepsilon_0(1/C - 1/C_o)$$

REFERENCES

[1] R. F. Pierret, *Field Effect Devices,* Vol. IV in *Modular Series on Solid State Devices,* Addison-Wesley Publ. Co., Reading, MA, 1983.

[2] G. W. Neudeck, *The PN Junction Diode,* Vol. II in *Modular Series on Solid State Devices,* Addison-Wesley Publ. Co., Reading, MA, 1983.

[3] M. Zerbst, "Relaxation Effects at Semiconductor-Insulator Interfaces" (in German), Z. Angew. Phys., *22,* 30–33, May, 1966.

[4] J. S. Kang and D. K. Schroder, "The Pulsed MIS Capacitor—A Critical Review," Phys. Stat. Sol., *89a,* 13–43, May 16, 1985.

[5] J. van der Spiegel and G. J. Declerck, "Theoretical and Practical Investigation of the Thermal Generation in Gate Controlled Diodes," Solid-State Electr., *24,* 869–877, Sept., 1981.

[6] P. U. Calzolari, S. Graffi, and C. Morandi, "Field-Enhanced Carrier Generation in MOS Capacitors," Solid-State Electr., *17,* 1001–1011, Oct., 1974.

[7] R. F. Pierret, "A Linear Sweep MOS-C Technique for Determining Minority Carrier Lifetimes," IEEE Trans. Electr. Dev., *ED-19,* 869–873, July, 1972.

[8] M. Miyake and H. Harada, "A New Analyzing Method for Non-Uniformly Doped MOS Capacitor C-t Characteristics in Lifetime Evaluation," Jap. J. Appl. Phys., *20,* L797–L800, Nov., 1981.

[9] R. F. Pierret and D. W. Small, "A Modified Linear Sweep Technique for MOS-C Generation Rate Measurements," IEEE Trans. Electr. Dev., *ED-22,* 1051–1052, Nov., 1975.

[10] W. D. Eades, J. D. Shott, and R. M. Swanson, "Refinements in the Measurement of Depleted Generation Lifetime," IEEE Trans. Electr. Dev., *ED-30,* 1274–1277, Oct., 1983.

[11] A. S. Grove and D. J. Fitzgerald, "Surface Effects on pn Junctions: Characteristics of Surface Space-Charge Regions Under Non-Equilibrium Conditions," Solid-State Electr., *9,* 783–806, Aug., 1966.

[12] R. F. Pierret, "The Gate-Controlled Diode s_0 Measurement and Steady-State Lateral Current Flow in Deeply Depleted MOS Structures," Solid-State Electr., *17,* 1257–1269, Dec., 1974.

[13] R. G. Mazur and D. H. Dickey, "A Spreading Resistance Technique for Resistivity Measurements in Silicon," J. Electrochem. Soc., *113,* 255–259, March, 1966.

[14] R. Galloni and A. Sardo, "Fully Automatic Apparatus for the Determination of Doping Profiles in Silicon by Electrochemical Measurements and Anodic Stripping," Rev. Sci. Instr., *54*, 369–373, March, 1983.

[15] J. Albers, P. Roitman, and C. L. Wilson, "Verification of Models for Fabrication of Arsenic Source-Drains in VLSI MOSFETs," IEEE Trans. Electr. Dev., *ED-30*, 1453–1462, Nov., 1983.

[16] J. Hilibrand and R. D. Gold, "Determination of the Impurity Distribution in Junction Diodes from Capacitance-Voltage Measurements," RCA Rev., *21*, 245–262, June, 1960.

[17] W. C. Johnson and P. T. Panousis, "The Influence of Debye Length on the C-V Measurement of Doping Profiles," IEEE Trans. Electr. Dev., *ED-18*, 965–973, Oct., 1971.

[18] E. H. Nicollian and J. R. Brews, *MOS Physics and Technology,* J. Wiley & Sons, New York, 1982, p. 393.

[19] K. Ziegler, E. Klausmann, and S. Kar, "Determination of the Semiconductor Doping Profile Right Up to Its Surface Using the MIS Capacitor," Solid-State Electr., *18*, 189–198, Febr., 1975.

[20] S. M. Sze, *Physics of Semiconductor Devices,* 2nd Edition, J. Wiley & Sons, New York, 1981, p. 78.

PROBLEMS

2.1 Switch S_1 in Fig. P2.1 is switched from ground to V_{G1} at $t = 0$. Draw the resultant C-V_G curves immediately after S_1 is closed and at $t = \infty$ and C-t curves for the three cases of switch S_2 in position (a) ground, (b) open circuit, and (c) $V_{D1} > V_{G1}$. The MOS structure is ideal — i.e., $V_{FB} = 0$. The capacitance measurement circuit is not shown.

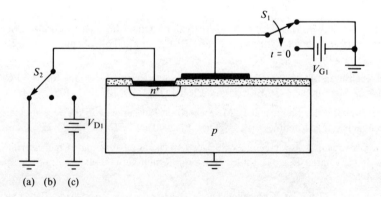

Fig. P2.1

2.2 Derive eq. (2.14).

2.3 The *C-t* data from a pulsed MOS capacitor are:

t (s)	C (pF)	t (s)	C (pF)	t (s)	C (pF)
0	5.53	100	8.26	200	13.79
5	5.62	105	8.45	205	14.17
10	5.72	110	8.65	210	14.55
15	5.83	115	8.85	215	14.94
20	5.95	120	9.08	220	15.34
25	6.06	125	9.29	225	15.72
30	6.18	130	9.53	230	16.10
35	6.30	135	9.76	235	16.48
40	6.42	140	10.01	240	16.81
45	6.54	145	10.26	245	17.09
50	6.68	150	10.53	250	17.29
55	6.81	155	10.81	255	17.43
60	6.94	160	11.09	260	17.53
65	7.10	165	11.39	265	17.58
70	7.24	170	11.71	270	17.62
75	7.40	175	12.03	275	17.64
80	7.55	180	12.36	280	17.64
85	7.72	185	12.71	285	17.64
90	7.89	190	13.05	290	17.65
95	8.08	195	13.42	295	17.65

For $x_o = 1100$ Å, $N_B = 3.5 \times 10^{14}$ cm^{-3}, $A = 3.45 \times 10^{-3}$ cm^2, $T = 300$ K, $K_o = 3.9$, and $K_s = 11.8$, calculate τ_g' and s' using the Zerbst technique. Hint: it is useful to plot $(C_o/C)^2$ vs. t and differentiate this curve graphically.

2.4 Solve eq. (2.3) for C as a function of t for a constant generation rate—i.e., $dQ_N/dt = -K$. For $K = qn_i^2 D_n/N_B L_n$, show how L_n can be found from an experimental *C-t* curve. This condition holds for an MOS-C at elevated temperature where the quasineutral bulk generation rate dominates and the back surface generation velocity can be neglected.

2.5 Calculate and plot the current–gate voltage curves for a gate-controlled diode with circular n^+p diode of radius $r = 5 \times 10^{-2}$ cm surrounded by an annular gate, as in Fig. 2.8, of inner radius $r_1 = 5 \times 10^{-2}$ cm and outer radius $r_2 = 7.5 \times 10^{-2}$ cm. Use eqs. (2.27) to (2.29) to calculate the current with $\tau_g(J) = 100$ μs, $\tau_g(G) = 75$ μs, $s_0 = 1.5$ cm/s, $n_i = 1.4 \times 10^{10}$ cm^{-3}, N_D in n^+ region $= 10^{19}$ cm^{-3}, N_A in p substrate $= 10^{15}$ cm^{-3}, $K_s = 11.8$, $K_o = 3.9$, $x_o = 1000$ Å, $V_{FB} = 0$, $T = 300$ K. Assume surface generation to start at $\phi_s = \phi_F$ and to terminate at $\phi_s = V_D + 2\phi_F$.

Calculate and plot the current for $V_G = 0$ to 10 V for (a) $V_D = 1$ V and (b) $V_D = 5$ V.

2.6 *C-V* measurements of two Si reverse-biased p^+n junctions of area 7.9×10^{-3} cm^2 at $T = 300$ K gave the following values:

V(V)	C_1 (pF)	C_2(pF)	V(V)	C_1(pF)	C_2(pF)
0.3	191	273	6.9	83.4	180
0.6	172	257	7.5	80.8	177
0.9	159	246	8.1	78.4	175
1.5	140	230	8.7	76.2	173
2.1	127	219	9.6	73.3	170
2.7	117	210	10.5	70.7	167
3.3	109	204	11.4	68.4	165
3.9	103	198	12.3	66.3	163
4.5	98	194	13.2	64.4	161
5.1	93.5	190	14.1	62.8	159
5.7	89.7	186	15	61.2	157
6.3	86.4	183			

Calculate and plot n vs. W over the voltage range measured.

2.7 For doping-concentration measurements with an MOS capacitor, it is important for the device to be in deep depletion with no inversion charge. This can be ensured by varying the gate voltage rapidly. It is furthermore desirable that there be no interface states at the Si/SiO$_2$ interface that result in interface state capacitance.

Explain the effect on the resultant doping-concentration profile if there are interface states that respond to the ac probing frequency.

3 / Charge-Coupled Devices–Fundamentals

3.1 INTRODUCTION

In Chapters 1 and 2 we discussed the concept of deep-depletion MOS capacitors and their use as characterization test structures. Now we turn to their application as circuit elements. They are extensively used in charge-coupled devices (CCD's) and dynamic random access memories (DRAM's). CCD's form the basis for most solid-state imaging arrays and, as such, are beginning to penetrate the consumer market as lightweight, low-power television cameras. DRAM's are the memory elements of most computers. For these two applications alone, MOS-C's are fabricated by the millions every day all over the world. This is a very good reason for becoming familiar with them and understanding their modes of operation.

The introduction of CCD's in 1970[1] generated an enormous world-wide interest and activity in virtually every major semiconductor laboratory and a very large output of papers, reports, and books. Over 1000 papers were published within a decade of their invention, and the first product — a CCD imager — was demonstrated only three years after the charge-coupled concept was introduced.

What precipitated this remarkable surge of activity for this new device? It was partly the vast background of MOS technology and expertise built up during the 1960's and partly the promise of a device that appeared to be deceptively simple to fabricate and suitable for a variety of applications. After all, the CCD is basically just a series of MOS capacitors requiring diodes only at the input and the output. It could be used as a shift register, a memory, a signal processor, and an imager. There seemed to be no end of new applications.

Its operation conformed very closely to theoretical prediction, allowing both theoreticians and experimenters to complement one another very effectively. What was predicted by theory was quickly put into practice and verified. A whole gamut of new structures and applications emerged. However, after a few years it was realized that the fabrication was not so simple after all. Some of the applications vanished, because other semiconductor technologies also advanced. In fact, some of the more traditional devices profited from the better semiconductor understanding that CCD's generated. They incorporated some of the CCD features and in turn replaced CCD's.

A classic example is the dynamic random-access memory. For a while it looked as if CCD's might find a large market as DRAM's, even though charge-coupled devices were serially, not randomly, addressed. This did not come about, but the CCD concept was applied to conventional DRAM's, allowing higher-density memory arrays. Another example can be found in signal processing. Digital signal processing has certain advantages over analog CCD's. This largely displaced CCD's in the signal-processing field. It is in the imaging field, where interestingly CCD's made their first contribution, that they find their main application today.

In this chapter we discuss the fundamental aspects of CCD's. Applications of CCD's are treated in Chapter 4. We give a brief historical discussion and then describe in this chapter the various types of charge-coupled devices. Next we develop the relevant equations for surface potential, charge confinement, and charge transfer. Then, charge input and output structures are discussed, followed by the concept of charge transfer and how carrier ballistics and interface states affect charge transfer. Finally, bulk-channel CCD's are described, and their performance is compared with that of surface channel CCD's.

3.2 BASIC CONSIDERATIONS

3.2.1 Charge-Transfer Device Structures

A CCD is a shift register in which sampled values of an analog signal are stored in the form of charges on a series of capacitors. Switches between capacitors transfer the charge from one capacitor to the next, following a command from an applied voltage pulse. The idea of making a shift register for analog signals and using it as a delay line dates to the early 1950's.[2] Shift registers were first implemented with bipolar transistors in 1965 and with MOS transistors in 1969. However, a truly practical realization had to await the development of the integrated circuit for both the capacitor and the switch to be implemented on the same semiconductor chip. The first MOS version was the *bucket-brigade device* (BBD) shown in Fig. 3.1.

The cross section in Fig. 3.1a shows the device to consist of a *p*-type substrate with *n*-diffusions overlaid by an insulator and a series of gates. They resemble metal-oxide-semiconductor field-effect transistors (MOSFET's) with source, drain, and gate. The detail of Fig. 3.1b shows how the electrically floating diffusions act simultaneously as the drain of one transistor and the source of the next. In other words, they are merely regions through which electrons flow from channel to channel and are, therefore, sometimes forward and sometimes reverse biased.

There is a certain amount of feedback from drain to source in the BBD, which modulates the threshold voltage of the MOSFET and limits the efficiency with which charge is transferred to approximately 0.999 per transfer. The transfer efficiency is a parameter describing the completeness of charge transfer from one element to the next. A value of 0.999 may appear sufficiently close to unity to be considered satisfactory.

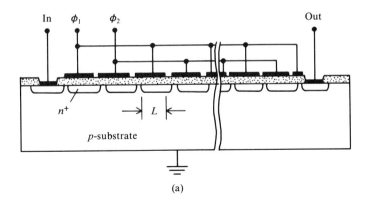

(a)

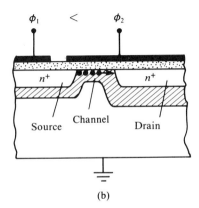

(b)

Fig. 3.1 MOS bucket-brigade device (BBD). In (a), charge is stored in n^+ islands; (b) shows the gate overlapping two n^+ islands, which act as source and drain in turn. Reprinted after Ref. [4] with permission.

But if only 0.999, or 99.9%, of the charge transfers, then after many transfers the output signal is a very distorted replica of the input. In modern charge-transfer devices, several thousand transfers are made between input and output.

Note that in a BBD the charge consists of **majority carriers** when in the diffused regions and **minority carriers** when in the channel between these regions. It is when the charge leaves a diffused source that it leaves a small fraction behind, because a potential barrier exists at the boundary between the source and the channel. **Complete** charge transfer is therefore impossible in this embodiment. If the diffused islands are removed, higher charge transfer becomes feasible. This occurs in the CCD, because there are no diffused islands.

The operation of the BBD is possible with only two sets of gates and two different applied potentials as shown in Fig. 3.1. For example, we see in Fig. 3.1b, for voltage

V_{G2} on gate 2 and V_{G1} on gate 1 and for $V_{G2} > V_{G1}$, that the right n-island acts as a drain and the left n-island as a source, and that the charge flows from source to drain. Once the charge is in the drain, the gate voltages are reversed. The sources become drains, and vice versa, and the charge flows to the next drain, and so on until it reaches the output. Clearly, connecting every odd-numbered gate together as phase 1 (ϕ_1) and every even-numbered gate as phase 2 (ϕ_2), and applying time-varying voltages to them, ensures unidirectional charge transfer.

When the sources and drains are removed, then three gates must be used in order to have unidirectional charge transfer. Such a three-phase CCD is shown in Fig. 3.2. We will discuss the number of CCD gates in more detail in a later section. The charge, sometimes called a *charge packet* because it is a small amount of charge held under one gate as minority inversion carriers, is stored under the gate with the highest potential. In other words, it is stored in potential wells created by the gate voltage. By periodically varying the electrode or gate voltages, the potential wells are shifted along the semiconductor. The charge, being located in these potential wells, moves with them.

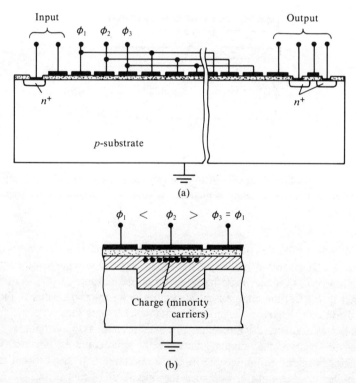

Fig. 3.2 Surface-channel charge-coupled device (SCCD). (a) shows a three-phase structure, and (b) shows the charge stored at the surface as minority carriers. Reprinted after Ref. [4] with permission.

Changing the frequency of the applied voltages, also called *clock voltages,* varies the time required to shift the charges through the device. The ability to vary the delay time electronically by merely varying the frequency of the gate voltages is a very desirable property of CCD's.

When the charge resides at the semiconductor surface, as in Fig. 3.2, the device is called a *surface-channel CCD* (SCCD). It has several shortcomings which we will discuss later on. An obvious one is the interaction of the charge with interface states. In Chapter 2 we saw interface states to be active generation-recombination centers. It is quite clear, then, that as charge packets are transferred through the device, some of the charge will be captured in interface states, causing charge loss or nonperfect transfer efficiency. An interesting solution to this problem was the invention of the *bulk-channel CCD* (BCCD)[3] shown in Fig. 3.3. The charge location is moved away from the surface into the *n*-channel, where it no longer interacts with interface states. It

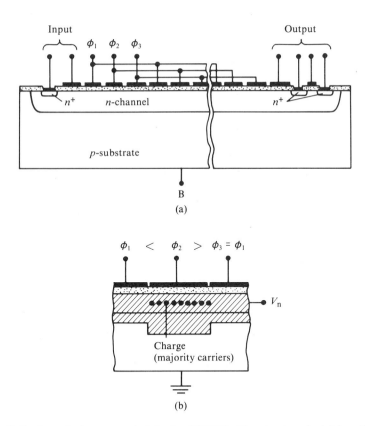

Fig. 3.3 Bulk-channel charge-coupled device (BCCD). The structure in (a) is a three-phase structure, showing the *n*-channel on a *p*-substrate; and (b) shows the charge stored in the *n*-channel as majority carriers. Reprinted after Ref. [4] with permission.

does, however, interact with bulk generation-recombination (G-R) centers present in the *n*-channel. Today's silicon process technology makes the bulk G-R center density easier to control than the interface-state density, giving the BCCD performance advantages over the SCCD. In spite of their increased process complexity, almost all of today's devices are BCCD's, because of their enhanced device performance.

Two slightly different types of BCCD's are found in the literature. The *buried-channel CCD* is generally fabricated by forming a thin *n*-channel by ion implantation. Thicknesses are typically less than one micron. In the *peristaltic CCD*, the *n*-channel is a thicker, epitaxially grown layer, with thicknesses of several microns. The bucket-brigade device and both types of CCD's utilize an MOS structure, with gates formed on an insulator. This is admirably suitable for Si devices with their high-quality, thermally grown SiO_2 film forming an interface with very low interface-state densities. It is much more difficult to make CCD's on other semiconductors for which such a good interface cannot be achieved. Attempts to make MOS-type CCD's with other semiconductors have been only partially successful, although they have been fabricated on Ge, InSb, and HgCdTe.

A solution to the insulator/semiconductor interface problem is the Schottky-barrier CCD shown in Fig. 3.4.[4] This CCD configuration can also be implemented by using *pn* junction barriers. Here, reverse-biased Schottky or *pn* junctions replace the gate-oxide portion of MOS CCD's. This approach is suitable for those materials, such as GaAs, for which it is virtually impossible to make good MOS structures. High-mobility GaAs is a good material for very-high-frequency CCD's. In fact, using the Schottky-barrier approach, GaAs CCD's have been fabricated with operational frequencies of 1 GHz. The fastest Si devices have been operated at several hundred MHz, with more typical frequencies being in the 10 to 20 MHz range. Charge-coupled and bucket-brigade devices form a class of devices more generally referred to as *charge-transfer devices* (CTD's).

3.2.2 Surface Potential

The surface-channel CCD is the easiest of the various CCD configurations to visualize, and we will therefore use it for all the basic device descriptions. We will subsequently extend the concepts to the other CCD configurations. We discussed the charge and capacitance behavior of the deep-depletion MOS-C in Chapter 1 and will repeat only the pertinent details. The device can exist in many charge or capacitance states. The capacitance values can range from the initial C_i to the final C_F for gate voltage V_{G1}, as shown in Fig. 3.5. As C varies between these two extremes, the charge must likewise vary because the voltage is constant.

The charge states corresponding to the three capacitance points A, B, and C in Fig. 3.5 are indicated in Fig. 3.6. Figure 3.6a shows a cross section through the device, indicating the scr by the shaded regions. For A there is no charge in the inversion layer, for B there is some charge, and for C the inversion layer has reached its maximum charge. The surface energy-band diagrams of E vs. x for each of the three

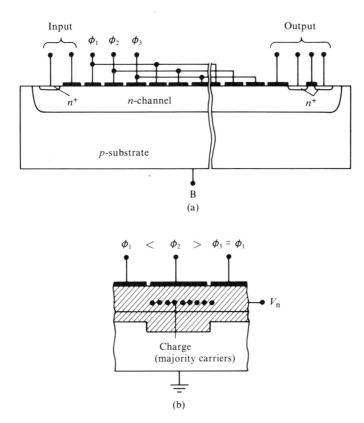

Fig. 3.4 Bulk-channel Schottky-gate charge-coupled device. The structure in (a) is a three-phase structure, showing the n-channel on a p-substrate; and (b) shows the charge stored in the n-channel as majority carriers. Reprinted after Ref. [4] with permission.

cases are shown in Fig. 3.6b. They can be thought of as being the energy equivalent of the spatial diagrams of Fig. 3.6a, and the minority-carrier inversion electrons that are physically located at the surface are shown at the bottom of these energy-band diagrams. The conventional energy-band diagrams that we encountered in Chapter 1 are shown in Fig. 3.6c as E vs. y. Here we see the minority electrons both at the surface, as in Fig. 3.6a, and at the various energies, as in Fig. 3.6b.

The quasi-Fermi levels of Chapter 1 are also shown along the surface as well as into the substrate. Furthermore, the surface potential, ϕ_s, is shown for each case. Recall that the surface potential is defined as the intrinsic level potential at the surface with respect to its zero value in the quasineutral bulk. For a given gate voltage, its magnitude clearly depends on the inversion charge, Q_N. This is quantitatively expressed by eq. (1.39).

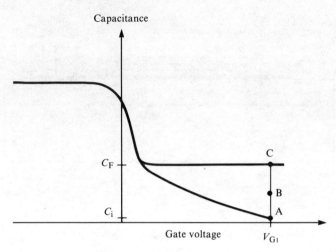

Fig. 3.5 Capacitance-voltage curves for an MOS-C. The CCD operates between points A and C at gate voltage V_{G1}.

The complete energy-band diagram is necessary to bring out all the features of the deep-depletion MOS-C. It is very tedious, however, to draw the conduction, valence, and intrinsic energies every time, especially since they are all parallel to one another. One energy would suffice, and any of the three could be chosen. Since the intrinsic energy level is used for the surface potential, it makes sense to choose it. So from now on we will show just one energy level, and it will represent the potential in the semiconductor. Remember, however, that the conduction and valence bands have the same shape.

An example is given in Fig. 3.7, where the oxide and semiconductor potentials are drawn to scale for a 5-V gate voltage for five charge states. The highest surface potential corresponds to zero inversion charge, and this is the lowest of the five curves. The potential increases downward on these plots while energy increases upward. The other curves correspond to charge increments of one-quarter maximum inversion charge. The potential from the surface into the semiconductor follows the relation

$$\phi(y) = \phi_s(\text{max})[1 - y/W_{\text{max}}]^2 \tag{3.1}$$

where $\phi_s(\text{max})$ is the maximum value of surface potential and W_{max} is the maximum scr width for each case.

The concept of *potential wells* is commonly used with CCD's. Such potential wells are shown in Fig. 3.7 at the surface where the inversion charge resides. There we see charge confinement only in the y-direction. The charge is obviously constrained to the surface by the semiconductor energy bands on the right and the oxide barrier on the left. To see the charge confinement in the x-direction, we turn to Fig. 3.8, which is the simplified version of Fig. 3.6b just as Fig. 3.7 is the simplified version of Fig. 3.6c.

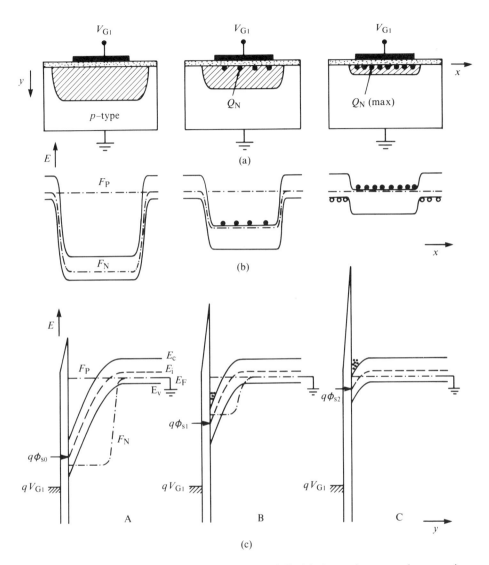

Fig. 3.6 MOS-C of Fig. 3.5 for points A, B, and C. (a) shows the space-charge regions, (b) shows the potential diagrams along x for $y = 0$, and (c) shows the potential diagrams along y into the semiconductor. The inversion charge is indicated by the solid circles.

Figure 3.8 is truly a surface potential diagram showing the potential at the very surface. It suggests an analogy to a real well. Its ultimate depth is a dry well. As water trickles into it, its depth — measured from the top of the well to the water surface — decreases, just as the surface potential decreases when charge flows into the potential well. In contrast to a real well, however, there is something odd about the potential

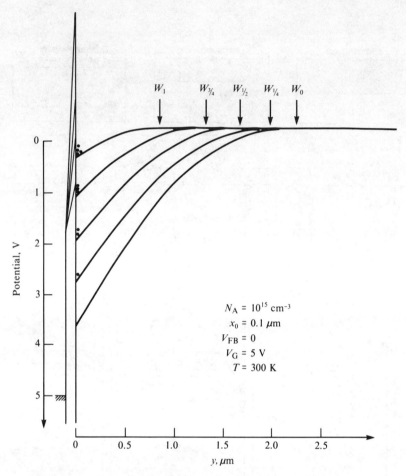

Fig. 3.7 The potential into the semiconductor for a deep-depletion MOS-C with zero, $\frac{1}{4}$, $\frac{1}{2}$, $\frac{3}{4}$, and full charge. The W's are the space-charge region widths corresponding to those charge states.

well. It cannot be filled to the top, because the surface potential of a full potential well (fully inverted surface) is given by

$$\phi_s = 2\phi_F \tag{3.2}$$

not zero. This is where our analogy ceases to exist. Nevertheless, we will find the analogy between charge and water useful in later CCD discussions.

The shaded areas in Fig. 3.7 correspond to inversion charge, with each segment being one quarter of the maximum charge. It should be clearly understood that the

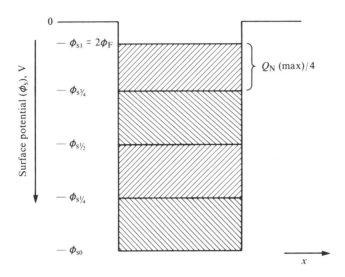

Fig. 3.8 The surface potentials along x for $y = 0$ for the charge states of the device shown in Fig. 3.7.

charge is physically located at the surface and that the potential-well picture is merely a convenient way of representing this.

3.2.3 Charge Confinement

The operation of a CCD depends on the confinement and transfer of charge packets consisting of **minority** carriers in an **SCCD** and **majority** carriers in a **BCCD**. How is the charge confined laterally? We know that it is confined in depth, or in the y-direction, by the potential barrier into the semiconductor. For lateral confinement, consider the SCCD in Fig. 3.9. It has many gates, four of which are shown. Every third one is connected together, resulting in three separate sets of gates, labeled ϕ_1, ϕ_2, and ϕ_3, where the "ϕ" here stands for *phase,* not potential. A CCD made of three sets of gates is called a *three-phase CCD*. A "phase" is one set of gates, e.g. all ϕ_1 gates. During device operation, all ϕ_1 gates have voltage V_{G1} applied, all ϕ_2 gates have V_{G2}, and all ϕ_3 gates have V_{G3}. The three-phase CCD was historically the first device to be demonstrated. There are also 1.5-, two-, and four-phase devices.

Now imagine $V_{G2} > V_{G1} = V_{G3}$. All gate voltages, however, are of such magnitude that the semiconductor under **all** gates is in deep depletion. But the surface under gate 2 is in deeper depletion than the surfaces under the other two gates. When there are no inversion charges under any gate, we have the situation depicted in Fig. 3.9a. Both the scr width and the surface potential are highest under ϕ_2. Note the similarity between the shape of the scr and the surface potential.

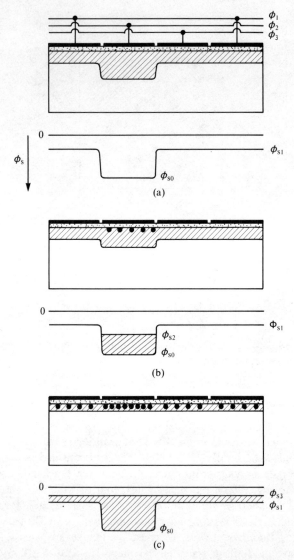

Fig. 3.9 Cross sections and surface potential plots of a three-phase CCD with $V_{G2} > V_{G1} = V_{G3}$: (a) no charge; (b) some charge in the potential well under ϕ_2; and (c) more charge than can be contained under ϕ_2, causing charge to spill through the entire device.

Now let minority carriers be introduced into the device by a brief flash of light, for example. Electron-hole pairs are produced, and the minority electrons are attracted to that part of the device with the highest surface potential. The electrons flow under gate 2, causing the scr to collapse slightly and the potential well to fill partially, as shown in Fig. 3.9b. The surface potential under gate 2 decreases from ϕ_{s0} to ϕ_{s2}, while that under gates 1 and 3 remains at ϕ_{s1}.

The charge is confined in its potential well by the potential barriers of height $\phi_{s1} - \phi_{s2}$ on both sides and can flow neither to the right nor to the left. If more charge is generated it will continue to flow into the potential well until it is full. As the well fills, the surface potential falls. When ϕ_{s2} reaches ϕ_{s1}, the well is no longer able to contain the charge. Any additional charge spreads out under **all** gates, and the surface potential becomes uniform at ϕ_{s3}, as shown in Fig. 3.9c. Charge confinement is lost, and the CCD ceases to function properly. Obviously, a CCD can be operated only under conditions where charge in one potential well never spills into adjacent wells.

What determines the surface potential and charge-storage capability? Let us restate the dependence of the surface potential on gate voltage and charge from eq. (1.39):

$$\phi_s = V_G' + Q_N/C_o - V_0\{[1 + 2(V_G' + Q_N/C_o)/V_0]^{1/2} - 1\} \qquad (3.3)$$

As an example of the utility of this equation, let us calculate the maximum charge that can be contained in the CCD of Fig. 3.9. We know that the surface potentials at maximum charge are $\phi_{s2} = \phi_{s1}$. From eq. (3.3) we find, by solving for that maximum charge, $Q_{N,m}$,

$$Q_{N,m} = -C_o(V_{G2} - V_{G1}) \qquad (3.4)$$

For typical values of $x_o = 0.1 \ \mu m$ and $V_{G2} - V_{G1} = 5$ V, we get $Q_{N,m} = -1.7 \times 10^{-7}$ coul/cm^2. This corresponds to $Q_{N,m}/(-q) = 1.06 \times 10^{12}$ electrons/cm^2 in the inversion layer. For a gate area of 10 $\mu m \times 50 \ \mu m$, this gives 5.3×10^6 electrons in the charge packet. The charge-packet size will, of course, vary with gate voltage, oxide thickness, and gate area, but typical values are in the range of 1 to 5×10^6 electrons for a full-potential well.

It should be noted that the maximum charge that can be handled by a CCD, given by eq. (3.4), is not identical to the maximum charge that can be stored under an isolated gate, given by eq. (1.47). This is because the former is determined by the potential barrier of surface potentials of adjacent gates, while the latter is determined by $2\phi_F$.

Adjacent gates confine the charge packet to its proper location along the charge-transfer direction. What about confinement orthogonal to that direction? Consider the charge packet shown shaded in Fig. 3.10a. It is to be transferred along the arrow in the central region—the CCD channel—between the dashed lines. In the horizontal or transfer direction, charge is confined by gate voltages, as shown in Fig. 3.10b. However, the gates cannot lie over the channel only. They extend vertically beyond the channel, either because there are other channels that are addressed by the same gates or because they must extend for contact to be made with them at the edge of the chip.

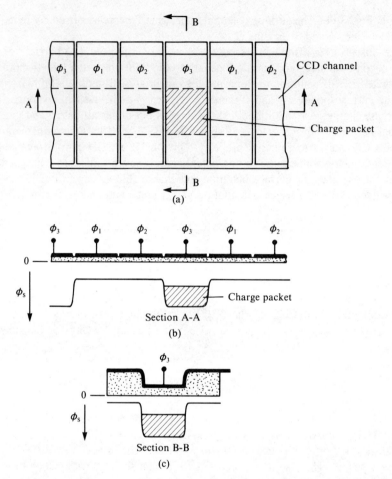

Fig. 3.10   Charge confinement in a CCD. The charge is the shaded region in (a). It is confined along A-A by the gate potentials, with $V_{G3} > V_{G1} = V_{G2}$, in (b), and along B-B by the two different oxide thicknesses in (c).

However, the charge must be confined to the channel and cannot be allowed to spread beyond it.

In order for the charge to be confined to the channel, it is necessary for the surface potential of the channel to be higher than the surface potential of the lateral region adjacent to it. An examination of eq. (3.3) reveals that either a thicker oxide or an increased doping concentration brings this about. For the thicker oxide, the oxide-voltage drop is enhanced, leaving less of the gate voltage to be dropped across the semiconductor. For the higher-doping case, the higher bulk scr charge makes inversion more difficult. The surface potential is lower in either case. We illustrate the thicker oxide version in Fig. 3.10c. Note the similarity between the shape of the gate over the varying oxide thickness and the surface potential.

Different oxide thicknesses produce steps on the device surface that can present fabrication difficulties, for the oxide must be sufficiently thick to prevent channel formation. It is for that reason that usually both **higher doping** and **thicker oxides** are used in the nonchannel regions. The thickness of the oxide is more flexible if doping is also used in the channel-stop regions. This applies not only to CCD's, but also to most conventional integrated circuits where such "channel stops" are required to prevent adjacent devices from coupling one to another. This unintentional coupling of adjacent devices is sometimes referred to as *crosstalk*.

3.2.4 Charge Transfer

Now that we know how to confine charge in the correct channel area, we turn to charge transfer. A cross section of a three-phase CCD is shown in Fig. 3.11a. As before, all ϕ_1 gates are connected to each other. So are all ϕ_2 and ϕ_3 gates. Hence only three gate voltages need be supplied to the device, regardless of how many gates there are. From our earlier discussion, it should be obvious that for proper CCD action, where one charge packet is not allowed to mix with others, a minimum of three gates is required for each charge packet. Such a set of gates constitutes a unit cell called a *stage* or a *cell*. Clearly, a 500-stage, three-phase device has 1500 gates, a 500-stage, two-phase CCD has only 1000 gates, while a 500-stage, four-phase version has 2000 gates. A stage or cell is the minimum unit necessary to contain one charge packet.

The gate voltages, also called *clock voltages,* for this example are shown in Fig. 3.11c. They have equal amplitudes, but are shifted in time with respect to each other. Let us consider the four times t_1, t_2, t_3, and t_4. At $t = t_1$, the gate voltage on phase 2 is "high," meaning that it has the high voltage V_{G2} supplied to it, while ϕ_1 and ϕ_3 are "low." The low voltage V_{G1} must be sufficiently high for the surface to be always in depletion. This keeps majority holes from the surface, preventing recombination of minority carriers with majority carriers. Remember, an SCCD is a minority-carrier device just as a MOSFET is, but not in the same sense as a bipolar transistor is. In a **bipolar** device, such as a bipolar junction transistor or *pn* junction diode, both majority and minority carriers are physically close to each other, allowing recombination. In a **unipolar** device, such as an SCCD or MOSFET, the minority carriers in the channel are physically separated from the majority carriers by the reverse-biased scr, and the two cannot recombine. So it is important that there always be a reverse-biased scr between them. This is ensured by the appropriate value of V_{G1}. We will return to this point when we discuss the effects of interface states.

The scr distribution and the surface potentials for $t = t_1$ are shown in Fig. 3.11a and b. Three potential wells are shown. Two contain charge and one is empty. At $t = t_2$, ϕ_3 goes "high" and the charge spreads over two gates. At $t = t_3$, the ϕ_2 gate voltage is in transition from "high" to "low." The decreasing surface potential pushes the charge to the right into the ϕ_3 potential well. This type of waveform is called a

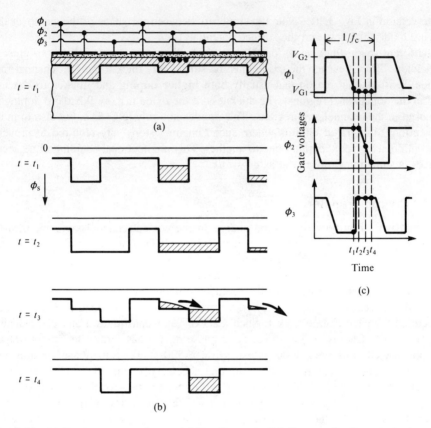

Fig. 3.11 (a) Device cross section, and (b) surface potential diagrams for times t_1, t_2, t_3, and t_4 shown on the clock-voltage waveform diagram in (c).

push clock, because it pushes the charge from one potential well to the next. Charge transfer is complete at $t = t_4$, when ϕ_2 has reached its low potential and the charge has moved one gate length. It took only a portion of the complete gate-voltage waveform cycle time to move the charge one gate length. Using the same arguments, one can show that it takes a time $t = 1/f_c$, where f_c is the clock frequency, to transfer the charge packet through one complete stage comprising all three gates. The clocks, of course, run continuously, and so the charge packet transfers through the entire device.

It should be obvious by now why in a CCD with uniform channel oxide thickness and doping concentration, three gates are necessary per stage. As shown by the $t = t_2$ plot of Fig. 3.11b, at the time when two adjacent gates are at high potential, the third gate establishes a potential barrier both to the right and to the left of the charge packet to prevent charge mixing. What is furthermore implied is that the gates are spaced sufficiently closely for there to be no potential barrier between two gates with identical gate voltages. If the spacing becomes too large, potential barriers are created and charge transfer is impeded. Close spacing is achieved in practice by having adjacent gates overlap, with an insulator between them as a separator. Typically, polycrystalline silicon is deposited and etched into the appropriate pattern for the first-level gates. It is then oxidized, and the next level is deposited. The spacing between levels is the oxide thickness.

A charge packet will change in size as it transfers through the CCD. For most cases it will **decrease** slightly, because a small fraction of the charge is trapped by interface states in surface-channel CCD's and by bulk G-R centers or states in bulk-channel CCD's. The trapped charge will eventually be released by thermal emission, but it will be lost from the original packet. Furthermore, a small fraction may stay behind in each potential well if the clock frequency is so high that the charge has insufficient time to transfer completely from well to well. Recombination does not occur, as mentioned earlier, and is therefore not a problem. Because the device is in deep depletion during its operation, thermally generated ehp will contribute charge to the packet, **increasing** its size. Whether or not this is significant depends on the total transfer time. The charge transfer time from stage to stage is variable and depends only on the clock frequency. A low frequency allows more time for thermal generation. Filling of an empty potential well thermally takes on the order of seconds to minutes. The total transfer time must therefore be a small fraction of this time. Thermally generated charge adds a negligible amount to the charge under those conditions. Whatever charge does add, however, is generated in a random manner and contributes noise to the device, and because it is random it cannot be utilized to make up for losses caused by charge capture in interface states.

We have now covered the basic CCD concepts. The reader should clearly understand *surface potential, potential well, charge confinement, charge transfer, cell, stage,* and *clock voltage.* For convenience, we repeat the surface-potential and charge-density equations for both *n*- and *p*-channel devices.

For *n*-channel SCCD's:

$$\phi_s = V_G' + Q_N/C_o - V_0\{[1 + 2(V_G' + Q_N/C_o)/V_0]^{1/2} - 1)$$
$$Q_N = -[V_G' - \phi_s - (2V_0\phi_s)^{1/2}]C_o$$

where V_G', ϕ_s, and $V_0 = qK_s\varepsilon_0(N_A - N_D)/C_o^2$ are positive and Q_N is negative.

For *p*-channel SCCD's:

$$\phi_s = V_G' + Q_P/C_o - V_0\{[1 + 2(V_G' + Q_P/C_o)/V_0]^{1/2} - 1\}$$
$$Q_P = -[V_G' - \phi_s + (2V_0\phi_s)^{1/2}]C_o$$

where V_G', ϕ_s, and $V_0 = -qK_s\varepsilon_0(N_D - N_A)/C_o^2$ are negative and Q_P is positive.

These are very important equations. The surface-potential expressions give the surface potential as a function of gate voltage, oxide thickness, and doping concentration and are frequently used design equations.

3.3 CHARGE INPUT AND OUTPUT

3.3.1 Charge Input

The charge stored and transferred within the CCD must first be injected into the device before it can be transferred. For imaging applications, the incident light creates ehp. The **optically** generated minority carriers are collected within each stage in that potential well with the highest surface potential. **Electrical** input makes use of an input diffusion and several input gates. Although there are several electrical input techniques, we will discuss only the most commonly used one, usually called the "*fill and spill*" or *potential equilibration* method.[5]

Consider the circuit in Fig. 3.12, consisting of an input diffusion, two input gates, and the first gate of the CCD channel. The diffusion and the first two gates can be viewed as a MOSFET with a source (the diffusion), a gate (G1), and a gate-induced drain (G2). The diode is initially reverse biased to V_{D1}, and the gate voltage V_{G1} creates the surface potential ϕ_{s1}. The input signal that is to be converted into charge packets is shown in the upper part of the figure. It consists of positive voltages only. If there are negative voltages, they can always be level-shifted to make them positive. The input signal is applied between gates G1 and G2 with G1 as the reference node, so that there is a voltage difference between the two gates given by the input voltage V_i.

The CCD, being a *sampled data* device, takes discrete samples of the analog input signal, each Δt wide, and converts them into a charge. If the signal has significant time variations over the time interval Δt, then the sampling process averages the signal. We see in Fig. 3.12 a fairly constant input voltage over Δt at $t = t_1$, and the surface-potential diagram in Fig. 3.12a corresponds to that time interval.

For a charge packet whose charge is proportional to the input voltage to be injected into the CCD, the diode is briefly pulsed from V_{D1} to V_{D2} and back again to V_{D1}, shown in Fig. 3.12b and c. This pulsing has to take place within the time interval Δt. During the $V_{D1} \rightarrow V_{D2}$ sequence, the surface potential is determined by the diode and momentarily becomes V_{D2}. The well under gate G2 floods with charge and overflows. During the $V_{D2} \rightarrow V_{D1}$ sequence, any charge that finds itself above the ϕ_{s1} surface potential level drains back into the diode. But the well under G2 remains full, because its charge is prevented from flowing back into the diode by the potential barrier on its left side. It also cannot flow into the CCD due to the potential barrier on its right side. We see, then, that the diode pulse sequence is an effective metering operation that leaves a precisely determined charge in the potential well, and the "fill and spill" designation is an apt descriptor.

The equality of the surface potential under the two gates, G1 and G2, allows eq. (3.3) to be easily solved for the metered charge as

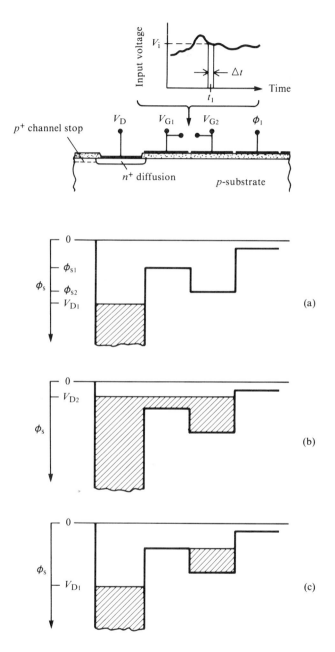

Fig. 3.12 The "fill and spill" input technique, showing the input waveform, the input circuit, and the surface potentials for three different times: (a) before "fill," (b) during "fill," and (c) after "spill."

$$Q_N = -C_o(V_{G2} - V_{G1}) = -C_o V_i \tag{3.5}$$

since $V_i = V_{G2} - V_{G1}$. So we see the metered charge packet to be proportional to the input voltage. This is exactly what is required for a linear conversion of voltage to charge. In eq. (3.5) we assume the flatband or threshold voltages to be identical under the two gates. This is a reasonable assumption since the two gates are right next to one another.

After the charge is metered, it is transferred into the CCD proper by driving phase ϕ_1 "high." This empties the metering well and prepares the input circuit for the next input cycle. In this manner the input voltage is partitioned into time increments, Δt, and converted into charge packets, each proportional to the average voltage during those time increments.

You will have noticed that a potential well under a gate has a definite bottom, and charge can exist only for potentials above that bottom. Actually we should say "top" for "bottom" and "below" for "above," because the surface potential increases downward, as seen in Fig. 3.12. For convenience we will occasionally use descriptive terms that are much like those used to describe water in a bucket.

A diode, in contrast, has no bottom. It can supply an infinite amount of charge since it cannot be emptied. How is that possible? It is possible by virtue of the electrical connection to it that keeps resupplying the charge drawn out. That is, of course, the reason that a current can flow through a diode forever. It is not because the diode has an infinite amount of charge in it, but because, as soon as one carrier leaves, another is supplied by the wire. Hence, we show diffused or ion-implanted regions as having no lower bound on potential diagrams. This does not hold for a **floating** diffusion. A floating diffusion can supply no more charge than it contains from the doping process.

It is impossible to withdraw all the charge if the region is heavily doped, because very large electric fields are set up that cause breakdown. Only lightly doped implanted islands can be totally depleted. Recall the relationship between electric field and charge from Gauss's law: $\mathcal{E} = Q/K_s\varepsilon_0$. For silicon with a typical breakdown field of 3×10^5 V/cm, we find $Q = 3.1 \times 10^{-7}$ coul/cm^2, or $Q/q = 1.9 \times 10^{12}$ cm^{-2}. Hence a doped region 1 μm thick can be doped only to 1.9×10^{16} cm^{-3}. For heavier doping, breakdown would occur before the region is depleted.

The charge in a potential well, created by a gate voltage, can be totally emptied, because it has no wire contact to it to resupply the charge. This allows **total** charge transfer and makes the CCD such a high-performance device. Recall that bucket-brigade devices have floating diffusions throughout the channel that can never be entirely depleted.

3.3.2 Charge Output

The output circuit is slightly more complex than the input circuit. Imagine the CCD as a delay line. The input voltage has been converted into charge packets. The charge packets have been clocked through the three-phase device, and, at some instance in time, one of them is located under gate ϕ_3 in Fig. 3.13a as "signal charge."

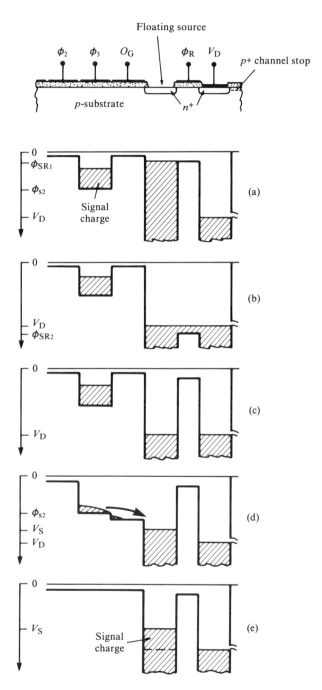

Fig. 3.13 The floating diffusion output, showing the main output circuit and the potentials at various stages, as discussed in the text.

The output circuit consists of an output gate, OG, and a MOSFET with a floating n^+ source, a reset gate, ϕ_R, and a drain biased to the dc voltage V_D. A short reset pulse, applied to ϕ_R, changes its surface potential briefly from ϕ_{sR1} to ϕ_{sR2}, as shown in Fig. 3.13b. Then it is lowered again to ϕ_{sR1}. For $\phi_{sR2} > V_D$, the surface potential under the reset gate and the potential of the floating diffusion become V_D, because any charge above V_D will flow into the drain. Using the water analogy, we can think of the drain as a bucket with a hole that always keeps the water level equal to that of the hole. The hole corresponds to the dc drain voltage.

At the end of the reset pulse, the surface potential under the reset gate returns to its original value, but the floating n^+ island remains at V_D, as shown in Fig. 3.13c. Through this reset operation, there is now an isolated, reverse-biased diode. The diode will not remain in this state for long, however. Thermal generation will return it to zero bias in typically a few seconds. But we do not give it that much time.

Pulsing the output gate to raise its surface potential above ϕ_{s2} allows the signal charge to flow into the floating diode, lowering its potential to V_s, as shown in Fig. 3.13d and e. This is the key in this output circuit. The potential of a floating diffusion drops in response to a charge flowing into it. The voltage change, $\Delta V = V_D - V_s$, depends on the amount of charge that flows into it and on its capacitance through

$$\Delta V = Q_N/C \qquad (3.6)$$

We saw earlier a value for Q_N of -1.7×10^{-7} coul/cm^2. For typical gate areas of 10 μm $\times$ 50 μm, this gives around -10^{-12} coul for the charge. For a diode biased to 5 V on a moderately doped substrate, and an optimized area that is smaller than a typical CCD gate area, C is on the order of 10^{-12} F, giving $\Delta V \approx -1$ V. This is a sufficiently large voltage to be useful. This output circuit implementation allows the detection of very small charges, largely because the capacitance can be made very small.

The next question, then, is "How do we make use of this high sensitivity?" Clearly, a floating diffusion is useless if we cannot measure its potential. Fortunately, there is a way of contacting the diffusion, yet keep it floating. It is connected to the gate of a MOSFET located directly beside the diffusion, as shown schematically in Fig. 3.14. The MOSFET is biased for a nominal drain current to flow through it. Its gate voltage, however, is not applied by an external power supply, but rather by the floating diffusion potential. If that potential varies by 1 V as a result of charge flowing into it, then the MOSFET experiences that same 1-V change on its gate, and its drain current changes accordingly. Of course, the gate will add a small capacitance to the capacitance of the diode, but it does not affect the operation in any significant way. The charge in the floating diffusion cannot drain away, because the MOSFET gate is a very-high-impedance point. After the MOSFET current change is detected, the floating diffusion charge is dumped into the drain, as shown in Fig. 3.13a and b, and the output circuit is ready to receive the next charge packet.

What this circuit has achieved, then, is a capacitive contact to the floating diffusion which has the important property of being an impedance converter. The impedance of

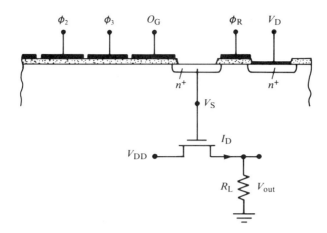

Fig. 3.14 The complete output circuit, showing the floating diffusion connected to the gate of a source-follower MOSFET on-chip amplifier.

a reverse-biased diode is very high. By coupling it to the MOSFET gate and taking the output voltage across the load resistor of a source-follower MOSFET connection, the output impedance is low and therefore can be easily coupled to an off-chip amplifier.

3.4 MULTIPHASE STRUCTURES

The simple three-phase CCD with gaps between adjacent gates is well suited to an introductory discussion and was, in fact, the first CCD structure fabricated. However, in practice, difficulties arise with both its operation and its fabrication. The surface potential between the gates is not well controlled and can assume values that create potential barriers, because there is usually some mobile charge on the surface that drifts in response to the gate voltages. Such potential barriers impede charge transfer. Later designs incorporated overlapping gate structures. Another problem is of a topological nature—i.e., it is necessary to cross over or under one of the gate connection lines to address all the electrodes.

A *four-phase CCD* requires four electrodes and four gate voltages. This would seem to make it more complex. However, clocking voltages are easier to generate due to their symmetry, and, because there is a double potential barrier between successive charge packets, performance is closer to ideal. Fabrication is also more direct. On an oxidized silicon wafer, a conductor, usually polysilicon, is deposited. It is etched into the appropriate pattern and oxidized.

Next a second layer of polysilicon is deposited and etched as shown in Fig. 3.15a. Note the overlapping gate structure, which eliminates the gap problem. The only gap between gates is now the oxide thickness, and even it is covered by a gate.

A structure with all gates on the same thickness insulator can be fabricated only if the first gate is deposited on an insulator that does not oxidize during the subsequent

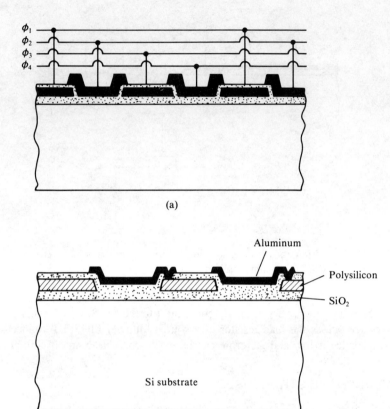

Fig. 3.15 (a) A planar four-phase CCD with overlapping gates, and (b) a two-phase nonplanar structure with overlapping gates.

polysilicon oxidation cycle. Such an insulator is silicon nitride. If the nitride layer is absent during polysilicon oxidation, the oxide between the first-level gates will grow when the gates are oxidized. It will therefore be thicker **between** the gates than **under** the first-level gates. This will result in an asymmetrical structure whose symmetrical operation is perturbed. Such an asymmetrical structure is shown in Fig. 3.15b. The first gate consists of polysilicon, and the second gate is made of aluminum. They are connected to each other, forming one gate.

This asymmetry can be exploited and is the basis of the *two-phase CCD* implemented in the two versions shown in Fig. 3.16a. In the first method, which is very similar to that shown in Fig. 3.15b, varying oxide thicknesses provide the asymmetry necessary for unidirectional charge transfer. According to eq. (3.3), the surface potential for such a structure will be as shown in Fig. 3.16b. In the second method, the asymmetrical surface potential is the result of a more heavily doped region under half

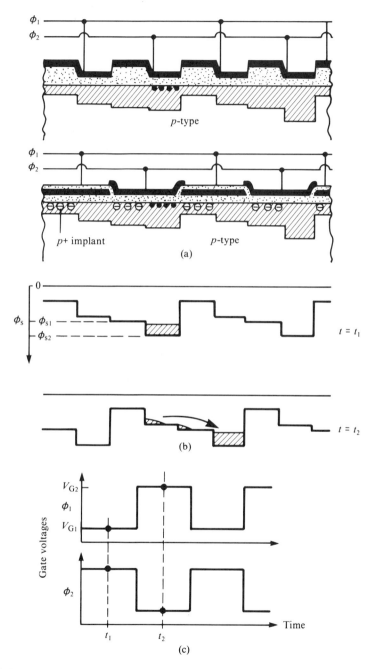

Fig. 3.16 A two-phase CCD. (a) Two methods for achieving asymmetry; (b) the surface potentials at times t_1 and t_2 shown on the clock-voltage diagram in (c).

of each gate. For a p-type structure, a more heavily doped p^+ region is formed by ion implantation. This is indicated by the negative charges representing the ionized acceptors. The p^+ doping reduces the surface potential under that portion of the gate.

The surface potential distributions for times t_1 and t_2 of the clock waveform in Fig. 3.16c are shown in Fig. 3.16b. Only two gates per stage are required for unidirectional operation of such a two-phase CCD. Two gates constitute the one stage necessary to store one charge packet, just as three gates are required in a three-phase device and four gates in a four-phase CCD. Only two clock voltages suffice, and they need not overlap. A clever use of multiple ion implantations has allowed a CCD implementation with only **one** gate level and only one clock voltage. This is the *virtual-phase CCD*.[6]

A limitation of the two-phase device is its lower charge-storage capability. We saw in Fig. 3.9 and eq. (3.4) that the charge in a three-phase device is determined by the gate voltages and oxide capacitance. The larger the $(V_{G2} - V_{G1})$ difference, the larger the charge packet. The same is true for a four-phase device, because the potential barrier is also set by the gate voltages. This is no longer true for the two-phase CCD. Here we see in Fig. 3.16b that the maximum charge is determined by $\Delta\phi_s = \phi_{s2} - \phi_{s1}$, the surface potential difference under the **same** gate, not under adjacent gates. Although use of higher gate voltages will increase $\Delta\phi_s$, this is not nearly as effective as varying adjacent gate voltages in the three- or four-phase case. Hence we find the charge-storage capability of a two-phase CCD to be largely determined during device design by oxide-thickness or implant-doping variations.

3.5 CHARGE TRANSFER

3.5.1 Charge-Transfer Efficiency

We have so far assumed charge transfer from one potential well to the next to be perfect with **all** charge transferred, leaving an empty well behind. In reality, charge transfer is imperfect because (i) there may be insufficient time for the charge to flow from well to well during the allotted time determined by the clock frequency, (ii) some charge is captured in interface states and the emission time is longer than the transfer time, and (iii) there may be potential barriers between the wells. For proper device design, there are no potential barriers, and transfer is not impeded because of this, so the third mechanism is usually not considered.

The effectiveness of charge transfer is expressed by either the *charge-transfer efficiency*, η, or the *charge-transfer inefficiency*, ε. The two are related by

$$\eta = 1 - \varepsilon \tag{3.7}$$

When there is *charge loss*, λ, we have

$$\eta = 1 - \varepsilon - \lambda \tag{3.8}$$

Charge loss occurs, for example, when during device operation the surface becomes accumulated and majority carriers are allowed to recombine with minority carriers that have been captured by interface states. When the device is properly operated, this should not happen. The usual assumption is that $\lambda = 0$, and we will not consider it further.

The charge-transfer process can be characterized by the charge-transfer inefficiency per elemental transfer, which is the fraction of charge left behind when charge is transferred from one well to the next. However, charge is stored in a *stage,* not under each gate, and the charge-transfer inefficiency per stage transfer is sometimes used. We will use the following definitions: ε = charge-transfer inefficiency per elemental transfer, n = number of elemental transfers in the CCD, P = number of clocking phases, N = number of stage transfers, and α = charge-transfer inefficiency per stage. It follows that $n = PN$ and $\alpha = P\varepsilon$.

Consider the charge Q in a potential well. After N transfers, the charge is no longer localized in one well, but due to charge-transfer inefficiency is spread out over several trailing wells. The charge distribution in these wells, normalized by the original charge, is given by the dispersion[7]

$$D_{i,N} = Q_i/Q = [N!(1 - \alpha)^i \alpha^{N-i}]/[(N - i)! i!] \tag{3.9}$$

where i is the stage number, with $i = 0$ being the stage containing the main part of the charge, $i = 1$ being the next stage, and so on. The dispersion caused by the transfer inefficiency for the first two transfers is shown in Fig. 3.17. Note the decreasing size of the charge packet with transfer. The charge deficit from the leading charge packet is found in the trailing packets. Overall, of course, there is charge conservation if the loss term, λ, is zero. The total charge in all of the stages must add up to the original charge.

The fractional deficit from the original charge packet after N stage transfers is given by

$$\text{Deficit} = 1 - D_{N,N} = 1 - (1 - \alpha)^N = 1 - (1 - P\varepsilon)^{n/P}$$
$$\approx N\alpha = n\varepsilon \tag{3.10}$$

for $N\alpha \ll 1$ and $n\varepsilon \ll 1$. The word "deficit" here means the charge loss from the leading charge packet that is found in the trailing packets. It is a temporary, not a permanent, loss.

Note that transfer inefficiency has two effects. One is the charge loss from the leading packet, shown in Fig. 3.17a, b, and c. The other is charge mixing. If there is a charge packet following the one in question, then clearly the charge left behind by one packet will add to the trailing packet. This is shown in Fig. 3.17d, where the charge increment lost by the first packet is added to the second one. For digital signals, where threshold levels determine the "ones" and "zeros," this presents no problem provided

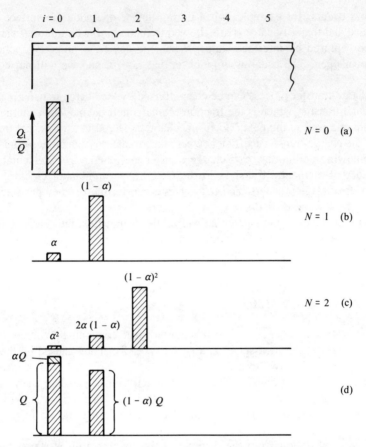

Fig. 3.17 Effects of transfer inefficiency on the normalized charge in a potential well after (a) one, (b) two, and (c) three transfers; (d) shows charge mixing.

that the charge loss of the first packet does not reduce its size below the threshold level.

Let us demonstrate this charge mixing with an example. Consider a 500-stage, three-phase digital delay line in which the threshold levels are such that 50% of full charge or more corresponds to a **1** and less than 50% is a **0**. For $\varepsilon = 1 \times 10^{-4}$, eq. (3.10) gives the remaining charge after 1500 transfers as $(1 - \text{loss}) = (1 - 3 \times 10^{-4})^{500} = 0.86$. Now suppose the input charge is not a full well, but 80% of a full well. The output is then $0.86 \times 0.8 \approx 0.7$, and the distinction between **1** and **0** is preserved. If the transfer inefficiency increases to $\varepsilon = 3 \times 10^{-4}$, we find that $(1 - \text{loss}) = 0.64$, and the output becomes $0.64 \times 0.8 \approx 0.51$. It is no longer possible to distinguish clearly between a **1** and a **0**. In this example, transfer inefficiency has blurred the ability to discriminate between the logic values of digital information. This is obviously not permissible in a digital circuit.

For analog signals the situation is worse, because there are no threshold values. It is the **magnitude** of each charge packet that carries the desired information. Transfer inefficiency distorts the information content. This is known as *crosstalk*. The name is particularly appropriate for CCD imagers in which crosstalk, or charge mixing between adjacent stages, appears as a smeared image in the display. After N stage transfers, the crosstalk between adjacent stages ($i = N$ and $i = N - 1$) is, from eq. (3.9),

$$D_{N-1,N}/D_{N,N} = N\alpha/(1 - \alpha) = n\varepsilon/(1 - P\varepsilon) \tag{3.11}$$

A considerable crosstalk reduction is effected if charge is held in every second stage, keeping an empty well between charge packets. Then we have

$$D_{N-2,N}/D_{N,N} = [N(N - 1)/2]/[\alpha/(1 - \alpha)]^2 \tag{3.12}$$

For the transfer inefficiencies of the digital delay line example considered previously, we find 15% and 45% crosstalk for charge in adjacent stages and 1.1% and 10% when an empty well is provided between charge packets. These examples show the importance of good transfer efficiency on CCD performance for either digital or analog use.

3.5.2 Charge-Transport Theory

The importance of transfer inefficiency is clear from the previous section. Now we examine the charge transfer in more detail. There are two primary mechanisms that determine charge-transfer efficiency. For surface-channel CCD's, *interface-state trapping* dominates at low and intermediate frequencies, and *carrier ballistics* dominate at high frequencies. For bulk-channel devices, bulk traps dominate at low and intermediate frequencies and carrier ballistics again limit the high-frequency performance. Because these two mechanisms operate at different frequencies, it is usual practice to analyze each separately and sum the resulting transfer efficiency predictions. We will follow that same procedure. First, carrier ballistics will be examined, and then interface and bulk-state trapping.

The physical mechanisms which lead to carrier motion from potential well to potential well are the same as those determining carrier motion in any semiconductor device—namely, drift and diffusion. In a MOSFET, as was shown in Volume IV, the drain current is due mainly to drift, with diffusion contributing only a minor part. In a *pn* junction diode, diffusion plays a very important role, especially in the quasineutral regions near the scr. In CCD's drift dominates. CCD gates are very narrow, and the intergate spacing is on the order of the insulator thickness. When the gate voltages on adjacent gates differ by several volts, appreciable electric fields are produced in the direction of charge transfer by these external voltages. Furthermore, when transfer is initiated due to the induced variation in carrier concentration from point to point under the gate, the large carrier concentrations in charge-containing wells lead to significant electric fields in the direction of charge transfer.

There is, of course, only one lateral electric field value at any given point in a CCD structure. It is common practice, however, to divide the lateral electric field into two components: the *fringing field* associated with the x-direction field spreading from one gate to the next, and the *self-induced field* associated with the variation in carrier concentration from point to point under the transfer gate. Charge transfer is frequently divided into three parts. We illustrate this in Fig. 3.18.

Initially, the voltages on phases 2 and 3 are taken to be equal, and lower than the phase 1 voltage, as shown by the dashed line in Fig. 3.18. Subsequently, the voltage on phase 2 is raised to a value larger than that on phase 1, and the charge begins to flow into the potential well under gate 2. The initial charge-transfer phase is shown in Fig. 3.18. During the early transfer stages, self-induced drift is dominant. It can be thought of as carriers pushing one another into the empty well and diminishes as the carrier concentration in the **discharging** well becomes small. During the intermediate stages of transfer, the fringing-field component is dominant. Here the electric field of the **receiving gate** reaches under the **discharging gate** and pulls the carriers into the receiving well. The shorter the gates, the more important this component is. Finally,

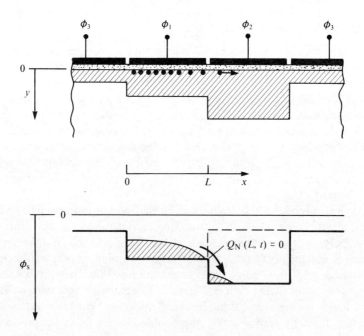

Fig. 3.18   Schematic of charge flow from one potential well to the next.

when both of these mechanisms have become ineffective, the last charge remnant moves by thermal diffusion. This is the slowest of the three components.

For short-gate-length CCD's, fringing-field transfer can be effective for most of the transfer period, effectively eliminating the diffusive component. This is especially true for bulk-channel CCD's, where fringing fields are much more effective because the charge is located not at the surface but within the semiconductor. The operational frequencies in those devices are much higher for that very reason.

CCD charge-transport theory requires a solution to the continuity and to Poisson's equations, as does the solution for other semiconductor devices. This approach is very difficult and in general necessitates computer solutions. Various approximations are usually made to make the problem tractable. These approximations permit "decoupling" of the continuity and Poisson's equations. Usually, the concept of fringing and self-induced fields is introduced. A good example of this type of solution can be found in Ref. [8].

A powerful alternative to the generalized solution, simplified by appropriate approximations, is the *charge-control solution*. It allows closed-form solutions that closely approximate exact computer solutions. Yet physical insight, so necessary for a good understanding of semiconductor devices, is retained.

The charge-control approach was originally developed to simplify the transient analysis of bipolar transistors,[9] and has since been applied in analyzing the transient response of other semiconductor devices. The main contribution of the charge-control approach is the removal of the functional dependence of ordinary differential equations on the spatial coordinates, by integrating the continuity equation in terms of the minority-carrier density over some physical dimension. The physical dimension is the base width in bipolar transistors and the gate length in CCD's. The continuity equation becomes a first-order, *ordinary* differential equation with time as the independent variable. Under dynamic conditions, charge control assumes the time rate of change of charge to be low enough for the instantaneous charge distributions to be a succession of steady-state distributions.

With integration of the continuity equation, some detail is obviously lost, but the resulting simplification is often worth this sacrifice. For CCD's, the final results of the charge-control analysis are remarkably similar to detailed computer analyses.[10] An additional advantage is that calculations can be made with relatively little effort and simple computer programs.

Following the classical approach to charge-control theory, the starting point is the continuity equation expressed in terms of the CCD electron charge:

$$\partial Q_N(x,t)/\partial t = \partial J_N(x,t)/\partial x - Q_N(x,t)/\tau_s \qquad (3.13)$$

In contrast to the usual continuity equation, in which minority-carrier recombination is considered, here the second term on the right side of the equation accounts for charge capture by interface states. τ_s is the effective time constant for electron capture. Interface state capture will be discussed in the next section. We repeat here that the charge captured by interface states is only temporarily lost. It is eventually released from the interface states, but is, of course, missing from the original charge packet and is added to trailing packets.

The continuity equation is integrated with respect to x over the CCD gate length L. This gives

$$\int_0^L [\partial Q_N(x, t)/\partial t]\, dx = \int_0^L [\partial J_N(x, t)/\partial x]\, dx - (1/\tau_s) \int_0^L Q_N(x, t)\, dx \qquad (3.14)$$

To remove the functional dependence of the spatial coordinate x from eq. (3.14), we define a **charge per unit width**, $Q_z(t)$, as

$$Q_z(t) = \int_0^L Q_N(x, t)\, dx \qquad (3.15)$$

This allows eq. (3.14) to be written as the basic charge-control equation

$$dQ_z(t)/dt = J_N(L, t) - J_N(0, t) - Q_z(t)/\tau_s \qquad (3.16)$$

Eq. (3.16) shows the rate of change of charge to be governed by the current inflow at $x = 0$, the current outflow at $x = L$, and the rate at which charge vanishes by inter-face-state capture. The transient behavior of the total charge in the discharging well is determined by the boundary conditions and by the model used to represent interface charge trapping during transfer to the receiving well.

The boundary condition at the left end of the discharging gate is

$$J_N(0, t) = 0 \qquad (3.17)$$

because the barrier in Fig. 3.18 prevents charge flow to the left. At the right end we have current flow so that, for $0 < x \le L$,

$$J_N(x, t) = D_n\, \partial Q_N(x, t)/\partial x + \mu_n Q_N(x, t)\mathscr{E} \qquad (3.18)$$

where the electric field, $\mathscr{E}$, is a combination fringing field, $\mathscr{E}_{xf}$, and self-induced field, $\mathscr{E}_{xs}$. The self-induced field is due to the surface potential gradient $\phi_s(x, t)$, or one can think of it as due to the charge gradient in the well.

The surface potential was earlier shown to be given by

$$\phi_s(x, t) = V_G' - [Q_N(x, t) + Q_B(x, t)]/C_o \approx V_G' - Q_N(x, t)/C_{eff} \qquad (3.19)$$

Here Q_B is the bulk charge density and C_{eff} is an effective surface capacitance per unit area. The linear approximate relationship is good for thin oxides and low substrate doping concentrations.

The self-induced field is given by

$$\mathscr{E}_{xs} = -\partial\phi_s(x,t)/\partial x = (1/C_{eff})\,\partial Q_N(x,t)/\partial x \tag{3.20}$$

and eq. (3.16), in conjunction with eq. (3.18), becomes

$$dQ_z(t)/dt = \{D_n\,\partial Q_N(x,t)/\partial x + [\mu_n\,Q_N(x,t)/C_{eff}]\,\partial Q_N(x,t)/\partial x + \mu_n\,Q_N(x,t)\mathscr{E}_{xf}\}_{x=L}$$
$$- Q_z(t)/\tau_s \tag{3.21}$$

An analytical solution of eq. (3.21) can be obtained only by transforming it into an ordinary differential equation with known time-dependent coefficients. The charge-control method circumvents this by postulating instantaneous charge distribution during the transient decay. This may seem unreasonable until it is realized that any disturbance within the charge packet redistributes itself very rapidly. Typically, this redistribution time is the dielectric relaxation time of the charge packet, which is on the order of 10^{-12} s. Since the dielectric relaxation time is dependent on the carrier density, it obviously increases as the charge in the packet decreases. However, for charge-transfer times of 10^{-7} to 10^{-3} s, the charge redistribution can be assumed to be instantaneous for most applications. So we see that the charge-control approach is quite reasonable.

Separation of variables leads to

$$Q_N(x,t) = g(x)f(t) \tag{3.22}$$

implying that the shape function of the charge distribution, $g(x)$, remains unchanged during the transient. In other words, the charge always redistributes itself instantaneously to follow the shape of the initial distribution. Its magnitude is weighted by the time function $f(t)$ to satisfy the integral form of the transport equation.

The details of the solution of eq. (3.21) are discussed in detail in Ref. [10]. We will not repeat them here, because of their length. We merely quote the main results. What is the chief device parameter of interest? It is the transfer efficiency or inefficiency. It is, after all, the aim of the device designer to design a device that transfers its charge with maximum efficiency. The transfer efficiency is therefore a good device descriptor.

We define the fraction of charge remaining in the discharging potential well as $\varepsilon(t)$. This quantity is clearly the charge-transfer inefficiency discussed earlier. But now we see that it is a function of time. Physically this is quite reasonable, for if the time allowed for charge transfer is very short, then only a small fraction of the charge packet will have time to transfer, and ε will be correspondingly high. Similarly, if we allow a long time, ε will decrease accordingly.

The temporal behavior of the charge-transfer inefficiency is, from Ref. [10],

$$\varepsilon(t) = K \exp(-Kt/t_{tr})/\{K + (\pi^2 Q_{av}/8C_{eff})[1 - \exp(-Kt/t_{tr})]\} \qquad (3.23)$$

where $K = \pi^2 D_n/4\mu_n + \pi L \mathscr{E}_{xf}/2$, $t_{tr} = L^2/\mu_n$, the transit time for 1-V bias, and Q_{av} = average initial charge density per unit area.

Eq. (3.23) is plotted in Fig. 3.19 for a given Q_{av}/C_{eff} and various fringing-field values $\mathscr{E}_{xf}$. For zero fringing field, the curve shows an initial rapid drop in ε due to the self-induced field, followed by the slower diffusion tail. The exact numerical solution is also shown for comparison, and the agreement is seen to be very good. The effect of fringing fields is obvious in this figure. As the fringing field increases from 0 to 1000 V/cm, ε decreases drastically. A combination of electric field and sufficient transfer time can make ε arbitrarily small. In practice, this is observed to some extent, but the transfer inefficiency levels off at some lower value. It does not go to zero. The reason for this is interface-state trapping, which we have neglected in this discussion.

The time scale of Fig. 3.19 is the normalized transit time. For CCD operation, the time allowed for charge transfer is set by the clock frequency. For a given frequency or the corresponding transfer time, the transfer inefficiency is found from Fig. 3.19 for that particular time. Clearly, the longer the time allotted for charge transfer, the lower the transfer inefficiency.

3.6   INTERFACE-STATE TRAPPING

3.6.1   A Qualitative Description

The results of the previous section indicate that when the charge packet is given sufficient time, the transfer inefficiency can be made arbitrarily small. This is not observed experimentally. A typical transfer inefficiency vs. clock frequency curve has the form shown in Fig. 3.20. For frequencies less than f_1, ε is reasonably constant, while for frequencies greater than f_1, ε rises sharply. In this steep part of the curve, transfer inefficiency is limited by carrier ballistics, while in the constant part it is limited by interface states in SCCD's and by bulk states in BCCD's. We treat only the effect of interface states. Bulk state behavior is similar. To understand how interface-state trapping can lead to transfer inefficiency, let us consider what happens when a charge packet is transferred into an empty potential well.

We saw in Section 1.2.4 that interface states at the semiconductor/oxide interface are generally distributed in energy throughout the band gap. This was originally shown in Fig. 1.12, and we show it again in Fig. 3.21. Consider that a large number of *zeros* — i.e., no charge — have traversed the CCD. Thermal electron and hole emission has established some steady-state energy level below which the interface states are filled with electrons and above which they are empty of electrons. This condition is

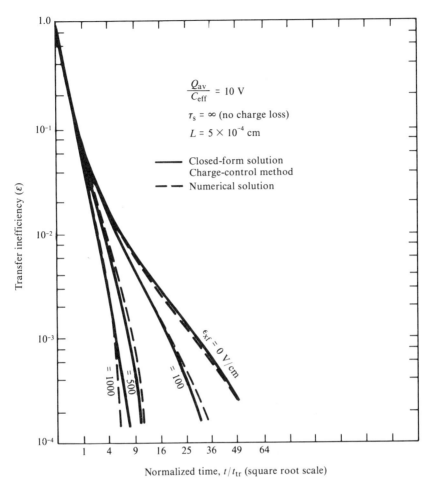

Fig. 3.19 Charge-transfer efficiency vs. normalized time as a function of fringing field for the charge-control approach and full numerical solution. Reprinted after Ref. [12] by permission of IEEE (© 1972, IEEE).

shown in Fig. 3.21a. When a **one**—i.e., a charge packet—enters the empty well, some electrons from the charge packet are captured by empty interface states. The capture time is on the order of 10^{-9} s, and interface states are filled to a new, higher energy level shown in Fig. 3.21b. The new energy level is the quasi-Fermi level F_N, determined by the charge density in the well.

When the charge packet is transferred to the next potential well, the discharging well becomes empty. Some of the electrons captured earlier by interface states are emitted as shown in Fig. 3.21c. The emission time constants depend exponentially on

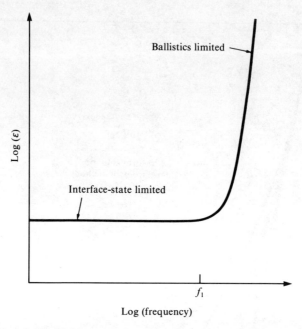

Fig. 3.20   Transfer inefficiency vs. clock frequency. Both are shown in log-log form.

the energy levels of the interface states below the conduction-band edge. There is, therefore, a wide spectrum of emission-time constants, each corresponding to one energy level.

Those electrons emitted in time to join the departing charge packet will obviously be transferred with it. Those whose emission times are longer than the time governed by the clock frequency cannot join the original packet and remain in the discharging well (Fig. 3.21d). Note that in Fig. 3.21d there are more occupied interface states than in Fig. 3.21a. The extra electrons in these occupied states are the same ones lost by the departing charge packet. The result is that the transferring charge packet will leave some electrons in each potential well through which it moves, and at the output will appear to have lost charge, because it will be smaller in magnitude than it was when it entered the CCD. The "lost" charge, of course, is not permanently lost, but only temporarily captured and will therefore appear as the delayed output shown in Fig. 3.17.

This type of charge-transfer degradation can be substantially improved by maintaining a *bias charge* in each potential well of the CCD. Such a bias charge is a small fraction of the maximum charge that the well can accommodate. The bias charge is electrically introduced at the CCD input by a *fill-and-spill* input circuit, for example, whether or not there is signal charge in the well. It is sometimes called a *fat zero* and serves to keep the slowest-emitting interface states occupied by electrons at all times.

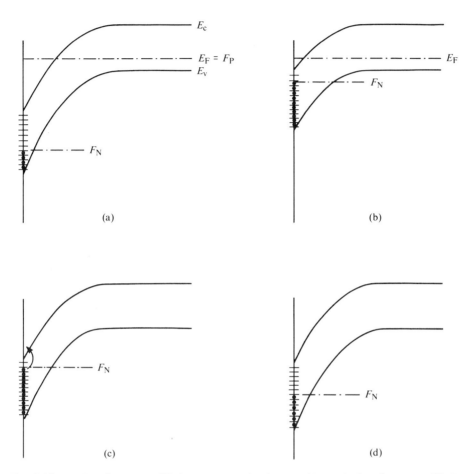

Fig. 3.21 (a) Interface states filled to an energy level near midgap, (b) interface states filled to the electron quasi-Fermi level, F_N, (c) electrons emitted from interface states join their original charge packet, and (d) electrons not emitted during the transfer time remain behind in interface states.

Let us illustrate this with an example. The band diagram of Fig. 3.22 represents the semiconductor energy-band diagram. Those solid circles within bracket (1) represent electrons in interface states with neither bias nor signal charge in the well. For a charge packet in the well, interface states fill up to the level F_N (full packet), so that bracket (2) and bracket (3) electrons represent those electrons captured from the charge packet. Now suppose that the clock frequency is such that only bracket (3) electrons join the transferring packet. Clearly, the bracket (2) electrons are lost from the charge packet. If a bias charge is introduced to keep the bracket (2) interface states filled with elec-

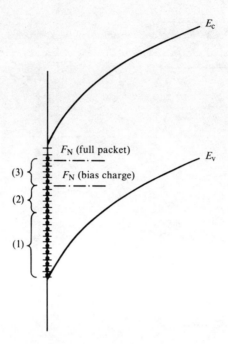

Fig. 3.22 (1) Electrons in interface states for no bias charge and no signal charge, (2) electrons in interface states from the bias charge, and (3) electrons in interface states from the signal charge; they are re-emitted to join their charge packet.

trons at all times, then the charge packet will not lose any charge as it transfers through the CCD. The effectiveness of this procedure is very nicely illustrated in Fig. 3.23. The transfer inefficiency is very high in the absence of a bias charge, but in its presence it drops significantly. The transfer inefficiency does not become zero. However, it does become quite small. For frequencies above 1 MHz in this example, carrier ballistics dominate charge transfer and bias charge has little influence because interface-state trapping no longer dominates.

3.6.2 A Mathematical Description

Interface states at a semiconductor/oxide interface are continuously distributed in energy throughout the band gap. Any theory dealing with recombination or generation should therefore employ an integration in energy over the band gap, as discussed in Section 1.2.4. For simplicity we will first apply Shockley-Read-Hall recombination-generation theory to an interface with N_{it} interface states per unit area at energy E_{it} in the band gap. Being concerned with both capture and emission, we use eqs. (1.57) to (1.60) and write the time rate of change of electron-occupied interface states, n_{it}, as

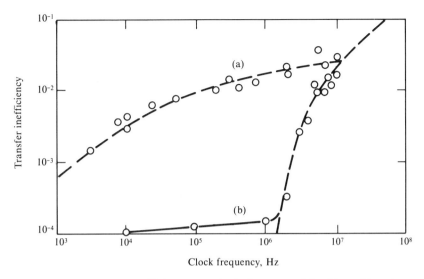

Fig. 3.23 Charge-transfer inefficiency vs. clock frequency (a) without bias charge, and (b) with bias charge. Reprinted after Ref. [11] by permission of Solid-State Technology, published by Technical Publishing, a company of Dun and Bradstreet.

$$dn_{it}/dt = (c_{ns}n_s + e_{ps})(N_{it} - n_{it}) - (c_{ps}p_s + e_{ns})n_{it} \qquad (3.24)$$

Let us now examine two solutions that are somewhat simplified but that bring out the main points of electron capture and emission: (i) If all the interface states are initially occupied by electrons at $t = 0$, the solution to eq. (3.24) for $t > 0$ is

$$n_{it}(t) = \tau N_{it}[(c_{ns}n_s + e_{ps}) + (c_{ps}p_s + e_{ns}) \exp(-t/\tau)] \qquad (3.25)$$

(ii) If all the interface states are initially empty of electrons at $t = 0$, the solution for $t > 0$ is

$$n_{it}(t) = \tau N_{it}(c_{ns}n_s + e_{ps})[1 - \exp(-t/\tau)] \qquad (3.26)$$

where the time constant is $\tau = 1/(c_{ns}n_s + e_{ns} + c_{ps}p_s + e_{ps})$. The concentrations n_s and p_s are assumed to be time-independent for all $t > 0$ in deriving these solutions. What do these equations mean? Suppose that the CCD has had zero charge for some time. This implies $p_s = n_s = 0$, and eqs. (3.25) and (3.26) give

$$n_{it}(t \to \infty) = N_{it}/(1 + e_{ns}/e_{ps}) \qquad (3.27)$$

This represents the steady-state occupancy of the interface states and is determined by the two emission rates only.

For n-channel CCD's, **electron** capture and emission are of main interest. The hole concentration and hole capture and emission can be neglected, and the time constant simplifies to

$$\tau = 1/(c_{ns}n_s + e_{ns}) = 1/\{c_{ns}n_s + c_{ns}n_i \exp[(E_{it} - E_i)/kT]\} \qquad (3.28a)$$

$$\tau = 1/\{c_{ns}n_s + c_{ns}N_c \exp[-(E_c - E_{it})/kT]\} \qquad (3.28b)$$

When a charge packet enters an empty well, electron **capture** dominates. Consider a packet with 10^{12} electrons/cm^2 in an inversion layer 100 Å thick. Assuming the electrons to be uniformly distributed within the inversion layer, the electron volume density is $n_s = 10^{18}$ cm^{-3}. For $v_{th} = 10^7$ cm/s and $\sigma_{ns} = 10^{-15}$ cm^2, we have $c_{ns} = v_{th}\sigma_{ns} = 10^{-8}$ cm^3/s. Furthermore, using $N_c = 10^{19}$ cm^{-3}, we get for the **capture-time constant, τ_c:**

$$\tau_c = 1/\{10^{10} + 10^{11} \exp[-(E_c - E_{it})/kT]\} \qquad (3.29)$$

For interface states with energy of $3kT$ or more below E_c, we find

$$\tau_c \approx 10^{-10} \text{ s} \qquad (3.30)$$

The capture-time constant is independent of energy. For those states closer to E_c, the capture time is even shorter. So, on most CCD operational time scales, electron capture is essentially instantaneous.

When the charge packet is transferred into the next potential well, the electron concentration, n_s, in the discharging well decreases to zero. Electron capture ceases, and electron **emission**, given by the emission-time constant, τ_e, is

$$\tau_e = 1/\{c_{ns}N_c \exp[-(E_c - E_{it})/kT]\} \qquad (3.31)$$

For the same parameters as above, we find

$$\tau_e \approx 10^{-11} \exp[(E_c - E_{it})/kT] \qquad (3.32)$$

which, in contrast to τ_c, is very dependent on the interface-state energy.

For transfer-efficiency purposes, it is important to know how many electrons are emitted in the time allowed by the clock frequency. The probability, $\mathscr{P}$, of an electron captured on an interface state at energy E_{it} being emitted in time t is given by

$$\mathscr{P} = 1 - \exp(-t/\tau_e) \qquad (3.33)$$

The electron charge per unit area, Q_N, emitted in time t from interface states distributed in energy throughout the band gap, all occupied by electrons at $t = 0$, is given by

$$Q_N(t) = q \int_0^{E_G} D_{it}(E)\{1 - \exp[-t/\tau_e(E)]\}\, dE \qquad (3.34)$$

Here we have simplified eq. (3.31) to read

$$\tau_e(E) = 1/[\sigma_{ns}(E) v_{th} N_c \exp(-E/kT)] \qquad (3.35)$$

by replacing $(E_c - E_{it})$ with E, where E is measured from the bottom of the conduction band, with E_c as the reference energy.

A solution of eq. (3.34) requires a knowledge of the energy dependence of both $D_{it}(E)$ and $\sigma_{ns}(E)$. Neither one is generally known for a given device unless detailed measurements are performed. Assuming both of these factors to be constant, we leave it to the reader to show (see Problem 3.5) that

$$Q_N(t) \approx qkT D_{it} \ln(\sigma_{ns} v_{th} N_c t) \qquad (3.36)$$

is valid for $1/(\sigma_{ns} v_{th} N_c) \ll t \ll \tau_e$ at $E = E_G/2$. For Si CCD's, eq. (3.36) can be expected to be valid in the time range from 10^{-10} to 10^{-3} s, making it applicable for most CCD applications.

Let us now see the effects of interface-state trapping on transfer inefficiency. Consider a CCD in which a series of **ones** is transferred, filling the interface states. They are followed by n_z **zeros**, allowing some of the captured electrons to be emitted. The time available for electron emission is

$$t_1 = n_z/f_c + 1/Pf_c \qquad (3.37)$$

where P is the number of clocking phases and f_c the clocking frequency. When now a single **one** is transferred, the time for electron emission is

$$t_2 = 1/Pf_c \qquad (3.38)$$

and the **one** will lose

$$Q_N(\text{loss}) = [Q_N(t_1) - Q_N(t_2)] \qquad (3.39)$$

charge to interface states. The first term represents the empty states ready to capture electrons from the **one**, while the second represents those captured electrons that are re-emitted to join the **one**.

Using eqs. (3.36) to (3.39) gives

$$Q_N(\text{loss}) = qkT D_{it} \ln(1 + Pn_z) \qquad (3.40)$$

With the transfer inefficiency defined by $\varepsilon = Q_N(\text{loss})/Q_N$, we find

$$\varepsilon = [qkTD_{it}/Q_N] \ln(1 + Pn_z) \qquad (3.41)$$

where Q_N is the charge in the charge packet prior to capture. For $D_{it} = 10^{10}$ cm^{-2} eV^{-1}, $Q_N/q = 10^{12}$ cm^{-2}, $P = 3$, and $n_z = 5$, we find $\varepsilon = 7 \times 10^{-4}$.

Eq. (3.41) shows very clearly the effect of the charge concentration. When Q_N becomes small, the transfer inefficiency increases. That is why a bias charge keeps ε low. If the charge concentration consists of both signal charge, $Q_N(\text{sig})$, and bias charge, $Q_N(\text{bias})$, the transfer inefficiency becomes

$$\varepsilon = \{qkTD_{it}/[Q_N(\text{sig}) + Q_N(\text{bias})]\} \ln(1 + Pn_z) \qquad (3.42)$$

If $Q_N(\text{sig})$ is small for low-level signals, an appropriate bias charge ensures a low transfer inefficiency. This is very graphically demonstrated in Fig. 3.23. Eq. (3.42) also shows an increase in ε with more **zeros** between **ones**. That should be obvious. The longer the time between **ones**, the more time there is for electrons to be emitted from interface states and the more interface states are ready to capture electrons from the first **one**. Bias charge reduces this effect by always keeping interface states occupied to a certain energy level.

3.7 BULK-CHANNEL DEVICES

Bulk-channel CCD's (BCCD's) are functionally very similar to their surface-channel counterparts. However, they are different and use some interesting device concepts. Their chief difference is found in the location of the charge packet. In an SCCD the charge is located at the surface, while in a BCCD it is located within the semiconductor, away from the surface. An n-channel BCCD consists of an n-island in a p-substrate with an oxide and a series of gates, as shown in Fig. 3.24a. When the n-region is typically a few microns thick and formed by epitaxy, the device is generally called a *peristaltic CCD*. When it is very shallow, typically less than one micron, and formed by ion implantation, it is generally called a *buried-channel CCD*.

The SCCD is basically a two-terminal device — one terminal on the gate, and another on the substrate. In addition, of course, there are input and output gates, not considered here because they are common to both SCCD's and BCCD's. The BCCD is a three-terminal structure — one terminal on the gate, a second on the substrate, and a third on the n-island.

Consider, for the moment, the gates and the substrate grounded and a positive voltage V_n applied to the n-layer. The voltage V_n reverse biases the np junction as well as the surface under the gate, and the scr spreads into the n-layer from both the top and the bottom. For V_n sufficiently high, the two scr regions merge, and the n-layer is then totally depleted. This is shown in Fig. 3.24a and b for phases ϕ_1 and ϕ_3. A potential minimum is created in the n-layer. Charge introduced into the device alters the energy-

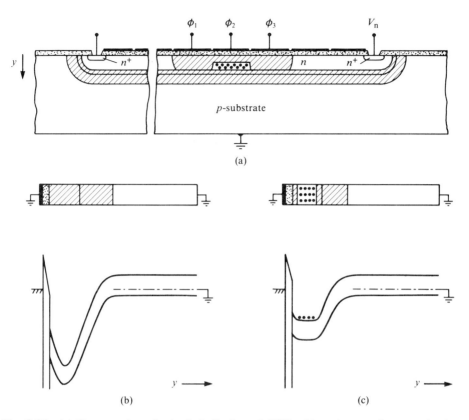

Fig. 3.24 (a) Cross section of a basic bulk-channel CCD without input and output circuits; (b) energy-band diagram from gate to substrate with no charge, as under gates 1 and 3; and (c) diagram similar to (b), but with charge, as under gate 2.

band diagram, as under gate 2 in Fig. 3.24a and c. The charge is stored as **majority** carriers in the potential minimum, surrounded on all sides by reverse-biased space-charge regions.

There are two major deviations from SCCD's. First, the charge consists of majority carriers instead of minority carriers, and second, it is not located at the surface but resides in the bulk. This second feature has removed the interaction of charge with interface states, resulting in higher device performance.

The electrical input and output are similar to those of SCCD's, with the exception that injection of **majority** carriers requires an **ohmic** rather than a minority-carrier-injecting pn-junction contact. This is indicated by the n^+ input and output diffusions in Fig. 3.24a. The actual input and output structure details, however, are not shown in Fig. 3.24a.

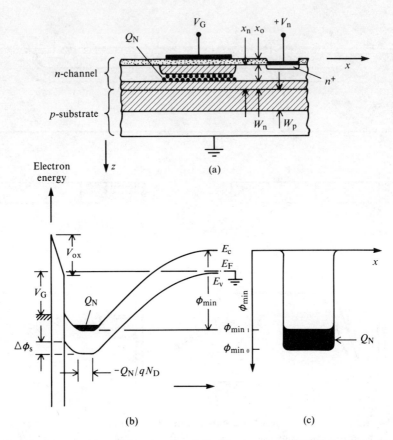

Fig. 3.25 Cross section (a), and energy-band diagrams perpendicular (b) and parallel (c) to the surface. Note that the potential well diagram (c) is not at the surface, but at the potential minimum.

Figure 3.25 shows more detailed cross-section and energy-band diagrams. The diagram in Fig. 3.25b is similar to that in Fig. 3.24c, while that in Fig. 3.25c shows a potential well along the x-direction, located within the n-island. The gate voltage in Fig. 3.25 is a positive value, no longer zero as in Fig. 3.24.

A detailed derivation of the BCCD equations is given in Ref. [12]. We only quote the most relevant equations here. The minimum potential, defined in Fig. 3.25b, is the potential at which the charge resides and is given by

$$\phi_{min} = [V_{G1} + V_{01} - (2V_{G1}V_{01} + V_{01}^2)^{1/2}][1 + N_A/N_D] \qquad (3.43)$$

with $V_{G1} = V_G' + V_1 - Q_N/C_e$, $V_1 = qN_Dx_n(x_o/K_o\varepsilon_0 + x_n/2K_s\varepsilon_0)$, $C_e = x_o/K_o\varepsilon_0 + (x_n - W_n - Q_N/2qN_D)/K_s\varepsilon_0$, $W_n = \{2K_s\varepsilon_0\phi_{min}/[qN_AN_D/(N_D + N_A)]\}^{1/2}$, $V_{01} =$

$qK_s\varepsilon_0N_A/C_1^2$, $C_1^{-1} = x_o/K_o\varepsilon_0 + x_n/K_s\varepsilon_0$, and Q_N = magnitude of the charge density per unit area in the potential well. Eq. (3.43) reduces to eq. (3.3) when $x_n \to 0$, $N_D \to \infty$, and ϕ_{min} is replaced by ϕ_s. The bulk-channel CCD becomes a surface-channel device in that case.

Similar to the energy-band diagrams of Fig. 3.7, we show in Fig. 3.26a the energy-band diagrams for varying amounts of charge in the potential well. The charge ranges from zero to maximum or saturation charge in increments of $Q_N/4$. These curves are for zero gate and zero substrate voltage. The effect of gate voltage on the energy bands with half the maximum charge is depicted in Fig. 3.26b. The gate voltage shifts the potential minimum up or down and, by proper sequencing of the gate voltages, causes charge transfer through the device.

One of the advantages of a BCCD over an SCCD is the location of the charge packet away from the oxide/semiconductor interface. This is described by the potential barrier $\Delta\phi_s$ in Fig. 3.25b. It is given by

$$\Delta\phi_s = (qN_D/2K_s\varepsilon_0)(x_n - W_n + Q_N/qN_D) \tag{3.44}$$

where Q_N is negative for *n*-channel devices.

A disadvantage of the BCCD is its lower charge-storage capability. Figure 3.27 shows cross sections through both an SCCD and a BCCD. Both devices have an oxide

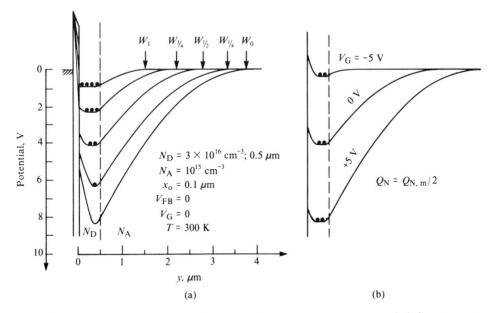

Fig. 3.26 The potential into the semiconductor for a BCCD with (a) zero, $\frac{1}{4}$, $\frac{1}{2}$, $\frac{3}{4}$, and maximum charge at zero gate and substrate voltage and (b) $\frac{1}{2}$ maximum charge for three gate voltages.

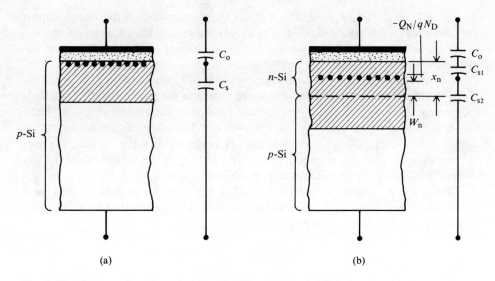

Fig. 3.27 Cross sections through (a) an SCCD and (b) a BCCD, showing the charge location and the capacitances in each case.

capacitance in series with a reverse-biased scr capacitance. For the SCCD in Fig. 3.27a, the minority-carrier charge is located at the surface and is given by

$$Q_{N,m} = -C_o(V_{G2} - V_{G1}) \tag{3.45}$$

This equation was derived earlier as eq. (3.4). The capacitance in this expression is the oxide capacitance.

For the BCCD, the charge is located within the semiconductor, shown in Fig. 3.27b. The charge-storage capability now is

$$Q_{N,m} = -C_e(V_{G2} - V_{G1}) \tag{3.46}$$

with the effective capacitance given by

$$C_e = (1/C_o + 1/C_{s1})^{-1} \tag{3.47}$$

where

$$1/C_{s1} = (x_n - W_n + Q_N/2qN_D)/K_s\varepsilon_0 \tag{3.48}$$

All three terms in the parentheses represent portions of the n-layer. The first term, x_n, is the thickness of the n-layer itself; W_n is the width of the np junction scr that extends into the n-layer; and $-Q_N/qN_D$ is the width occupied by the charge in the potential well. Half of that width applies to C_{s1} and the other half to C_{s2} in Fig. 3.27b.

From the same figure we find that the width $-Q_N/qN_D$ cannot be larger than $(x_n - W_n)$. This gives the maximum charge that can be stored under an isolated gate as

$$Q_N(\text{max}) = -qN_D(x_n - W_n) \qquad (3.49)$$

The maximum charge in a full-potential well is furthermore determined by the gate voltages, as

$$Q_{N,m} = C_o(V_{G2} - V_{G1})/[1 + K_o(x_n - W_n)/2K_s x_o] \qquad (3.50)$$

From eqs. (3.45) and (3.50) we find the ratio of BCCD to SCCD charge storage to be

$$Q_{N,m}(\text{BCCD})/Q_{N,m}(\text{SCCD}) = 1/[1 + K_o(x_n - W_n)/2K_s x_o] \qquad (3.51)$$

For most BCCD's, $N_D \gg N_A$, so that $W_n/x_n \ll 1$ and the ratio in eq. (3.51) becomes approximately $(1 + K_o x_n/2K_s x_o)$. For a device with $x_n = 0.5 \ \mu m$ and $x_o = 0.1 \ \mu m$, we find the BCCD to be able to hold only 0.55 of the charge of the SCCD. This is the charge-handling penalty of the BCCD. It can hold only 50 to 75% of the charge of an SCCD with identical oxide thickness, gate area, and clock-voltage swings.

So far we have shown the charge location within the semiconductor to be an operational penalty, because the charge-storage capability of the BCCD is reduced in comparison with that of an SCCD. Yet, the BCCD has become the workhorse of the charge-transfer device family. The main reason for this is the very charge location that reduces the charge-storage capacity. Because charge is not located at the surface, interactions with interface states are eliminated. This alleviates a major cause of charge-transfer inefficiency. It is true that the charge interacts with bulk states, but it is easier to reduce the bulk-state density than it is to reduce the interface-state density. It is typically found that BCCD's have lower transfer inefficiencies than SCCD's of comparable geometry. When a bias charge is introduced, transfer inefficiencies as low as 10^{-5} have been achieved. Such values are very difficult to obtain with SCCD's.

A further, very important operational advantage of BCCD's can also be traced to the charge location—that is, the maximum clock frequency before a major degradation of transfer inefficiency sets in. Clearly, the fringing field that we discussed earlier is more effective the further the charge is removed from the surface. This is indeed observed. For peristaltic CCD's, in which the n-layer is quite thick, Si devices have been operated with clock frequencies up to 200 MHz. These frequencies are lower for the shallow ion-implanted BCCD's, but they are still higher than those of comparable SCCD's. It is for these reasons—namely, lower transfer inefficiency and higher operational frequencies—that BCCD's are largely used today, in spite of their lower charge-handling capacity and added fabrication complexity.

3.8 SUMMARY

We have described the fundamentals of charge-coupled devices in this chapter. The concept of charge packets, and their transfer and input and output, were discussed. Charge-coupled devices fall into the two basic categories of surface-channel and bulk-channel CCD's. Their similarities and differences were pointed out. For either type, there must always be a way to confine charge to prevent charge mixing. Charge confinement varies with the number of phases per stage, and techniques of confining charge were described. We have seen how charge transfer is affected by interface or bulk states at low frequencies and by carrier ballistics at high frequencies. Bulk-channel CCD's have advantages for both of these reasons, and they are the preferred configuration for most of today's CCD's.

Important equations in this chapter are the surface potential

$$\phi_s = V_G' + Q_N/C_o - V_0\{[1 + 2(V_G' + Q_N/C_o)/V_0]^{1/2} - 1\}$$

and the charge density that can be stored in the potential well

$$Q_N = -[V_G' - \phi_s - (2V_0\phi_s)^{1/2}]/C_o$$

Both of these equations apply to n-channel devices. Approximate expressions for the charge-transfer efficiency are

$$\varepsilon(t) = K \exp(-Kt/t_{tr})/\{K + (\pi^2 Q_{av}/8C_{eff})[1 - \exp(-Kt/t_{tr})]\}$$

when carrier ballistics dominate, and

$$\varepsilon = \{qkTD_{it}/[Q_N(\text{sig}) + Q_N(\text{bias})]\} \ln(1 + Pn_z)$$

when interface-state capture and emission dominate.

REFERENCES

[1] W. S. Boyle and G. E. Smith, "Charge-Coupled Semiconductor Devices," Bell Syst. Techn. J., *49*, 587–593, April, 1970.

[2] For an excellent discussion of the early history of solid-state shift registers and charge transfer devices, see L. J. M. Esser and F. L. J. Sangster, "Charge Transfer Devices," in *Handbook on Semiconductors* (C. Hilsum, ed.), Vol. 4, p. 335–421, North-Holland Publ. Co., Amsterdam, 1981.

[3] R. H. Walden, R. H. Krambeck, R. J. Strain, J. McKenna, N. L. Schryer, and G. E. Smith, "The Buried Channel Charge-Coupled Device," Bell Syst. Techn. J., *51*, 1635–1640, Sept., 1972.

[4] D. K. Schroder, "Schottky Barrier Charge-Coupled Devices," in *Metal-Semiconductor Schottky Barrier Junctions and Their Applications* (B. L. Sharma, ed.), p. 293–333, Plenum Press, New York, 1984.

[5] M. F. Tompsett, "Surface Potential Equilibration Method of Setting Charge in Charge-Coupled Devices," IEEE Trans. Electr. Dev., *ED-22,* 305–309, June, 1975.

[6] J. Hynecek, "Virtual Phase Technology: A New Approach to Fabrication of Large-Area CCDs," IEEE Trans. Electr. Dev., *ED-28,* 483–489, May, 1981.

[7] D. F. Barbe, "Imaging Devices Using the Charge-Coupled Concept," Proc. IEEE, *63,* 38–67, Jan., 1975.

[8] J. E. Carnes, W. F. Kosonocky, and E. G. Ramberg, "Drift-Aiding Fringing Fields in Charge-Coupled Devices," IEEE J. Solid-State Circ., *SC-6,* 322–326, Oct., 1971; "Free Charge Transfer in Charge-Coupled Devices," IEEE Trans. Electr. Dev., *ED-19,* 798–808, June, 1972.

[9] D. J. Hamilton, F. A. Lindholm, and J. A. Narud, "Comparison of Large Signal Models for Junction Transistors," Proc. IEEE, *52,* 239–248, March, 1964; D. Koehler, "The Charge-Control Concept in the Form of Equivalent Circuits, Representing a Link Between the Classic Large Signal Diode and Transistor Models," Bell Syst. Techn. J., *46,* 523–576, March, 1967.

[10] H. S. Lee and L. G. Heller, "Charge-Control Method of Charge-Coupled Device Transfer Analysis," IEEE Trans. Electr. Dev., *ED-19,* 1270–1279, Dec., 1972.

[11] J. E. Carnes and W. F. Kosonocky, "Charge-Coupled Devices and Applications," Solid-State Technol., *17,* 67–77, April, 1974.

[12] D. F. Barbe and S. B. Campana, "Imaging Arrays Using the Charge-Coupled Concept," in *Advances in Image Pickup and Display,* Vol. 3, p. 171–296, Academic Press, New York, 1977.

PROBLEMS

3.1 In the two-phase CCD of Fig. P3.1, calculate the maximum number of electrons/cm^2 and the maximum number of electrons that can be handled. Use gate length $L = 10$ μm, gate width $Z = 50$ μm, $\phi_{ms} = -1$ V, $Q_f/q = 5 \times 10^{10}$ cm^{-2}, $K_o = 3.9$, and $K_s = 11.8$.

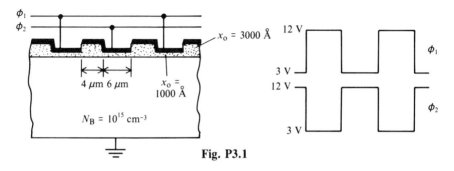

Fig. P3.1

3.2 Figure P3.2 shows cross sections through a CCD line array. The cross section along the charge-transfer direction is shown in (a), and two cross sections perpendicular to charge transfer are shown in (b) and (c).

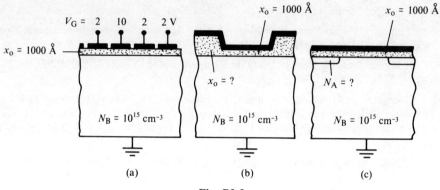

Fig. P3.2

For the gate voltages shown, find:

(i) How many electrons can be stored under the 10-V gate?

(ii) For case (b), how thick must the thick oxide be for charge to be confined? The requirement is: ϕ_s (under the thick oxide) at $V_G = 10$ V $\leq \phi_s$ (0.1 μm oxide thickness) at $V_G = 2$ V.

(iii) For case (c), what must the doping concentration in the heavily doped surface layer be? The requirement for surface potential is identical to that in (ii). Assume the highly doped regions to be sufficiently thick to contain the scr completely. $K_o = 3.9$, $K_s = 11.8$, gate length $= 10$ μm, gate width $= 100$ μm, $V_{FB} = 0$.

3.3 Show that for the high-low step semiconductor profile of an MOS-C in Fig. P3.3, the surface potential is:

$$\text{for } x \leq x_1: \quad \phi_s = V_G' - V_{01}[(1 + 2V_G'/V_{01})^{1/2} - 1]$$

$$\text{for } x > x_1: \quad \phi_s = V_G' - V_{12} - V_{02}\{[1 + 2(V_G' - V_{12})/V_{02}$$
$$- (V_2/V_{02})^2(N_{A1} - N_{A2})/N_{A2}]^{1/2} - 1\}$$

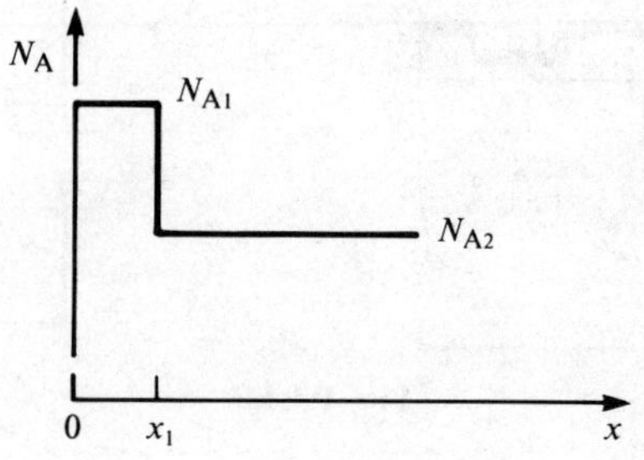

Fig. P3.3

where $V_{01} = qK_s\varepsilon_0 N_{A1}/C_o^2$, $V_{02} = qK_s\varepsilon_0 N_{A2}/C_o^2$, $V_{12} = V_1 - V_2$, $V_1 = qN_{A1}x_1/C_o$, $V_2 = qN_{A2}x_1/C_o$.

3.4 This problem is concerned with the charge-handling capability of three- vs. two-phase CCD's.

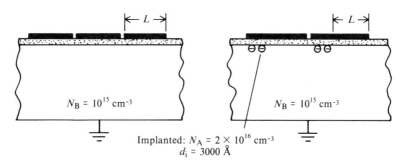

Fig. P3.4

For each of the two structures shown in Fig. P3.4, calculate the maximum number of electrons that can be handled for normal unidirectional flow — i.e., no charge is allowed to flow backward. $K_o = 3.9$, $K_s = 11.8$, $x_o = 0.05$ μm, $A_G = L \times Z = 2 \times 10^{-6}$ cm^2, $V_{FB} = 0$, gate voltages vary between 3 and 10 V.

Hint: Use the surface-potential equations of Problem 3.3.

3.5 Electrons are emitted from occupied interface states with an emission-time constant

$$\tau_e = 1/[\sigma_{ns}v_{th}N_c \exp(-E/kT)]$$

The mean electron-charge density, Q_N, emitted in time t from initially occupied interface states, is

$$Q_N(t) = q \int_0^{EG} D_{it}[1 - \exp(-t/\tau_e)] dE$$

For D_{it} and σ_{ns} constant and independent of energy, show that

$$Q_N(t) \approx qkTD_{it} \ln(\sigma_{ns}v_{th}N_c t)$$

3.6 In the bulk-channel CCD of Fig. P3.6, the n- and p-regions are uniformly doped to N_D and N_A, respectively. $N_A = N_D$ and $V_{FB} = 0$.

(i) Draw the energy-band diagram for $V_G = 0$ and $V_n = 0$.

(ii) Draw the energy-band diagram, the charge-density profile, and the electric-field profile for the gate charge $Q_G = 0$ and V_n such that the n-region is entirely depleted.

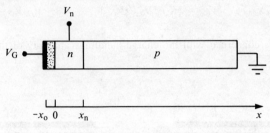

Fig. P3.6

(iii) Draw the energy-band diagram, the charge-density profile, and the electric-field profile for the gate voltage $V_G = 0$ and V_n such that the n-region is entirely depleted.

(iv) Is V_n in (ii) larger or smaller than V_n in (iii)? Explain.

3.7 Leakage current adds charge in CCD's. Consider the case of Fig. P3.7, which shows the device cross section and the surface-potential diagram for one particular time interval. A three-phase, 500-stage CCD delay line is operated at a clock frequency of 100 kHz. Well #1 is empty and well #2 has 10^{12} cm^{-2} electrons in it at the input to the line. The space-charge region leakage current expression is: $I_{leak} = qAn_i(W/\tau_g + s_0)$

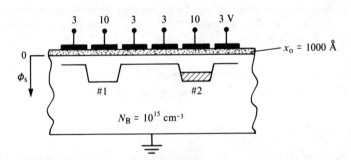

Fig. P3.7

Calculate the electrons added to each potential well by thermal generation when the charge packets reach the output of the delay line at (i) 27 °C and (ii) 75 °C. $K_o = 3.9$, $K_s = 11.8$, $\tau_g = 100$ μs and temperature-independent, $s_0 = 1$ cm/s, $A = 10^{-5}$ cm^2, $V_G = 3$ and 10 V, $V_{FB} = 0$, $n_i = 3.87 \times 10^{16} T^{1.5} \exp(-0.605/kT)$. For simplicity, assume nonoverlapping pulses, where at any one time only **one** of the three potential wells is at the high potential.

4 / Charge-Coupled Devices–Applications

4.1 INTRODUCTION

The main feature that distinguishes charge-coupled devices from most other semiconductor devices is their ability to transfer charge from one stage to the next at high transfer efficiency and low noise. We have already seen how this is implemented in one dimension. In this section we will extend such transfer to two dimensions. The charge is first shifted in one direction and then orthogonal to that direction. This implementation is particularly useful for imaging applications.

Three chief application areas were originally envisioned for CCD's: **memories, signal processors,** and **imagers**. Continued advances in non-CCD random access memories have virtually eliminated CCD's from the memory market. For signal-processing applications, CCD's were initially thought to be the answer to many signal-processing problems. But again, other approaches, mainly digital signal processing, have eliminated CCD's from many of the original proposed applications. However, CCD's have found use where their electronically variable delay is the key feature. In fact, the first large-scale application of CCD's was as *comb filters* in television receivers, sometimes referred to as *electronic combs*. Their electronically variable delay line features are also the key for their use in some oscilloscopes.

An application that is just beginning to emerge, and that appears to be a very large market, is the solid-state imager or television camera for home and industrial use. The very first CCD device to be demonstrated was used as the sensing element in a TV camera. Imaging has been important all along in CCD development, and there have been a variety of applications. For example, most astronomical photography is done with CCD's today. In this application it has almost entirely replaced film, largely because of its higher quantum efficiency and its linear-transfer characteristics relating the digital output to the incident light. The digital output can be stored in a memory, allowing point-by-point calibration and subtraction of background due to the night sky.[1] When a signal is in electronic form, other signal-processing functions can, of course, be performed that are difficult to do with film.

We limit the discussion of CCD applications in this chapter to signal processing and imaging. We choose the comb filter and the transversal filter as signal-processing examples because they demonstrate the unique capability of CCD's in this field very nicely. Comb filters are also commonly used in television receivers. In the imaging field, we describe both line and area arrays. Frame-transfer and interline-transfer geometries form subgroups within the area-array discussion. Both are utilized in today's imaging arrays in solid-state cameras.

4.2   SIGNAL PROCESSING

A CCD has several features that place it in a unique position in the realm of signal processing. It operates directly with analog signals, eliminating the analog-to-digital and digital-to-analog conversion necessary in digital signal processing. It allows electronically variable time delay by merely changing the clock frequency. The signal in the CCD can be accessed at each transfer stage, allowing its use as a multiplexer or transversal filter.

Historically, the bucket-brigade device was the first charge-transfer device used for signal-processing applications. Later use, however, has shifted almost totally to CCD's. Here we will confine our discussions to CCD's. In particular, we will use delay lines and transversal filters as examples of CCD versatility for signal processing. But first we must define several signal-processing terms.

4.2.1   Definitions

Bandwidth

The CCD is an analog device that does not require analog-to-digital conversion. But, because it is a sampled data device, an analog signal applied to the input is sampled at the clock frequency, f_c, as shown in Fig. 3.12. The Nyquist sampling theorem states that for a faithful reproduction of a band-limited signal of bandwidth B, the sampling frequency must be at least $2B$. Hence the maximum bandwidth that can be processed without distortion is $B = f_c/2$ for a CCD operated at f_c. For conventional CCD's, the highest clock frequency consistent with good transfer efficiency is around 10 MHz. This implies that bandwidths of up to 5 MHz can be comfortably processed. This places the device in a good position to handle television signals, whose bandwidth is slightly more than 4 MHz. Special devices with f_c values of several hundred MHz have been made and shown to work. These are for special-purpose applications. For example, a CCD is used in a 60-MHz oscilloscope.[2]

Delay Time

Once the analog signal has been sampled and transferred into the CCD, it consists of discrete charge packets. The transfer sequence is depicted in Fig. 3.11, and an extension of the discussion of that figure shows the time to transfer a charge packet by one stage given as $t = 1/f_c$. For an N-stage device, the total signal delay becomes

$$t_d = N/f_c \tag{4.1}$$

This equation shows clearly that by simply varying f_c, the delay time can be changed. Electronic tunability is very desirable, and is impossible to achieve in the conventional glass delay lines that are used in some systems.

While the delay time is variable, it cannot be made arbitrarily short or long. The lower limit is set by the maximum clock frequency for which the CCD still has an acceptable transfer inefficiency. The upper limit is determined by thermally generated leakage current that adds charge to the potential wells, thus distorting the signal. Clearly, the total delay time must be short compared with the time to fill the wells thermally. Fortunately, this fill time is on the order of one second or more for good devices, and delay times are generally much shorter than one second.

For a signal to be passed through a linear system without any distortion, the system response must have a constant-amplitude characteristic over the frequency spectrum of the input signal, and its phase shift must be linear over that frequency range. A **sinusoidal** signal of frequency f, transferred through a lossless delay line with delay t_d, experiences a phase shift, $\Delta\Phi$, given by

$$\Delta\Phi = \omega t_d = 2\pi f t_d \tag{4.2}$$

The transfer function of such a delay line is

$$H = \exp(-j\omega t_d) \tag{4.3}$$

The transfer inefficiency of a CCD causes an additional phase shift in the delayed signal of[3]

$$\Delta\Phi_1 = n\varepsilon \, \sin(2\pi f/f_c) \tag{4.4}$$

where f is the frequency of the sinusoidal signal transferred through the CCD at clock frequency f_c. Eq. (4.4) is plotted in Fig. 4.1a. It shows a maximum phase shift at $f = 0.25 f_c$. The phase shift, $\Delta\Phi_1$, is equivalent to an additional time delay of $t_{d1} = \Delta\Phi_1/2\pi f$. The total delay time then becomes

$$t_d = N/f_c + (n\varepsilon/2\pi f) \sin(2\pi f/f_c) \tag{4.5}$$

For most applications, the transfer-inefficiency component of the delay time can be neglected, giving eq. (4.1) as a very good approximation for the delay time.

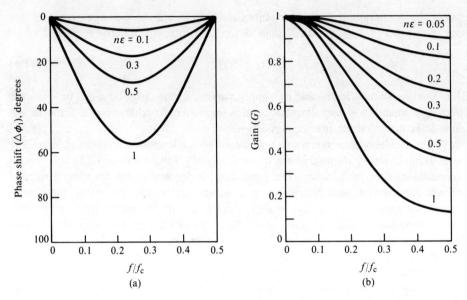

Fig. 4.1 Effects of transfer inefficiency on (a) the phase shift and (b) gain vs. frequency of a sinusoidal signal as a function of the "transfer inefficiency–number of elemental transfers" product.

A figure-of-merit frequently used in signal-processing applications is the product of the maximum bandwidth that the system can handle and the delay time that the signal experiences traversing the system. For a CCD, the delay time–bandwidth product is

$$Bt_d = (f_c/2)(N/f_c) = N/2 \qquad (4.6)$$

Modulation Transfer Function

The modulation transfer function (MTF) is analogous to an electrical circuit transfer function. It is the ratio of output to input signal as a function of frequency for a sinusoidal input waveform. For a CCD with perfect transfer efficiency, the output signal would be a perfect replica of the input signal, except for a phase shift caused by the time delay. The CCD, however, does not have perfect charge transfer, and the output is a distorted version of the input. We have already seen that an additional phase shift is introduced.

The amplitude is also changed, as shown by the gain expression[3]

$$G(f) = \exp\{-n\varepsilon[1 - \cos(2\pi f/f_c)]\} \qquad (4.7)$$

and plotted in Fig. 4.1b. The gain is also called the modulation transfer function. We will designate it as MTF_t, the MTF due to nonperfect charge transfer. In a later section dealing with imaging, we will develop expressions for other MTF's.

$G(f)$ is unity at low frequencies and then drops sharply with frequency for large $n\varepsilon$ values. However, for $n\varepsilon \leq 0.1$, the gain is larger than 0.8, and $\Delta\Phi_1 \leq \pi/10$. These gain and phase shift limits are acceptable for most applications. For example, for a 500-stage, three-phase CCD, a requirement of $n\varepsilon \leq 0.1$ means that ε must be less than 6.7×10^{-5}. These considerations show clearly the exacting demands placed on CCD's.

Signal-To-Noise Ratio

The output signal of a CCD is degraded not only as a result of imperfect transfer efficiency, but also because noise is added to the signal. Noise is introduced from various sources in the device. It begins with the introduction of the signal. Whether the signal is introduced electrically or optically, noise is added during the input process. The charge packet interacts with interface states in SCCD's and bulk states in BCCD's as it transfers through the device. This interaction is in the form of random electron capture and emission. Any time that a process proceeds randomly, it introduces noise. Thermal carrier generation or leakage current is also a random process, adding electrons to the packet during its passage through the CCD and introducing additional noise. At the output, both on-chip and off-chip amplifiers add noise.

It would appear that the signal is significantly degraded after passing through the CCD. In fact, the CCD is one of the lowest-noise devices compared with other devices that perform similar functions. This is partly the result of the manufacturing process technology that has evolved over the years. Silicon devices can be made with very low interface- and bulk-state densities, keeping the interface- and bulk-state noise, as well as the leakage-current noise, low. Input and output noise depend critically on the capacitances of the input and output nodes. These can be made very small, typically less than one picofarad, ensuring low input and output noise. Correlated double sampling at the output further reduces the output noise.[4,5] For a detailed discussion on noise, the reader is referred to Refs. [5] and [6].

4.2.2 The Comb Filter

Delay lines have many applications in electronic systems. We will describe two such applications to demonstrate the utility of CCD's. The first is the *comb* or *notch filter* found in many recent television receivers,[7] and the second is the *transversal filter*. In the standard NTSC (National Television System Committee) color television system, both the luminance (brightness) and chrominance (color difference information) are contained in a common communications channel. Because it is not possible to filter these two exactly, one sometimes notices erroneous colors in television displays. This is particularly obvious when the scene contains fine horizontal lines. A phenomenon known as *cross color* is observed. Additionally, at the edges of color transitions one sees *dot crawl*. These artifacts not only introduce colors that are not in the original scene, but they also cause the picture to flicker. The comb filter alleviates many of these problems and produces a markedly sharper picture.

An input signal, $V_i(f)$, applied to the comb filter in Fig. 4.2 is equally divided into two components. One component is fed through a CCD delay line whose transfer function, $H(f)$, is the product of its gain and phase shift, given by

$$H(f) = G(f) \exp(-j2\pi f t_d) \tag{4.8}$$

The other component is not delayed. After summation, the output is

$$V_o(f)_+ = V_i(f)[1 + G(f) \exp(-j2\pi f t_d)] \tag{4.9}$$

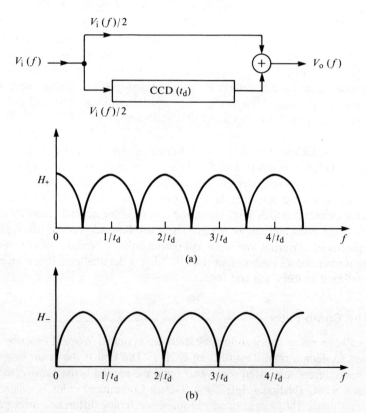

Fig. 4.2   Schematic of (a) an additive comb filter and its transfer function; (b) shows the transfer function for a subtractive circuit.

Eq. (4.9) contains both phase and amplitude information. We will consider only the **amplitude** transfer function $H_+ = |V_o(f)_+/V_i(f)|$ given by

$$H_+ = [1 + G(f)^2 + 2G(f)\cos(2\pi f t_d)]^{1/2} \qquad (4.10)$$

The gain is less than unity, but for good CCD's it is close to unity. Hence we approximate it as $G(f) \approx 1$. This allows eq. (4.10) to be simplified to

$$H_+ = 2|\cos(\pi f t_d)| \qquad (4.11)$$

which is plotted in Fig. 4.2a.

The important characteristic of eq. (4.11) for a comb-filter application is the fact that $H_+ = 0$ at $f = (n + 1/2)t_d$, where $n = 0, 1, 2 \ldots$. The transfer function has zeros at well-defined and periodic frequencies. No information passes through such a filter at these null frequencies. This is exactly what is required to remove unwanted or *alias* frequencies from a periodic signal like a television signal. The frequency nulls are determined by the delay time, which in turn is determined by the clock frequency according to eq. (4.1). The clock frequency is derived from the television signal with very high precision. The delay time of interest here is the time required to scan one TV line.

By using output subtraction, instead of addition, the transfer function becomes

$$H_- = 2|\sin(\pi f t_d)| \qquad (4.12)$$

which has zeros at $f = n/t_d$, where $n = 0, 1, 2 \ldots$ This function is shown in Fig. 4.2b. Note the well-defined nulls and the frequency shift between H_+ and H_- at which these nulls occur. This is exactly what is required for the luminance and chrominance signal filtering. All frequencies that occur at the nulls are filtered out.

A conventional low-, high-, or band-pass filter does not have such narrow, repetitive stop bands and cannot achieve this type of filtering. A CCD is ideally suited for comb-filtering applications, because the delay time is precisely controlled by the TV signal-derived clock frequency. The integrated circuit CCD filter is very stable, because it is not influenced by temperature or humidity.

4.2.3 The Transversal Filter

A *transversal filter* is an electronic system with which any desired linear filter can be implemented. A given filter function is implemented by designing the appropriate transfer function of the transversal filter. Since a CCD is well suited for this application, it is worthy of a more detailed discussion. Consider the electrical network in Fig. 4.3a. The network is characterized by the transfer function $H(f)$ in the frequency domain and the response $h(t)$ in the time domain.

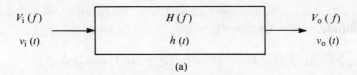

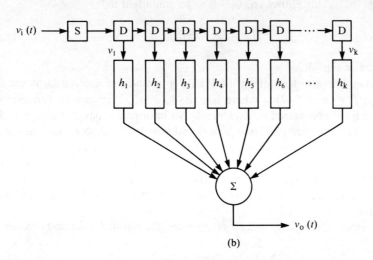

Fig. 4.3 A linear filter represented by its transfer function; (b) a transversal filter consisting of an input, delay stages, and weights. The delayed and weighted signals are summed to give v_o.

The output voltage, V_o, is the product of the input voltage, V_i, and the transfer function. In the frequency domain it is

$$V_o(f) = H(f)V_i(f) \tag{4.13}$$

In the time domain, the relationship between the input and the output voltages is not a simple multiplication, but rather the *convolution* of the input voltage with the transfer function, expressed by

$$v_o(t) = \int_{-\infty}^{\infty} h(\tau)v_i(t - \tau)\, d\tau \tag{4.14}$$

Note the distinction between the frequency and the time domain. In the frequency domain the functions are multiplied, whereas in the time domain they are convolved.

Let us suppose that the input voltage is a unit impulse or delta function, $\delta(t)$. Then we find in the time domain

$$v_o(t) = \int_\infty^\infty h(\tau)\delta(t - \tau)\,d\tau = h(t) \tag{4.15}$$

while in the frequency domain

$$V_o(f) = H(f) \tag{4.16}$$

For an impulse response input, the output is the transfer function itself.

What are the implications of this for a CCD? Consider the configuration of Fig. 4.3b. It is a device consisting of a sampling or input stage, S, followed by N delay stages, D, each with a delay time $t_d = 1/f_c$. The signal is nondestructively sampled at each delay stage, multiplied by a weighting coefficient h_k, where $k = 1, 2 \ldots N$, and the weighted outputs are summed to give

$$v_o(t) = \sum_{k=1}^{N} h_k v_i(n - k) \tag{4.17}$$

This equation is the discrete version of the integral equation (4.14). The arrangement in Fig. 4.3b is a *transversal filter*. It can be used to implement a linear filter by merely choosing the weights appropriately.

How is an actual design implemented? The designer decides what the frequency response of the filter should be. For example, let us consider a low-pass filter. It should have the amplitude-frequency response approaching that shown in Fig. 4.4a, with amplitude A over the frequency range 0 to f_p. The real system, of course, is concerned only with positive frequencies and can only approximate this ideal response function. For completeness, however, we show the entire ideal response for both positive and negative frequencies. The low-pass frequency response for positive frequencies would be obtained for an impulse input if the filter transfer function in the *frequency* domain were that of Fig. 4.4a.

The signal travels through the actual device in the *time* domain. It becomes necessary, then, to find the equivalent time-domain transfer function. It is well known from circuit analysis that the time- and frequency-domain responses are related by the Fourier transform. Using Fourier integrals, the time-domain expression for the example of Fig. 4.4a becomes

$$h(t) = (1/2\pi) \int_{-\omega_p}^{\omega_p} A \,\exp(j\omega t)\,d\omega = 2Af_p[\sin(2\pi f_p t)/(2\pi f_p t)] \tag{4.18}$$

This familiar $\sin(x)/x$ function is shown in Fig. 4.4b.

To implement this filter in a transversal filter format, it is necessary to create weights according to the function of eq. (4.18). These weights should not impede charge transfer. One method that has been successfully used is the nondestructive sens-

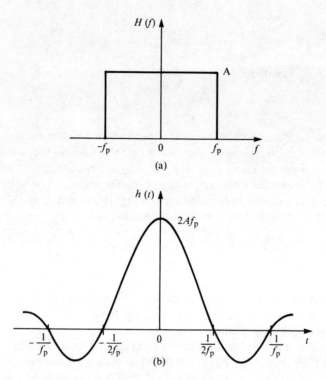

Fig. 4.4 A low-pass filter in (a) the frequency domain and (b) the time domain.

ing of charge under a CCD gate by integrating the current that flows in the clock line during charge transfer.[8] This is illustrated in Fig. 4.5 for a three-phase CCD.

When charge flows in a CCD channel from one electrode to the next, it induces a current flow in the receiving electrode. This induced current is proportional to the CCD charge. For conventional CCD's, the gates are continuous over the CCD channel and the current is not measured. In the CCD transversal filter, some of the gates are split, as shown in Fig. 4.5. Weighting coefficients with $-1 < h_k < +1$ are implemented by splitting each ϕ_3 gate as shown in the figure. The upper portions of each ϕ_3 gate are connected to a common clock line (ϕ_3^+), and similarly the lower portions are connected to the common ϕ_3^- line. The currents in the two lines are subtracted from each other by a differential amplifier.

The actual weights are assigned to each ϕ_3 gate by the location of the break in the gate electrode. It is split so that a fraction $(1 + h_k)/2$ is connected to ϕ_3^+ and a fraction $(1 - h_k)/2$ is connected to ϕ_3^-. If the split is in the center, then $h_k = 0$, while a split near the end of the ϕ_3^- electrode gives $h_k = 1$. Similarly, any other value between -1 and $+1$ can be assigned. A photograph of a CCD with the gate pattern exhibiting the $\sin(x)/x$ pattern and its corresponding frequency response are shown in Fig. 4.6. The

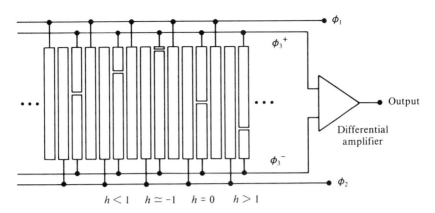

Fig. 4.5   CCD implementation of a transversal filter using the split gate concept.

frequency response very clearly displays the low-pass filter characteristic expected from such a design.[9] Other filter functions can be implemented by appropriate changes in the split-gate pattern.

4.3 IMAGING

Imaging, or, more precisely, electronic imaging, is the detection, read-out, and storage or display of a one- or two-dimensional array of photons from a scene being imaged. It is performed by an image sensor, whose function it is to generate a time-varying video signal corresponding to the spatial variations in the incident optical image. Traditionally, this has been done by electron-beam scanned television camera tubes. They have been used for many years, are very reliable, and are of excellent quality. Solid-state imagers, first developed in the late 1960's,[10] are smaller and lighter, and consume less power, than electron-beam scanned tubes. They have recently reached the degree of perfection necessary for them to compete with TV camera tubes. Wide acceptance has, in the past, been hampered by poorer picture quality and higher prices.

The task of producing high-quality solid-state imager chips is formidable indeed. Such a chip has several hundred thousand picture elements and a size on the order of 1 cm^2. Memory arrays are also of this complexity, but in contrast to memory arrays, imaging arrays do not have built-in redundancy. Memory arrays have extra rows of memory elements on the chip that can be activated to replace defective elements within the array. This cannot be done for imaging arrays, because the image is continuous in nature. Essentially all elements in the array must function properly. Any faults in the chip result in blemishes in the displayed picture. The eye is a very critical detector of such blemishes.

The concept of a CCD imager is illustrated in Fig. 4.7. We show a three-phase device with clock voltages that give the scr and surface potential distribution indicated

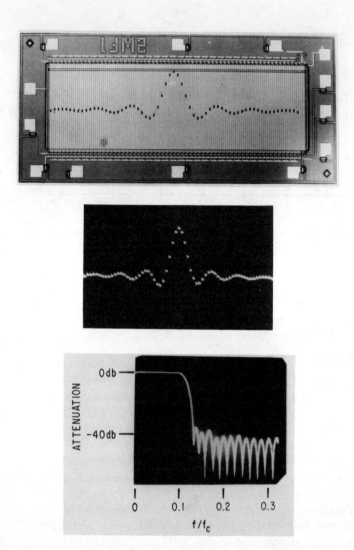

Fig. 4.6 Photograph of a low-pass CCD transversal filter, showing clearly the $\sin(x)/x$ pattern in the split gates, the impulse response, and the frequency response of the filter. Courtesy of R. D. Baertsch, General Electric Co.

there. The spatially varying image or scene is incident on either the front or rear surface. Rear irradiation is shown. Those photons absorbed in the semiconductor generate electron-hole pairs. Photons in the visible and near-infrared wavelength band generate one ehp per absorbed photon. For visible light, almost all photons are absorbed within the common semiconductors Si, Ge, and GaAs. Photons with energy near the band gap

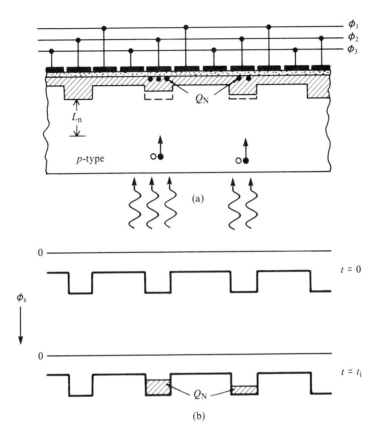

Fig. 4.7 (a) Cross section through a three-phase CCD imager, and (b) the surface potential profiles at $t = 0$ and after integration of the charge for time t_i.

have very long absorption lengths, and only a small fraction of them are absorbed. The remainder pass through the semiconductor unabsorbed.

Of the two carrier types generated, *minority carriers* are of main interest. Those minority carriers generated in the scr are collected without loss, since the scr electric field separates them from the majority carriers almost instantly. Recombination is therefore very unlikely. Minority carriers generated in the quasineutral bulk find themselves in a sea of majority carriers. Those minority carriers within about one minority-carrier diffusion length from the edge of the scr experience a diffusion gradient, aiding their diffusion toward the scr for collection. Once they reach the scr, recombination ceases, because they become separated from the majority carriers by the electric field in the scr. The minority carriers generated beyond one diffusion-length distance from the scr edge have a high probability of recombination, and few of them are collected.

Once the carriers enter the scr, they are collected under those gates with the most attractive potentials. In Fig. 4.7, they are collected under the ϕ_2 gates. The collected charge, Q_N, is proportional to the intensity of the irradiation and is the result of integrating the carriers for an integration time, t_i. The charges are subsequently transferred through the CCD, as discussed in Section 3.2.4. At the output amplifier, the charge is converted to a voltage which is proportional to the light intensity of the imaged scene. The CCD imager can be thought of as a photon $\rightarrow$ charge $\rightarrow$ voltage converter.

In conventional NTSC television, the displayed picture consists of two interlaced pictures. Of the approximately 500 displayed lines on a TV screen, first the odd lines, making up one-half of the picture, are displayed for a field time of $1/60$ s. Then the even lines, making up the other half of the picture, are displayed for the second field time of $1/60$ s. In effect, this gives 60 half-pictures per second and results in a more pleasing, flicker-free picture than would be produced by displaying the full picture 30 times per second.

The imager must be capable of integrating the scene for one field time and reading it out during the next field time. The reader may have noticed a potential problem. During the first integration period, the charge is collected in the potential wells. It is then read out. But during the read-out time, which also lasts $1/60$ s, the next field must be integrated. This is clearly impossible. One cannot read out the integrated charge of one field and, at the same time, begin to integrate charge for the next field in the same imaging array without charge mixing or signal smearing.

There are two solutions to this problem. Either the read-out time is made very short compared with the integration time, making signal mixing negligible, or the integration and read-out functions are performed in different parts of the imager. The latter solution is generally adopted. This, of course, increases the chip size, because there are in effect two stages needed for each storage site or picture element (pixel). One stage is for charge integration and the other for read-out. The details are left for a later section.

4.3.1 Definitions

Dark Signal

Dark signal is the imager output when there is no irradiation present. It is also referred to as *dark current* or *dark charge*. We discussed in Chapter 2 the various sources of thermal ehp generation. For silicon devices operated at room temperature, ehp generation in the scr dominates over that in the quasineutral region. The CCD scr-generated bulk and surface current density is

$$J_{scr} = qn_i(W/\tau_g + s) \tag{4.19}$$

We have used the surface generation velocity s, rather than s_0. Recall from Section 2.1.2.1 that s_0 is the surface generation velocity for a **depleted** surface. When there is charge in a CCD well, the surface is clearly not depleted, and surface generation is reduced from that of a depleted surface empty well. Another point that is frequently overlooked is the variation of W with charge. As charge is introduced into the potential well, the scr width decreases. Consequently, the dark current decreases also.

In other words, the more charge there is in the potential well, the lower the dark current, because surface generation and scr width are both reduced.

For good-quality CCD imagers, typical values of $W = 2 \ \mu m$, $\tau_g = 1 \ ms$, and $s = 0.5 \ cm/s$ give $J_{scr} = 1.7 \times 10^{-9} \ A/cm^2$ at a temperature of 300 K, using $n_i = 1.4 \times 10^{10} \ cm^{-3}$. This is the current density that flows into the potential well during the integration time. The total thermally generated carrier density collected during a frame or integration time of $1/60$ s is 4.8×10^8 electrons/cm^2. Here we have taken into account that while charge in a three-phase device is collected only in one potential well, ehp generation proceeds over all three wells.

Considering that the maximum charge of a full potential well is on the order of $10^{12} \ cm^{-2}$, we see that the dark charge is very small indeed. It is the dark charge *variation* across an imaging array that can be a problem. The variation is particularly severe when material defects give rise to localized spots of high ehp generation. The potential wells can fill up with charge even in the absence of light, and the output signal is identical to that of high-brightness parts of the scene. Bright spots appear on the display.

For applications requiring very long integration times, the room-temperature dark current becomes significant. In the above example, the potential well would be completely filled with dark charge in about 50 s. For some applications it is necessary to integrate for longer times than this. Astronomical imaging, for example, requires very long integration times, because the light from distant stars is extremely weak. The CCD imagers are then cooled to reduce the dark current.

Quantum Efficiency

Quantum efficiency is an important optical-device descriptor, because it is a measure of how well the device converts incident photons into collected CCD charge. It is defined by the ratio of the **collected** photon-generated minority-carrier density, Q_N, to the **incident** integrated photon flux density, F, as

$$\eta = -(Q_N/q)/(Ft_i) = -(J_{coll}t_i/q)/(Ft_i) = -J_{coll}/qF \qquad (4.20)$$

where J_{coll} is the collected photocurrent density and t_i is the integration time. The negative sign accounts for the negative inversion charge and the fact that J_{coll} and F are in opposite directions.

In order to relate the quantum efficiency to device parameters, it is necessary to derive an expression for the photocurrent density. For a photon flux density, F, incident on a semiconductor, as shown in Fig. 4.8a, the portion RF is reflected back from the surface, where R is the surface reflectivity. The portion $(1 - R)F$ enters the semiconductor. The change in photon flux density due to absorption inside the semiconductor, F_i, as a function of distance is

$$\Delta F_i(x) = F_i(x + \Delta x) - F_i(x) \qquad (4.21)$$

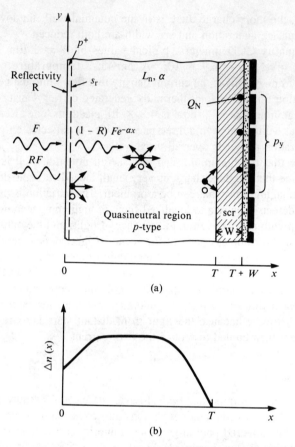

Fig. 4.8 A rear-irradiated CCD imager in (a), and (b) the excess minority-carrier distribution in the device.

For a homogeneous material, $\Delta F_i(x)$ is related to the distance traversed, Δx, and the flux density, $F_i(x)$, according to

$$\Delta F_i(x) = -\alpha F_i(x)\Delta x \tag{4.22}$$

where α is the optical absorption coefficient. The negative sign indicates a reduction in F_i. Writing eq. (4.22) as

$$dF_i(x)/dx = -\alpha F_i(x) \tag{4.23}$$

and integrating this expression gives

$$F_i(x) = F_i(0) \exp(-\alpha x) = (1 - R)F \exp(-\alpha x) \tag{4.24}$$

This is the well-known *Lambert-Beer* exponential law of absorption.

If we assume each **absorbed** photon to generate one ehp, then the volume generation rate (ehp/cm^{3}s) at which ehp are optically generated is given by

$$G(x) = -dF_i(x)/dx = (1 - R)F \alpha \exp(-\alpha x) \tag{4.25}$$

To calculate the quantum efficiency, we must find the minority-carrier concentration actually **collected** by the CCD.

Figure 4.8a shows the CCD with rear irradiation. The photon flux density inside the semiconductor generates excess ehp, shown by the solid and open circles in Fig. 4.8a and the curve in Fig. 4.8b. The electric field in the quasineutral region is very small, and the minority carriers move chiefly by diffusion. The minority carriers diffuse randomly in all directions, indicated by the arrows in Fig. 4.8a. Those that reach the scr are collected. Some recombine in the quasineutral bulk. Bulk recombination is characterized by the diffusion length L_n. Others recombine at the back surface. That recombination is characterized by the surface recombination velocity s_r.

Under the assumption of zero electric field in the quasineutral region, the *steady-state* one-dimensional electron-continuity equation is

$$d^2\Delta n/dx^2 - \Delta n/L_n^2 = -G(x)/D_n \tag{4.26}$$

where Δn is the *excess minority-carrier density*, D_n is the diffusion constant, and $G(x)$ is the generation rate of eq. (4.25). To solve eq. (4.26), we use the following boundary conditions.[11] At $x = 0$, surface recombination gives the first boundary condition:

$$d\Delta n/dx = s_r\Delta n(0)/D_n \tag{4.27}$$

and at $x = T$ the electric field in the reverse-biased scr collects essentially all of the minority carriers incident upon the scr. Hence it keeps Δn at the edge of the scr near zero. This gives a second boundary condition:

$$\Delta n(T) = 0 \tag{4.28}$$

The collected current is assumed to be diffusion current only, with

$$J_{coll} = qD_n\, d\Delta n/dx \qquad \text{at } x = T \tag{4.29}$$

The solution of eq. (4.26) is left as Problem 4.4. We merely quote the result for the quantum efficiency

$$\eta = \{(1 - R)\alpha L_n/[(\alpha L_n)^2 - 1]\}\{[(k + \alpha L_n)/\text{Den}]$$
$$- (\alpha L_n + A)e^{-\alpha T}\} + (1 - R)e^{-\alpha T}(1 - e^{-\alpha W}) \qquad (4.30)$$

where $A = [k \cosh(\zeta) + \sinh(\zeta)]/\text{Den}$, $\text{Den} = \cosh(\zeta) + k \sinh(\zeta)$, $\zeta = T/L_n$, and $k = s_r L_n/D_n$. Eq. (4.30) includes the carrier generation in the scr in addition to carrier generation in the quasineutral region.

A study of eq. (4.30) reveals that all the device parameters shown in Fig. 4.8a play a role in the quantum efficiency. Although it is not obvious from this rather complex expression, high η requires small ζ and low s_r. ζ can be made small by either reducing T or increasing L_n. The surface recombination velocity is reduced by forming a p/p^+ junction at the light-incident surface. Such a *low-high junction* presents a repulsive potential to minority electrons.[12]

The scene can be imaged onto the front or the rear CCD surface. Figures 4.7 and 4.8 show rear irradiation, but front irradiation is more common. Both have advantages and disadvantages. For rear irradiation, there is no obstruction to the incident photons, and good absorption is ensured in the semiconductor with ehp generation throughout the substrate. But, as we will see in the next section, the wafer must be thinned. This is a formidable fabrication disadvantage. Front irradiation does not require thinning, but additional reflection and absorption in the gate-insulator-semiconductor sandwich make the optical response less uniform and the quantum efficiency lower.

Theoretical and experimental quantum-efficiency curves are shown in Fig. 4.9. The curves in Fig. 4.9a are for rear-irradiated CCD's with substrates thinned to about 10 to 15 μm and bonded to glass backing plates.[13,14] The solid line (1) in Fig. 4.9a is a theoretical curve according to eq. (4.30). It agrees reasonably well with the experimental data for wavelengths above 0.55 μm. However, for lower wavelengths the agreement is poor due to one missing term in eq. (4.30).

The heavily doped p^+ layer of the low-high p-p^+ junction in rear-irradiated imaging devices has a very low recombination lifetime. Minority carriers generated in that layer have a very low probability of being collected. Hence, the p^+ layer can, to first order, be considered a passive or "dead" layer with thickness δ.[12] By multiplying eq. (4.30) by the term $\exp(-\alpha\delta)$, the theoretical quantum efficiency curve (1) in Fig. 4.9a is modified to curve (2). The modified curve agrees quite closely with the data points for $\delta = 500$ Å. The "dead" layer affects only the short-wavelength, short-absorption-depth (high absorption coefficient) light. The low reflectivity of $R = 0.15$ was chosen in the calculation, because these devices are bonded to glass backing plates that reduce reflectivity.

Experimental data for front-irradiated CCD's are shown in Fig. 4.9b.[15,16] For simplicity, we have not included theoretical curves. The theory must be modified for front irradiation to take into account multiple reflections in the gate-insulator-semiconductor sandwich and absorption in the gates.[17] Both of these effects are clearly shown in

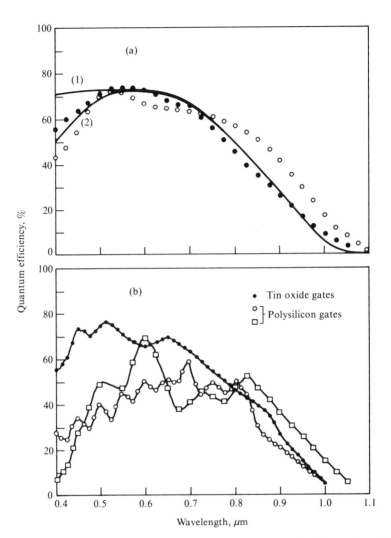

Fig. 4.9 Experimental quantum efficiency vs. wavelength data for (a) rear-irradiated and (b) front-irradiated CCD's. The theoretical curves in (a) are calculated from eq. (4.30), with $R = 0.15$, $L_n = 100 \ \mu m$, $D_n = 30 \ cm^2/s$, $s_r = 5000 \ cm/s$, $T = 10 \ \mu m$, and $W = 3 \ \mu m$. Curve (1) is for zero and (2) for 500-Å "dead" layer.

Fig. 4.9b. The low quantum efficiency at short wavelengths is significantly enhanced and the periodic η-λ variations greatly reduced when the polysilicon gates are replaced by optically transparent, electrically conducting tin oxide gates.[16,17]

Instead of the quantum efficiency, the *responsivity* is frequently given. It is defined as the ratio of collected current density to incident power density P. The power density is related to the photon flux density by

$$P = h\nu F = hcF/\lambda \tag{4.31}$$

where λ is the wavelength and the responsivity $\mathcal{R}$ becomes

$$\mathcal{R} = J_{coll}/P = J_{coll}\lambda/hcF = q\eta\lambda/hc \tag{4.32}$$

Modulation Transfer Function

The *modulation transfer function* (MTF) is a measure of the resolution of the device. It is defined as the response of the imager to a spatial, sinusoidally varying optical input image. The over-all system MTF is the product of the MTF's of the camera lens, the CCD, the electronic circuitry, and the display. We will address only the CCD component here, because it is generally the limiting factor.

The over-all CCD MTF consists of three components: (i) the charge-transfer inefficiency MTF_t, discussed in Section 4.2.1, (ii) the MTF_d due to minority-carrier diffusion in the quasineutral region of the device, and (iii) the MTF_s due to the discrete nature of the charge-collection wells. We consider only the last two here.

Minority carriers generated by absorbed photons diffuse randomly. Those generated by long-wavelength, low-α photons near the scr region in Fig. 4.8a are collected with little chance of lateral diffusion. We assume that the incident light travels through the semiconductor with no scattering. Short-wavelength light with high α is absorbed near $x = 0$. The minority carriers generated there must diffuse through the entire substrate to reach the scr. However, the random carrier diffusion makes the probability of being collected by another CCD stage along the y-direction very high. This results in MTF degradation.

Imagine a small light spot incident on the back of the wafer, generating ehp near the back surface. The minority carriers diffuse randomly in all directions and spread out laterally approximately the same distance as the wafer thickness. For a 300-μm-thick wafer, they also spread approximately 300 μm. For 15-μm spacing between CCD stages, the spot will spread over 20 stages or pixels with a drastic resolution loss. To overcome this limitation, it is necessary to thin the wafer. The quasineutral region thickness of the substrate should be roughly the pixel-to-pixel spacing or less.

Front-side irradiation has this problem to a much lesser extent. Short-wavelength light generates carriers in the scr with no resolution loss, and only long-wavelength, near-infrared photons are absorbed deep in the substrate. Near-infrared light is usually of little interest for visible imaging, and can be filtered out.

The main problem in the front-side-irradiated configuration is the absorption and reflection in the insulator and the gates. Polysilicon gates are of course preferred over aluminum gates, because polysilicon is at least partially transparent, but it does show significant absorption in the blue part of the spectrum. Optically transparent, electrically conducting gates made of tin oxide are preferred over polysilicon because they are more transparent and have lower reflectivity. We will show later that photodiodes, coupled to CCD's, are better yet. Photodiodes do not require gates, and their reflectivity can be substantially reduced with proper antireflection coating.

The MTF_d can be calculated by assuming the incident photon flux density to be modulated only in the y-direction. According to Ref. [18], we let

$$F(y) = (F/2)[1 + \cos(2\pi f_s y)] \quad (4.33)$$

where f_s is the spatial modulation frequency of the intensity variation in the y-direction. It is not the photon frequency. Eq. (4.33) gives $F(y) = F$ for $f_s = 0$, as it should. With this spatially varying irradiance, the generation rate becomes

$$G(x, y) = [(1 - R)F\alpha/2][1 + \cos(2\pi f_s y)] \exp(-\alpha x) \quad (4.34)$$

and the continuity equation becomes

$$\partial^2 \Delta n/\partial x^2 + \partial^2 \Delta n/\partial y^2 - \Delta n/L_n^2 = G(x, y)/D_n \quad (4.35)$$

Substituting the assumed photon flux density of eq. (4.33) into eq. (4.35) yields a variable separable equation. The solution to the resulting equation is again eq. (4.30).[19] However, in the new expression the diffusion length must be replaced by

$$L_n(f_s) = L_n/[1 + (2\pi f_s L_n)^2]^{1/2} \quad (4.36)$$

For uniform irradiation, $f_s \to 0$, and $L_n(f_s)$ becomes the conventional diffusion length. For $f_s \neq 0$, the new diffusion length is smaller. This in turn gives a lower quantum efficiency for the modulated irradiance.

The modulation transfer function due to minority-carrier diffusion is calculated from the ratio of the quantum-efficiency expressions[18]

$$MTF_d = \eta(f_s)/\eta \quad (4.37)$$

where $\eta(f_s)$ is eq. (4.30) with eq. (4.36) substituted for the diffusion length.

The CCD imager is a spatial sampled data device because the CCD cells are discrete entities, not a continuum. The discreteness results in a further MTF degradation. The y-modulated photon flux density of eq. (4.33) gives rise to a similar spatially varying ehp generation pattern. The electrons collected in the CCD potential wells are proportional to that pattern. The quantum efficiency is a measure of the conversion efficiency of photons to collected charge. Using eqs. (4.20) and (4.33), we can write the charge pattern as

$$Q_N(f_s) = -qF(y)t_i\eta = -(qFt_i/2)[\eta + \eta(f_s)\cos(2\pi f_s y)] \tag{4.38}$$

Eq. (4.38) reduces to $Q_N(0) = -qFt_i\eta$ when $f_s = 0$. For CCD cell or pixel center-to-center spacing p_y, we find the charge collected in a given CCD well to be

$$Q_N(f_s) = -(qFt_i/2p_y)\int_{-p_y/2}^{p_y/2} [\eta + \eta(f_s)\cos(2\pi f_s y)]\,dy \tag{4.39}$$

Integrating eq. (4.39) gives

$$Q_N(f_s) = -(qFt_i\eta/2)\{1 + [\eta(f_s)/\eta][\sin(\pi f_s p_y)/(\pi f_s p_y)]\} \tag{4.40}$$

The factor $[\eta(f_s)/\eta]$ is the diffusion modulation transfer function given by eq. (4.37). The factor $[\sin(x)/x]$ is the spatial modulation transfer function

$$\text{MTF}_s = \sin(\pi f_s p_y)/(\pi f_s p_y) \tag{4.41}$$

MTF_s is a fundamental limitation on device performance determined by the discrete nature of the CCD with cell spacing p_y.

Calculated modulation transfer functions are plotted in Fig. 4.10. MTF_d and MTF_s are plotted separately in Fig. 4.10a for the device of Fig. 4.9a curve 2. The diffusion modulation transfer function is very dependent on the quasineutral region thickness, T. That is intuitively obvious. The thicker the wafer, the more chance there is for the minority carriers to diffuse laterally, leading to resolution loss. The modulation transfer function due to MTF_d and MTF_s is

$$\text{MTF} = \text{MTF}_d \times \text{MTF}_s \tag{4.42}$$

It is shown in Fig. 4.10b. Note that for the example chosen in this figure, the resolution is almost entirely limited by diffusion. The over-all CCD modulation transfer function is given by

$$\text{MTF}_{CCD} = \text{MTF}_d \times \text{MTF}_s \times \text{MTF}_t \tag{4.43}$$

with MTF_t given by eq. (4.7).

The arrow at $f_s = f_N$ in Fig. 4.10 indicates the Nyquist-limited spatial frequency. This frequency corresponds to one spatial cycle falling on two CCD cells—i.e., $f_N = 1/2p_y$. In other words, at this frequency a bright line of the y-direction modulated

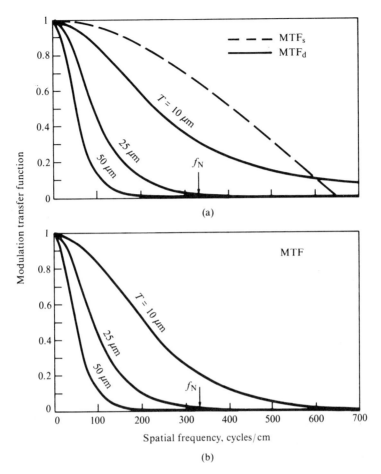

Fig. 4.10 Modulation transfer function vs. spatial modulation frequency. In (a) the MTF$_d$ and MTF$_s$ are plotted separately, and in (b) their products are plotted. The CCD device has the same parameters as in Fig. 4.9 except: $\lambda = 0.6$ μm, $p_y = 15$ μm, $\delta = 500$ Å, and the various T values shown.

sinusoidal excitation pattern falls on one cell and a dark line on the adjacent cell. This is the highest spatial frequency signal that can be imaged by the array without frequency distortion. Hence the imager of Fig. 4.10 can image undistorted frequencies only up to 330 cycles/cm. Any higher frequencies in the input scene introduce unwanted or alias frequencies into the displayed picture. To prevent this from happening, the input image must be prefiltered to remove those high frequencies. This can be done optically by defocussing the lens slightly.

4.3.2 Line Arrays

Imaging arrays fall into two broad categories: line arrays and area arrays. As the name implies, line arrays image one line at a time, while area arrays image an entire two-dimensional scene. Line arrays find use either where a line of information is sufficient, or where mechanical motion of the scene past the array provides the second dimension necessary for a two-dimensional picture. For example, a printed page can be imaged by moving the page past the line array. The line array must of course be read out repeatedly as the page moves by.

For some quality-control applications, the object under observation is already in motion. The diameter of a wire being extruded, for example, can be continuously monitored by imaging its diameter onto a line array. The output voltage from the array can be used in a feedback loop during the extrusion process to maintain a constant diameter. Similarly, many other industrial operations can be monitored with such linear-imaging arrays.

Another interesting application is in spectrometers.[20] Light is dispersed by a grating, spatially separating the wavelengths. The classical example is sunlight dispersed into its color spectrum by a prism. When the dispersed light is imaged onto a line array, the output from each imaging element in the array corresponds to a different wavelength of the dispersed light. The line array is, in effect, a wavelength → charge → voltage converter.

An example of the organization of a line array is shown in Fig. 4.11. It consists of a central imaging portion and two CCD read-out registers, one above and one below the imaging line. The charge is integrated in the central portion. At the end of the integration time the two transfer gates are pulsed high to shift the charge from the even-numbered imaging elements into the upper register, and from the odd-numbered elements into the lower register. The use of two read-out registers has two distinct advantages: (i) the imaging elements can be made approximately half the size of a CCD stage, and (ii) the clock frequency of each register is only half that of a single-register line array.

The central imaging array can be a CCD-like device in which a long central gate (not shown in Fig. 4.11a) keeps the semiconductor in deep depletion. Mixing of spatial information along the array is prevented by *zig-zag* channel stops. The transfer gates are held in their **low** state during charge integration. The channel stops and transfer gates isolate the charge in each imaging element during the integration period. At the end of the integration period, the transfer gates are pulsed **high** and the integrated charge flows into the read-out CCD's. The surface potential cross-sectional diagrams "before transfer" and "after transfer" into the read-out registers are shown in Fig. 4.11b and c.

The imaging elements can also be an array of photodiodes instead of the CCD array pictured in Fig. 4.11. Photodiodes have the advantage of not requiring a gate and can therefore be more easily optimized for high quantum efficiency, because the incident light is not absorbed by the gates or reflected by the gate/insulator structure. Most line arrays are, in fact, of the photodiode variety for this very reason.

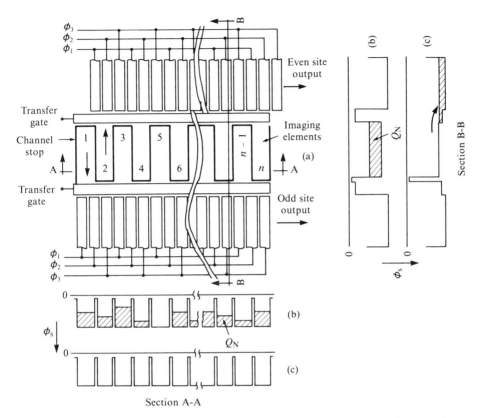

Fig. 4.11   (a) A CCD imaging line array. Two surface potential cross sections show the charge (b) during integration and (c) after transfer into the read-out registers.

The potential of the electrically floating photodiodes is set very much like that of the output diode in the CCD output circuit shown in Fig. 3.13. The transfer gates in their **high** state establish a surface potential, and all charge above that level flows from the diodes into the registers until the diodes reach that same potential. When the transfer gates go **low**, the diodes are isolated at that potential. Charge is subsequently collected during the integration period to discharge the diodes by an amount proportional to the light intensity on the array.

4.3.3   Area Arrays

Before discussing area arrays, we will review briefly a few points of the NTSC television system that are pertinent to area arrays. The TV picture consists of approximately 500 displayed lines. They are displayed in an interlaced format of two *fields*. The odd lines are displayed during the first field and the even lines are displayed during the second field. Each *field time* is 1/60 s, and 60 half-pictures are displayed each second.

It takes a *line time* of 53.5 μs for the electron beam within the picture tube of a TV receiver to scan one line from beginning to end. The time from the end of one line to the beginning of the next is the *line retrace time* (10 μs). The field time includes the *field retrace time* (900 μs), which is the time required for the beam to go from the end of one field to the beginning of the next. We refer to these times in the following discussion because the output from the TV camera must be exactly in synchronism with the electron beam in the picture tube.

CCD area arrays fall into two main design categories: the *frame-transfer* type and the *interline-transfer* type. Both designs include a light-integrating section and a read-out section. The frame-transfer type was historically the first to be demonstrated.[21] We show it schematically in Fig. 4.12. A two-phase CCD is used in this example for simplicity.

The frame-transfer imager consists of three sections with different functions. The upper section of Fig. 4.12a shows the *image area*. This is the only part of the imaging chip that is open to light. The rest is shielded from the light. The array can be irradiated from the front or from the rear provided that similar shielding is done on the back of the chip. The central section is the *storage area*. It serves the function of intermediate storage. The lower section is one CCD line—the *read-out register*. The gates in the upper two areas run across the chip horizontally. They are indicated by the short

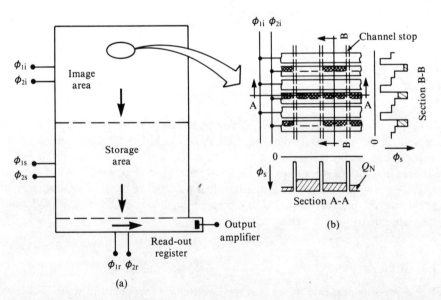

Fig. 4.12   (a) Schematic of a frame-transfer CCD imager, and (b) an enlarged section of the image area, showing the gate structure and surface potential profiles. A two-phase CCD is used.

horizontal clock lines ϕ_{1i}, ϕ_{2i}, ϕ_{1s}, and ϕ_{2s}. The charge moves vertically along the arrow direction. In the read-out register, the gates are vertical, indicated by ϕ_{1r} and ϕ_{2r}. The charge moves horizontally to the on-chip amplifier, discussed in Section 3.3.2.

The scene is imaged onto the imaging area. During the integration period, clocks ϕ_{1i} and ϕ_{2i} are stopped. As shown by the blown-up section in Fig. 4.12b, the phase 2 clock potentials in this example are more positive and charge is integrated under gates 2. Charge mixing is prevented in the vertical direction by the low ϕ_{1i} potentials. Channel stops prevent charge mixing in the horizontal direction. The integrated charge is indicated by the shaded regions in Fig. 4.12b.

The scene, imaged on the imaging area, is integrated for a *field time*. At the end of the field time, during the *field retrace time*, the contents of the entire imaging area are rapidly transferred to the storage area. This is accomplished by turning on both the imaging-area clocks (ϕ_{1i} and ϕ_{2i}) and the storage-area clocks (ϕ_{1s} and ϕ_{2s}). At the end of the retrace time the entire image is in the storage area and the image area is empty of charge.

The imaging-area clocks are once again stopped, and the empty image area is ready to integrate the next field. During this second field time, the pattern in the storage area is shifted down into the horizontal read-out register and read out one line at a time. The times are synchronized with those of the TV display.

During the image area $\rightarrow$ storage area shift, the lowest line in the image area is shifted into the read-out register. This line is read out in a *line time*. At the end of the line time, the read-out register is empty. During the *line retrace time*, the next line of the storage area is shifted into the register to be read out. This continues until the last line of the storage area is read out. Then the storage area is empty at the end of the second *field time*. The image area has integrated charge during this entire time and is now ready to shift the charge into the storage area during the next field retrace time. In this way it is possible to integrate one field while reading out the next.

The charge in the two upper areas is clocked at relatively low frequencies. Only the read-out register must run at the high frequency (around 8 MHz) associated with television signals. Note that the number of lines in the imaging area is only that of one **field**, or half of the displayed TV lines. This is because only one field is integrated at any one time. Of course, the storage area must also contain the same number of lines. So the **chip** must contain the necessary 500 "lines," where each "line" consists of P gates for a P-phase CCD.

The displayed picture is more pleasing if one field is integrated under gates 2 and the next under gates 1. This offsets the two images slightly and effectively doubles the number of vertical samples. It results in a significantly improved MTF, or a more continuous picture. In a three-phase device, it has been found that charge integrated under gate 1 during one field and under gates 2 and 3 during the second field gives the most pleasing picture.[22]

The second chip organization of area imaging arrays is the interline-transfer layout,[23] shown in Fig. 4.13. In contrast to the frame-transfer design, where the sensing and read-out functions are performed in separate sections of the chip, in the interline

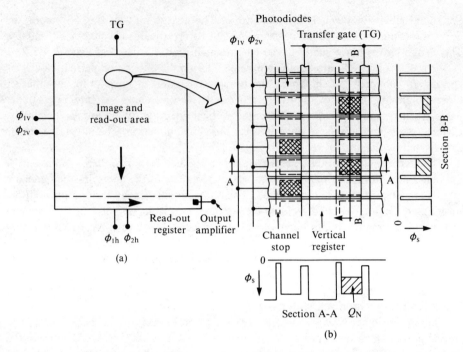

Fig. 4.13 (a) Schematic of an interline-transfer CCD imager, and (b) an enlarged section of the image area, showing the gate structure and surface potential profiles. A two-phase CCD is used.

organization the two are located next to each other. The imaging elements, located beside the read-out registers, need not be CCD sensors, but can be photodiodes. In this way they can be optimized for highest quantum efficiency.

Let us consider the interline-transfer array of Fig. 4.13. A two-phase CCD is shown. The CCD gates of the vertical registers run horizontally across the entire array. The transfer gates are at right angles to the vertical registers. The vertical registers, lying between the photodiodes and the transfer gates, are shielded from the incident light. Although not shown in this figure, the horizontal CCD gates are so arranged that they do not cover the photodiodes. They are routed around the diodes, but they must of course remain continuous across the entire array.

Let us follow the array operation. Through the appropriate combination of gate voltages, all photodiodes are reverse biased. The transfer gates are then turned off, isolating the diodes from the vertical registers. The diodes are isolated from each other by channel stops. The scene is imaged onto the entire array through the open photodiodes and integrated for a field time. The photodiodes can be thought of as little reservoirs, surrounded on three sides by dikes and on the fourth side by a water gate. Water trickles into these reservoirs and, after an appropriate period of time, is released by opening the gate.

Diodes under both gate 1 and gate 2 integrate charge. After one field time, the charge in photodiodes 1 is transferred into the vertical read-out registers by turning the transfer gates on momentarily. Once the charge is in the vertical registers, it is shifted down into the horizontal read-out register one line at a time, much the same as in the frame-transfer device. In this way one field is read out. At the end of the second field time, during the field retrace time, the charge in photodiodes 2 is transferred into the vertical read-out registers and the second field is read out.

The layout of Fig. 4.13 automatically gives an interlaced output, because field 1 is integrated in the odd-numbered diodes and field 2 in the even-numbered ones. Each diode actually integrates for two field times. After transfer of the integrated charge from diodes 1 into the vertical registers during the field retrace time, it takes 1/60 s to shift this field out of the array. Then the diode 2 charge is read out during the next field time. When it is time for diodes 1 to be transferred again, two field times have elapsed. With twice the integration time of a frame-transfer device, twice as much charge is collected in the photodiodes, assuming that the photosensitive areas are equal in the two arrays. Hence the photosensitive area of the interline-transfer array can be made half the size of that in a frame-transfer device for identical optical sensitivity.

Typical arrays consist of approximately 400 horizontal and 490 vertical pixels. The vertical number is governed by the TV line number and the digital address circuitry and the horizontal number by the resolution of the NTSC system. Non-NTSC systems can have different horizontal and vertical numbers of pixels. The interline-transfer array can be irradiated only from the front, because the charge in the read-out registers must be read out in the dark. This is ensured by a light shield. Irradiation from the rear causes charge in the registers to mix during integration and read-out.

One of the reasons for the popularity of interline-transfer arrays is the convenience of making "color chips." In a color camera it is necessary to generate a red, a green, and a blue signal. In a conventional studio television camera, there are three color-image tubes inside the camera. Each of the three tubes is equipped with a filter that transmits only one of the three colors. In a CCD camera, one could use three CCD imaging chips, each with a different color filter. Integrating all three colors onto one chip, however, is a more cost-effective approach. This is accomplished by placing small color filters over the individual photodiodes.[10] Some diodes have blue filters, others have green filters, and the rest have red filters. Through the appropriate output electronics, it becomes possible to separate the output signal into its three color components. It is easier to implement the color filters on interline-transfer arrays.

We have discussed the basic configurations of the main sensor architectures. There are many variations on these basic designs. Besides the basic concept, there are many factors that enter into the choice of a final design. The ease of fabrication, the yield of the process, the performance of the device, and the size of the chip are just a few. Recent designs have incorporated means of controlling light overload. When a very bright spot of light is contained within a scene, it is possible that during the integration time there is too much charge for the photosensor to hold. The excess charge spills into adjacent pixels and discharges them. In this way it is possible for a small, bright spot of light to bloom into a much larger "charge spot" in the array. Ultimately this translates into a big white spot on the TV screen. This is known as *blooming* and is clearly an undesirable condition. One solution is to build the array in a *p*-layer on an *n*-type substrate.[24] By providing a reverse bias between the *p*-layer and the *n*-substrate, it is possible to pull the excess charge due to a bright spot into the substrate rather than letting it spill into adjacent gates. Much effort is still being devoted to CCD imagers, and more innovations are likely to emerge.

4.4 SUMMARY

In this chapter we have presented several applications of CCD's whose fundamentals were described in Chapter 3. We chose examples from signal processing and imaging. Both lie at the heart of the chief CCD applications today. We discussed the necessary fundamentals — bandwidth, delay time, signal-to-noise ratio, dark signal, quantum efficiency, responsivity, and modulation transfer function — and then applied these fundamentals to comb filters, transversal filters, and line- and area-imaging arrays. We showed typical geometrical layout considerations and discussed those device aspects that influence system performance.

Important equations include the time-bandwidth product

$$Bt_d = (f_c/2)(N/f_c) = N/2$$

the quantum efficiency

$$\eta = \{(1 - R)\alpha L_n/[(\alpha L_n)^2 - 1]\}\{[(k + \alpha L_n)/\text{Den}] - (\alpha L_n + A)e^{-\alpha T}\}$$
$$+ (1 - R)e^{-\alpha T}(1 - e^{-\alpha W})$$

(see eq. (4.30) for definitions) the responsivity

$$\mathcal{R} = q\eta\lambda/hc$$

and the modulation transfer function

$$\text{MTF}_{\text{CCD}} = \text{MTF}_d \times \text{MTF}_s \times \text{MTF}_t$$

where

$$\text{MTF}_d = \eta(f_s)/\eta$$
$$\text{MTF}_s = \sin(\pi f_s p_y)/(\pi f_s p_y)$$
$$\text{MTF}_t = \exp\{-n\varepsilon[1 - \cos(2\pi f/f_c)]\}$$

REFERENCES

[1] W. K. Ford, Jr.,"Digital Imaging Techniques," Ann. Rev. Astron. Astrophys., *17*, 189-212, 1979; J. N. Bahcall and L. Spitzer, "The Space Telescope," Scient. Am., *247*, 40-51, July, 1982.

[2] H. Dollekamp, L. J. M. Esser, and H. de Jong, "P^{2}CCD in 60 MHz Oscilloscope with Digital Image Storage," Philips Tech. Rev., *40*, 55-60, May, 1982.

[3] C. H. Sequin and M. F. Tompsett, *Charge Transfer Devices,* Academic Press, New York, 1975.

[4] M. H. White, D. R. Lampe, F. C. Blaha, and I. A. Mack, "Characterization of Surface-Channel CCD Imaging Arrays at Low Light Levels," IEEE Trans. Solid-State Circ., *SC-9*, 1-13, Febr., 1974.

[5] D. F. Barbe and S. B. Campana, "Imaging Arrays Using the Charge-Coupled Concept," in *Advances in Image Pickup and Display,* Vol. 3, p. 171-296, Academic Press, New York, 1977.

[6] J. E. Carnes and W. F. Kosonocky, "Noise Sources in Charge-Coupled Devices," RCA Rev., *33*, 327-343, June, 1972.

[7] D. H. Pritchard, "A CCD Comb Filter for Color TV Receiver Picture Enhancement," RCA Rev., *41*, 3-28, March, 1980.

[8] D. D. Buss, D. R. Collins, W. H. Bailey, and C. R. Reeves, "Transversal Filtering Using Charge-Transfer Devices," IEEE J. Solid-State Circ., *SC-8*, 138-146, April, 1973.

[9] R. D. Baertsch, "Transversal Filters with Charge Transfer Devices," IEEE Trans. Nucl. Sc., *NS-24*, 312-315, Febr., 1977.

[10] P. K. Weimer and A. D. Cope, "Image Sensors for Television and Related Applications," in *Advances in Image Pickup and Display,* Vol. 6, p. 177-252, Academic Press, 1983.

[11] S. M. Sze, *Physics of Semiconductor Devices,* 2nd Edition, J. Wiley & Sons, New York, 1981, p. 802.

[12] T. M. Buck, H. C. Casey, J. V. Dalton, and M. Yamin, "Influence of Bulk and Surface Properties on Image Sensing Silicon Diode Arrays," Bell Syst. Techn. J., *47*, 1827-1854, Nov., 1968.

[13] E. D. Savoye, D. F. Battson, T. W. Edwards, W. N. Henry, D. R. Tshudy, L. F. Wallace, G. W. Hughes, W. F. Kosonocky, P. A. Levine, and F. V. Shallcross, "High Sensitivity Charge-Coupled Device (CCD) Imagers for Television in State-of-the-Art Imaging Arrays and Their Applications," Proc. Soc. Photoinstr. Eng., *501*, 32-39, 1984.

[14] R. H. Stanton, J. W. Alexander, E. W. Dennison, T. A. Glavich, P. M. Salomon, and R. E. Williamson, "ASTROS: A Sub-Arcsec CCD Star Trecker," Proc. Soc. Photoinstr. Eng., *501*, 256-282, 1984.

[15] T. H. Lee, T. J. Tredwell, B. C. Burkey, T. M. Kelly, R. J. Khosla, D. L. Losee, R. L. Nielsen, and W. C. McColgin, "A 360,000-Pixel Charge-Coupled Color-Image Sensor for Imaging Photographic Negative," IEEE Trans. Electr. Dev., *ED-32*, 1439-1445, Aug., 1985.

[16] W. F. Keenan and D. C. Harrison, "A Tin Oxide Transparent-Gate Buried-Channel Virtual-Phase CCD Imager," IEEE Trans. Electr. Dev., *ED-32*, 1531-1533, Aug., 1985.

[17] D. K. Schroder, "Transparent Gate Silicon Photodetectors," IEEE Trans. Electr. Dev., *ED-25*, 90-97, Febr., 1978.

[18] M. H. Crowell and E. F. Labuda, "The Silicon Diode Array Camera Tube," Bell Syst. Techn. J., *48*, 1481-1528, May/June, 1969.

[19] D. H. Seib, "Carrier Diffusion Degradation of Modulation Transfer Function in Charge Coupled Imagers," IEEE Trans. Electr. Dev., *ED-21*, 210-217, March, 1974.

[20] Y. Talmi and R. W. Simpson, "Self-Scanned Photodiode Array: A Multichannel Spectrometric Detector," Appl. Opt., *19*, 1401-1414, May, 1980.

[21] C. H. Sequin, D. A. Sealer, W. J. Bertram, Jr., M. F. Tompsett, R. R. Buckley, T. A. Shankoff, and W. J. McNamara, "A Charge-Coupled Area Image Sensor and Frame Store," IEEE Trans. Electr. Dev., *ED-20*, 244-252, March, 1973.

[22] C. H. Sequin, "Interlacing in Charge-Coupled Imaging Devices," IEEE Trans. Electr. Dev., *ED-20*, 244-252, June, 1973.

[23] D. F. Barbe, "Imaging Devices Using the Charge-Coupled Concept," Proc. IEEE, *63*, 38-67, Jan., 1975.

[24] Y. Ishihara, E. Oda, H. Tanigawa, A. Kohno, N. Teranishi, E. Takeuchi, I. Akiyama, and T. Kamata, "Interline CCD Image Sensor with an Antiblooming Structure," IEEE Trans. Electr. Dev., *ED-31*, 83-88, Jan., 1984.

PROBLEMS

4.1 A two-phase CCD is shown in Fig. P4.1. It consists of 512 polysilicon and 512 aluminum gates.

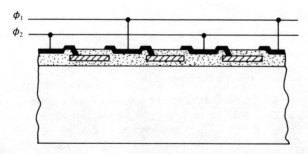

Fig. P4.1

(i) How many bits of information can this CCD handle?

(ii) What is the delay time experienced by a signal being clocked through the device at 1 MHz?

(iii) For a particular application, the delay time must be variable from 1 to 30 ms. What must be the range of clock-voltage frequencies to achieve these delay times?

(iv) What is the CCD's maximum time delay–bandwidth product?

4.2 Show the transfer function of a subtractive comb filter to be

$$H_- = 2|\sin(\pi f t_d)|$$

4.3 Derive the transversal filter time response function, $h(t)$, for a bandpass filter that is to pass frequencies between f_1 and f_2. Frequencies $f_2 < f < f_1$ should be attenuated.

4.4 (a) Derive an expression for $\Delta n(x)$ using eqs. (4.25) to (4.28).

(b) Derive η of eq. (4.30) using eqs. (4.25) to (4.29), adding the scr component.

(c) Plot $\log[\Delta n(x)]$ vs. x over the range $0 \le x \le T$. Use $R = 0.3$, $L_n = 100 \ \mu m$, $D_n = 30 \ cm^2/s$, $W = 3 \ \mu m$, $T = 250 \ \mu m$, $\alpha = 1000 \ cm^{-1}$, $F = 10^{15}$ photons/cm²s, and $s_r = 0$, 10^3, and $10^7 \ cm/s$.

(d) Plot η for the same R, L_n, D_n, W, and s_r values and $T = 10$, 25, and 250 μm using the λ-α values for Si:

λ	0.4	0.5	0.6	0.7	0.8	0.9	1.0	1.1 μm
α	70,000	11,000	4500	2200	1000	400	80	3 cm^{-1}

4.5 Derive an expression for the quantum efficiency of a **front-irradiated** CCD imager. Use R_{eff} as the effective reflectivity of the gate-insulator-semiconductor sandwich. Include scr collection.

4.6 Plot the MTF_d vs. f_s for the same R, L_n, D_n and W values as in Problem 4.4 and for $\alpha = 1000 \ cm^{-1}$, $s_r = 1000 \ cm/s$, $T = 10$, 25, and 250 μm, and $f_s = 0$ to 200 cycles/cm.

4.7 Calculate the over-all MTF for Problem 4.6 by including the spatial modulation transfer function MTF_s and the charge transfer modulation transfer function MTF_t. Use pixel-to-pixel spacing $p_y = 15 \ \mu m$, $f/f_c = 0.25$, $n = 1500$ transfers, and $\varepsilon = 10^{-4}$.

4.8 The vertical spatial modulation transfer function, MTF_s, of an interline-transfer CCD imager is better than that of a frame-transfer CCD imager if both use the same number of phases and same gate length. Discuss why this is so using a two-phase CCD as an example.

5 / Semiconductor Memories

5.1 INTRODUCTION

Memories are logic devices that store and manipulate information. The information is stored in a *binary* format utilizing one of two states of a storage element. The binary digit or *bit* is generally referred to as a logic **1** or a **0**. It is entered into the memory during the **write** cycle and subsequently interrogated during the **read** cycle.

Computer information storage or memory systems fall into one of several categories based on storage capacity and access time. Very large memories use magnetic tape or optical storage. Intermediate storage requirements utilize magnetic tape or hard and soft (floppy) disks. "Hard" disks consist of aluminum disks coated with a ferromagnetic material and usually are not removable from the computer. "Floppy" disks use a flexible plastic substrate coated with a ferromagnetic film and are easily removed from the disk drive. In the 10^7 to 10^8 bit range, semiconductor memories are dominant. Semiconductor chips capable of storing one million bits occupy an area of 0.5 to 0.6 cm^2 and are the driving force in the continued shrinkage of semiconductor devices.

Information stored in magnetic media is permanently stored. This is referred to as *nonvolatile* storage. When the power is interrupted, the information is not lost. In contrast, when the power is turned off with *volatile* storage, all information is lost. Many, but not all, semiconductor memories are of the volatile type.

There are basically two memory architectures: *random access* and *sequential access*. A random-access structure consists of a two-dimensional array of storage cells with address circuitry appropriate for accessing any storage location randomly. The access time is almost independent of the location of a particular storage element in the array. The random-access type of architecture is therefore eminently suitable for applications where short access time is important.

In a sequential-access organization, the stored information is accessed sequentially or serially. The access time is much longer. For example, to access a piece of information in the middle of a magnetic tape, the first half of the tape must be run past the reading head. Reading information from a magnetic disk is random in the sense that the "read" head can access any part of the disk along a given radius to find a particular track. Once the "read" head is located on a track, it must wait for the information on that track to move past the head sequentially by the rotational motion of the disk.

Random and sequential data acquisition have likely been experienced by the reader in a library. Any page in a journal can be accessed as easily as any other. The journal is a random-access information store. A microfilm, however, must be advanced to the particular page desired in a sequential manner. This is a more time-consuming process, especially if the information is not near the beginning of the microfilm.

We discuss MOS semiconductor memories in this book because they use MOS transistors and capacitors. The deep-depletion MOS-C is the storage element in the dynamic random-access memory. Bipolar memories, although similar to MOS memories, are not discussed. We begin the chapter with memory fundamentals and types and then treat inverters. Inverters are important for static memories and also for sense amplifiers in dynamic memories. Then we turn to static random-access memories and finally to dynamic random-access memories. We describe ways to write, read, and refresh the stored information, and finally we discuss a very important element of today's high-density memories with their very small amount of stored charge — the sense amplifier.

5.2 MEMORY FUNDAMENTALS

Semiconductor memories come in a variety of types, and it is instructive to review them briefly. They are two-dimensional arrays of regularly spaced memory or storage elements, made of bipolar or MOSFET transistors. Bipolar memories are used when fast access is required, but their packing density is lower than that of MOS memories. The power dissipation of bipolar memories is higher. The majority of high-density memories are of the MOS type.

A storage element is located at the intersection of two lines that are used to write and read the information stored there. This is shown schematically in Fig. 5.1. A 64-bit array, consisting of eight rows and eight columns, is shown. Memory arrays are always rectangular, but they need not be square. Each of the 64 cells is connected to one of eight horizontal "row lines" and to one of eight vertical "column lines." A particular memory location is addressed by specifying the row and column lines. This is done by giving the appropriate address codes to the row and column decoders.[1]

The row decoder takes the binary input number and translates it into the correct row to be selected. In the example shown in Fig. 5.1, the cell locations start with $(0, 0)$ in the upper left corner and end on $(7, 7)$ in the lower right corner. The row being addressed is row 3, and its row address is the binary number 011. It stands for decimal value 3. The binary 011 applied to the row decoder activates all eight cells in row 3, indicated by the shaded cells in that row. But we are only interested in the contents of cell $(3, 5)$. By activating column 5 with the binary 101 applied to the column decoder, all cells in that column are column-activated, shown by the shaded column 5 cells. Only cell $(3, 5)$ is addressed by both the row and the column select, and the contents of that cell are read by being routed and detected by the appropriate read-out circuitry.

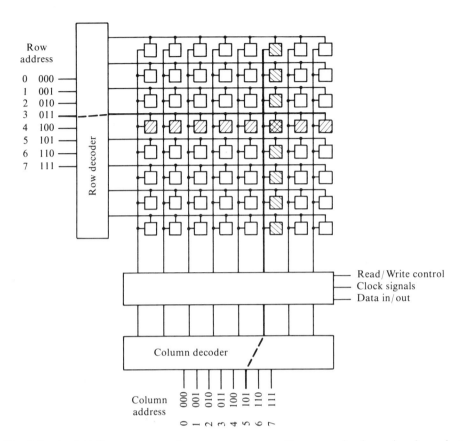

Fig. 5.1 An 8 × 8 array representing a memory array. The row and column decoders select the appropriate cell [cell (3, 5) here], and the rest of the circuitry is used for writing, reading, and refreshing the information. A "row address" selects an entire row, and a "column address" selects an entire column. Reprinted after Ref. [1] by permission of Scientific American, Inc.

It should be obvious that in this manner any one of the 64 cells can be read as easily as any other. A three-digit binary address on the row and column decoder allows $(2^3)^2$ cells to be addressed. So an n-digit binary address can select $(2^n)^2$ cells; that is, 65,536 cells can be addressed for $n = 8$ and 1,048,576 cells for $n = 10$. Semiconductor memories usually come in multiples of 1024 bits or 1 Kbit. The "K" stands here for 1024, **not** 1000. Hence, a 65,536-cell memory is generally called a 64 Kbit memory and a 1,048,576-cell memory is a 1000 Kbit or 1 Mbit memory.

Semiconductor memories are subdivided into volatile and nonvolatile types:[2]
Nonvolatile memories: The stored information is preserved when power to the memory is interrupted. In the *read-only memory (ROM)*, the information is perma-

nently stored. The stored code is built into the chip during fabrication in one of several ways. The code can be a particular metallization pattern of the array, formed by including or omitting the gates of MOSFET's, or it can be implemented by providing the MOSFET's with two different gate oxide thicknesses. The MOSFET's either do or do not conduct when addressed. The result is a stored **one** or **zero**. The memory can be read to retrieve stored information, but once the contents are set they cannot be altered. These memories are used as the microprogram storage in digital computers and as lookup tables for mathematical functions, for example. The ROM is clearly a non-volatile memory, since the stored pattern is permanently fixed and cannot be altered.

In the *programmable read-only memory (PROM)*, the information is written by the user after device fabrication by one of several techniques. The "write" operation is destructive, and once the memory is written the information cannot be erased. Mechanisms such as blowing nichrome or polysilicon fuse links on the chip are utilized. The PROM is useful when small quantities of memories are required and when it is uneconomical to generate the necessary mask sets required for ROM's. The PROM's are standard arrays that are easily produced and then custom-programmed by each user.

The *electrically programmable read-only memory (EPROM)* is also programmed by the user after device fabrication, like the PROM. However, the stored pattern, usually set by injecting charge into the insulator or onto a floating gate embedded in the insulator, can be altered. It takes large voltages to write the information, and the "write" operation is slow compared with that of dynamic random-access memories. EPROM's are used where the stored information does not have to be changed frequently, as for example during the debugging phase of software development. However, the information can be changed if needed. If the stored information needs to be altered, then, in one popular EPROM type, the chip is exposed to ultraviolet light for several minutes. The light discharges the stored information by allowing charge on a floating gate to escape. This type of memory is sometimes referred to as a *reprogrammable ROM (RePROM)*.

In the *electrically erasable programmable ROM (EEPROM)*, the information is written as in the EPROM by injecting charge into the insulator or onto a floating gate. The memory is, however, fabricated so that the information can be erased electrically by applying a pulse of polarity opposite to the charging pulse polarity. The voltage pulse causes the stored charge to be cleared by charge tunneling or charge injection. This type of memory is also known as an *electrically alterable read-only memory (EAROM)* and is used where occasional program or data updating is required.

Volatile memories: The stored information is lost when power is interrupted. The information in a *random-access read-write memory (RAM)* is rapidly and easily written into the memory and rapidly read. The architecture of the RAM is very similar to that of the ROM, but requires additional circuitry for refreshing the data in the storage cells, additional logic for controlling the "read" and "write" functions, and a more complex memory cell. The stored charge in a RAM is smaller than that in a ROM, and therefore very sensitive detectors or sense amplifiers must be used during the "read" operation. Nevertheless, the RAM is the workhorse of the semiconductor memory family because of its high density and low cost. It is the main data storage memory for mainframe computers, minicomputers, and microcomputers. Millions of these memory units are produced every month worldwide.

Within the RAM family are found the *static RAM (SRAM),* pronounced "ess-ram," and the *dynamic RAM (DRAM),* pronounced "dee-ram." The SRAM can hold its charge or stored information as long as there is power applied to the circuit without the need to refresh the stored information. The DRAM, on the other hand, cannot hold its charge for very long even when the power is uninterrupted. DRAM's use deep-depletion MOS capacitors as storage elements. Since deep-depletion MOS-C's operate in the nonequilibrium mode, their information content must be periodically refreshed whether the stored information is utilized or not. When the information is read out from a DRAM, the read-out is **destructive** and the contents of a memory cell are lost. In an SRAM, the read-out is **nondestructive** and the "read" operation does not disturb the stored information.

5.3 INVERTERS

We treat the dynamic RAM in detail, because it utilizes a deep-depletion MOS-C, which is the main theme running throughout this volume. However, for completeness, we also discuss the SRAM because it is a common memory circuit. Before describing its operation, it is instructive to consider the chief building block of the SRAM — the inverter — separately. The inverter is also important in its own right as a digital gate and as the basis of the sense amplifier in the DRAM.

An inverter is a MOSFET driver transistor in series with a load device, as shown in Fig. 5.2a. The driver is sometimes called the *pull-down* transistor. We show an *n*-channel enhancement-mode driver, T1, in series with a load, indicated by the box.[3] Transistor T1 has the usual three-terminal MOSFET drain current–drain voltage characteristics shown in Fig. 5.2b. Its gate voltage is the inverter input voltage, and its drain-to-source voltage is the inverter output voltage.

The two-terminal load device can take one of three configurations: (i) an enhancement-mode MOSFET with its drain connected to its gate, (ii) a depletion-mode MOSFET with its source connected to its gate, and (iii) a resistor. When the load consists of a transistor it is sometimes called the *pull-up* transistor. The current-voltage characteristics of these three load devices are shown in Fig. 5.2c. The current-voltage characteristics in this figure are those of each device measured by itself, i.e. not as a load device. Here we assume a grounded substrate for the *pull-up* transistor. The MOSFET symbols are standard for enhancement- and depletion-mode MOSFET's. Semiconductor device symbols are shown in Appendix III.

The MOSFET drain current–output voltage curves of T1 with the three two-terminal loads are shown by the $i_{DS1} - v_o$ curves with the appropriate load lines in Fig. 5.2d. Whenever a transistor is connected to a load, the device operates along the load line. This holds for the inverter, too. The input-output voltage-transfer curves, ob-

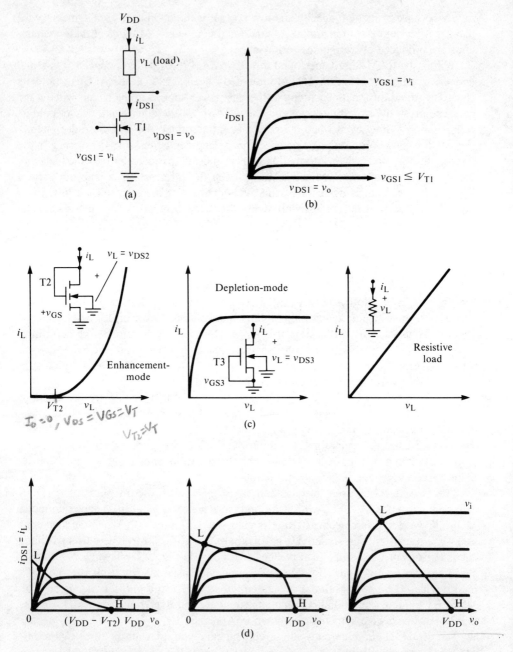

Fig. 5.2   (a) MOSFET inverter consisting of an enhancement-mode driver and a load; (b) the current-voltage characteristics of the driver; (c) three different load devices; (d) the driver current-voltage curves with the enhancement-mode, depletion-mode, and resistor load lines.

tained from the intersection of the load line with the transistor curves, are shown for all three cases in Fig. 5.3.

Let us consider the three loads in the order shown in Fig. 5.2c. The enhancement-mode load is a two-terminal device with its gate connected to its drain. This places the operation of the load MOSFET into the "above pinch-off" or saturation region. Neglecting the bulk charge for simplicity, the current-voltage relationship (see eq. 5.17 in Volume IV of this series) is given by

$$i_L = k_2(V_{GS2} - V_{T2})^2 = k_2(V_{DS2} - V_{T2})^2 \tag{5.1}$$

where $V_{GS2} = V_{DS2}$ and $k_2 = Z_2 \overline{\mu}_n C_o / 2L_2$. The subscript "2" is used for the enhancement-mode load, and "3" is used later for the depletion-mode load. With the gate connected to the drain, drain current does not flow until the gate voltage exceeds the threshold voltage, V_{T2}, as shown in Fig. 5.2c.

From Fig. 5.2a, we find $v_L = V_{DS2} = V_{DD} - V_{DS1} = V_{DD} - v_o$. Substituting for V_{DS2} in eq. (5.1) gives

$$i_{DS1} = i_L = k_2(V_{DD} - V_{T2} - v_o)^2 \tag{5.2}$$

For a very small or "low" input, T1 is **off** and $i_{DS1} \approx 0$ where we neglect the leakage current of T1. For logic devices, "low" and "high" refer to voltages that are typically

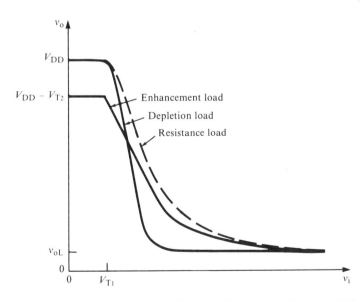

Fig. 5.3   The output-input voltage transfer curves for the three inverters of Fig. 5.2.

near 0 and 5 V, respectively. In Fig. 5.2d, these two states are designated L and H. For a negligibly small leakage current, we find for H

$$v_o = V_{DD} - V_{T2} \tag{5.3}$$

as indicated in Figs. 5.2d and 5.3. The output is "high," but less than the supply voltage V_{DD}. The output is $V_{DD} - V_{T2}$ because there is a voltage drop across the load transistor equal to its threshold voltage.

The astute reader will no doubt have noticed the different shape of the T_2 current-voltage characteristic when it is isolated (Fig. 5.2c) compared with when it is a load (Fig. 5.2d). The different shape is due to the threshold voltage behavior. The threshold voltage is constant when T_2 is measured by itself with constant substrate voltage as in Fig. 5.2c. We show a grounded substrate in Fig. 5.2c. V_{T2} is different with substrate bias but is still constant. When the MOSFET is connected as a *pull-up* load, its source-substrate potential is no longer constant. In Fig. 5.2a we see the source potential to be equal to the output voltage v_o, and the substrate is assumed to be grounded here. The substrate may not be grounded. That does not change the qualitative aspect of our discussion. With v_o varying during the $v_o \approx 0$ to $v_o = V_{DD} - V_{T2}$ transition, the T_2 source-substrate potential varies by the same voltage. Consequently, V_{T2} *increases* during this transition, and the current-voltage characteristic becomes less steep, as indicated in Fig. 5.2d. We have simply used V_{T2}, but it should be understood to be variable.

For a "high" input, T1 is **on** and is effectively a short circuit. It is not quite a complete short circuit, however, because there is a small voltage drop across any MOSFET in the highly conducting state. This is shown by v_{oL}, the "low" output voltage in Fig. 5.3. If the gate of the enhancement-mode load transistor were not shorted to its drain, but independently biased with gate voltage $V_{GS2} > (V_{DD} + V_{T2})$, T2 would operate in its linear region. The "high" output voltage for that connection becomes V_{DD}, because there is no longer a threshold voltage drop between the drain and source of T2. As high an output voltage as possible for a given input voltage is highly desirable for a logic device. An additional power supply is required for the enhancement-mode load to increase the output from $V_{DD} - V_{T2}$ to V_{DD} — a decided circuit disadvantage.

For the depletion-mode load, we see in Fig. 5.2d that a "low" input gives V_{DD} as the output voltage without an additional power supply. There is no threshold voltage drop across the depletion-mode load as there is for the enhancement-mode load. For a "high" input voltage, the output voltage is v_{oL}. Arguments similar to those of the depletion-mode load hold for the resistive load, with V_{DD} out for a "low" in. For all three loads we find that a "low" input gives a "high" output and a "high" input gives a "low" output.

The shape of the current-voltage characteristic for the depletion-load MOSFET T_3 also changes when it is connected as a load. This can be seen clearly by comparing Fig. 5.2c with Fig. 5.2d. For the constant substrate potential of Fig. 5.2c, the threshold voltage is constant. During inverter operation, the source-substrate potential varies in Fig. 5.2d just as it does for the enhancement-mode load even though the source-gate voltage is zero. But for the depletion-mode device, the threshold voltage V_{T3} *decreases* as the substrate potential increases. The MOSFET threshold voltage is discussed in more detail in Sections 6.1 and 6.2.

Of the three connections, the enhancement-mode load is rarely used. The rapidly changing load line of the enhancement-mode load in Fig. 5.2d forces the current through T2 to decrease during the entire switching process. For the depletion-mode load, the inverter current stays higher for a longer time when the input voltage switches from "high" to "low." Switching invariably requires the charging or discharging of a capacitor, and a higher current translates to a lower switching time for the depletion-mode load. The depletion-mode load device adds fabrication complexity because both depletion- and enhancement-mode devices are on the same chip. However, this poses no particular problem with today's ion-implantation processes, where any dopant type and concentration are easily implemented.

Resistive loads used to be difficult to implement. The required high resistances were difficult to fabricate within the space constraints of high-density chips. Recently, polysilicon resistors that give the high resistances required for low power dissipation have been used. Resistive loads have an additional advantage. The resistors can be placed on top of other circuit elements, resulting in smaller chip sizes. This could, of course, not be done if the resistors were made in the same single-crystal substrate as the rest of the circuit. Resistive loads are used a great deal today.

It is obvious from the circuit diagram of Fig. 5.2 that there is current flow through the inverter for "high" inputs, even though there is none for "low" inputs. For a high density of inverters, power dissipation can be significant. A technology that reduces power dissipation is the complementary MOS (CMOS) approach. CMOS consists of both *n*- and *p*-channel devices on the same chip. A typical CMOS inverter is shown in Fig. 5.4a. It consists of a *p*-channel MOSFET built in an *n*-type substrate and an *n*-channel MOSFET in a *p*-island or *p*-well formed within the *n*-substrate. CMOS circuits can also be built on *p*-substrates, in which case *n*-wells are formed that contain the *p*-channel devices. For some CMOS applications, both *n*- and *p*-wells are formed in the substrate.

CMOS devices are very important for high-density circuits, largely because of their low power dissipation. Let us, therefore, consider the inverter connection in Fig. 5.4b in some detail. The driver is the *n*-channel transistor T1, and the load is the *p*-channel transistor T2. The drains of the two transistors are connected together to form the output, and the gates connected to each other constitute the input. Both transistors are enhancement-mode devices.

The *n*-substrate and the source of the *p*-channel transistor are biased to V_{DD}. The two drains form the output. The *p*-well and the source of the *n*-channel transistor are grounded. With the *p*-well grounded and the *n*-substrate biased to V_{DD}, the *p*-well/substrate junction is reverse biased to V_{DD}. It follows, then, that the input voltage v_i must be larger than V_{T1} for T1 to conduct. For a "low" input, i.e., $v_{iL} \leq V_{T1}$, T1 is **off**. For that same input voltage the positive substrate voltage puts T2 in the **on** state. With T1

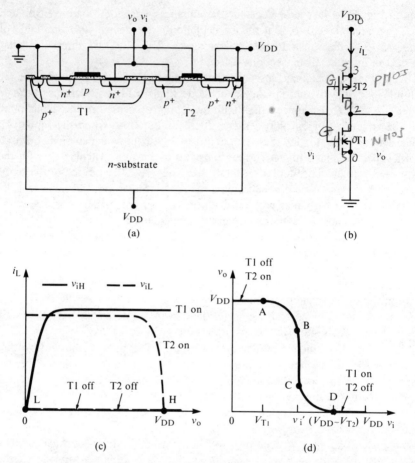

Fig. 5.4 A p-well CMOS inverter: (a) the device cross section, (b) the circuit, (c) the current-voltage curves with the n-channel driver and the p-channel load, and (d) the output-input voltage transfer curve.

on and T2 **off**, no current flows through the inverter. The logic state for this input voltage is shown as the "high" state H in Fig. 5.4c. It corresponds to the intersection of the two dashed current-voltage curves at "H."

What input voltage is required to turn T2 **off**? The input voltage must rise until V_{GS} of T2 is greater than V_{T2}. Recall that n-channel MOSFET's usually have positive threshold voltages and p-channel MOSFET's usually have negative threshold voltages. Let us use a numerical example to demonstrate the inverter operation with $V_{T1} = 1$ V, $V_{T2} = -1$ V and $V_{DD} = 5$ V. The p-well is grounded, and v_i is initially zero. T1 is **off** since its gate voltage, v_i, is below threshold. The T2 gate is at -5 V with respect to its substrate. The gate-substrate voltage is more negative than its threshold voltage, and T2 is **on**. Current flow through the circuit is essentially zero. The only current flow is the leakage current of the reverse-biased junctions. There is very little voltage drop across T2 when there is only leakage current flowing through it, and the output voltage is very close to V_{DD}.

Now consider v_i being raised above zero. When it reaches $V_{T1} = 1$ V, T1 begins to conduct, T2 continues to be **on**, and current flow begins. The output voltage drops. As v_i increases further, T1 goes into stronger conduction, but T2 begins to turn off. In fact, when v_i reaches 4 V, the gate voltage of T2 with respect to its substrate becomes -1 V. This is its threshold voltage, and T2 turns off. The current becomes approximately zero again, there is no voltage drop across T1, and the output voltage is very close to zero. This is shown by "L" in Fig. 5.4c. This point corresponds to the intersection of the two solid current-voltage curves. We note in passing that significant current flows only when the inverter switches from one state to the other. The power dissipation in either the "low" or the "high" state is due to leakage current only and is therefore very small. The main power dissipation occurs during switching.

The voltage transfer characteristic is shown in Fig. 5.4d. In the region from A to D, both T1 and T2 are **on**. In region A-B, T1 is in saturation while T2 is in its linear current-voltage characteristic region. In region C-D, T2 is in saturation while T1 is in its linear region. In region B-C, where the transfer characteristic has its steepest slope, both transistors are in saturation. We use v_i' as the input voltage in this steep part of the output characteristic where both transistors are in saturation. Their current-voltage equations are

$$i_{DS1} = k_n(V_{GS1} - V_{T1})^2 = k_n(v_i' - V_{T1})^2 \tag{5.4}$$

and

$$i_{DS2} = k_p(V_{GS2} - |V_{T2}|)^2$$
$$= k_p(V_{DD} - v_i' - |V_{T2}|)^2 \tag{5.5}$$

where $k_n = Z_n \overline{\mu}_n C_o / 2L_n$ and $k_p = Z_p \overline{\mu}_p C_o / 2L_p$. $Z_{n,p}$ and $L_{n,p}$ designate the gate widths and lengths of the n- and p-channel devices, respectively.

Eqs. (5.4) and (5.5) are equal to each other, because the current must be the same through both devices. Solving for v_i' gives

$$v_i' = [V_{DD} + V_{T1}(k_n/k_p)^{1/2} - |V_{T2}|]/[1 + (k_n/k_p)^{1/2}] \tag{5.6}$$

V_{T1}, V_{T2}, k_n, and k_p can be designed over a wide range of values. For the special case of $V_{T1} = |V_{T2}|$ and $k_n = k_p$, we find

$$v_i' = V_{DD}/2 \tag{5.7}$$

For $k_n/k_p = Z_n\overline{\mu}_n L_p/Z_p\overline{\mu}_p L_n = 1$, the geometry of the n- and p-channel transistors cannot be identical because $\overline{\mu}_n \approx 3\overline{\mu}_p$. The device geometry must be adjusted to give the desired k_n/k_p ratio.

In summary, we see that for any of the inverters, a "low" input gives a "high" output and a "high" input gives a "low" output. This relationship is clearly shown in the voltage-transfer curves of Figs. 5.3 and 5.4d. The CMOS inverter has a considerably more abrupt transition from the **on** to the **off** state and has the least power dissipation of all four. The abrupt transition is due to both transistors being in saturation, and small input-voltage changes cause large output-voltage variations.

5.4 STATIC RANDOM-ACCESS MEMORIES

Most static random-access memories use inverters in the form of *bistable multivibrators* or *flip-flops*. To understand such circuits, let us consider the double inverter circuit of Fig. 5.5a in some detail. For $v_i \le V_{T1}$, T1 is **off**. The voltage at point "a" and on the gate of T2 is $V_a = V_{DD} - V_{T3}$. This ensures that T2 is **on**, with a resultant output voltage v_{oL}, as shown in Fig. 5.5b. As the input voltage is raised and exceeds the threshold voltage of T1, transistor T1 turns on. The potential at point "a" will consequently fall, and T2 is turned off. The output voltage increases and saturates at $V_{DD} - V_{T4}$.

The circuit can operate anywhere along its solid line transfer characteristic in Fig. 5.5b. Note that, in contrast to an inverter which gives "high" out for "low" in, this circuit gives "low" out for "low" in. It does not invert the input signal. This immediately raises the question of whether such a circuit could not be connected in some kind of feedback arrangement to implement new circuit functions.

One feedback connection is shown by the dashed line in Fig. 5.5a, with the output fed back to the input. This adds a constraint to the circuit—namely, $v_o = v_i$—as shown by the dashed line in Fig. 5.5b. While the original circuit could operate anywhere along the solid line, the new circuit is constrained to operate at the intersection of the two lines. Only points A, B, and C are possible operating points.

Suppose the circuit is biased at D before the feedback connection with $v_i > v_o$. As soon as the feedback path is introduced, v_i is forced to be equal to v_o, and the operating point moves to C. Similar arguments show point E to move to A. What happens when the circuit is initially biased to point F? After the feedback connection, will it move to B or to C? It cannot remain at F. With the slope of the output characteristic at F greater than unity, the circuit gain is greater than unity, too. Hence the output voltage increases until F comes to rest at C. The circuit has only two stable states: A and C. Once it is biased at either one of these, it remains there as long as V_{DD} is supplied.[4]

To change the state, let us introduce the trigger voltage v_{tr} into the feedback loop and redraw the circuit to that in Fig. 5.6a. With v_{tr} initially zero, the circuit is biased at point C in Fig. 5.6b. When v_{tr} increases, the dashed 45° line moves to the right without slope change, since $v_i = v_o + v_{tr}$, and C changes to C'. Although the operating

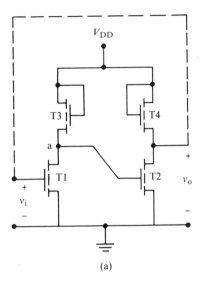

(a)

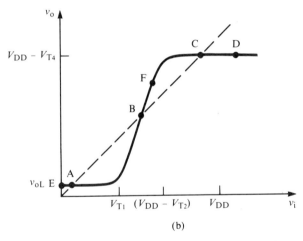

(b)

Fig. 5.5 A series-connected inverter: (a) the circuit diagram, and (b) the output-input voltage characteristic. The dashed line in (a) is a positive feedback connection; its effect on the transfer characteristic is shown in (b).

point has moved to a higher input voltage, the state of the circuit has not changed. Both input and output remain "high."

When v_{tr} becomes negative, the input voltage becomes $v_i = v_o - v_{tr}$ and the 45° line slides to the left. The operating point moves to the left of C, but remains in the "high" state until the line moves to the left beyond the upper portion of the voltage

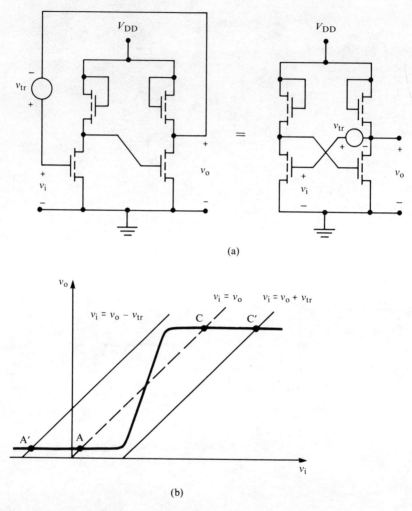

Fig. 5.6 A flip-flop with trigger voltage: (a) the circuit diagram, and (b) the voltage characteristic with positive and negative trigger voltages.

characteristic, shown by the "$v_i = v_o - v_{tr}$" line. Then the circuit switches to its stable point A'. Once the circuit is at A', the trigger voltage can be removed. The operating point then moves to A, but the circuit will remain stable and will not change its state.

Such a circuit is known as a *flip-flop*, because it flips back and forth between two stable states. To change its state it is only necessary to apply a trigger voltage of sufficient magnitude and duration for the "flip" to take place. Once the circuit has settled into its new stable state, the trigger voltage can be removed. A circuit of this type with two stable states is suitable as a memory, since a memory is nothing more than a circuit with two states. But there must be a mechanism to set the memory into one of these two states.

Such a circuit, the basic and well-known six-transistor cell, is shown in Fig. 5.7, in the dashed rectangle.[2] The circuit in Fig. 5.7 is part of a larger X-Y array not shown. X represents the rows, and Y represents the columns. We also show associated "write" and "read" circuitry to demonstrate its operation. Each cell in the overall array can be addressed randomly.

To demonstrate the "write" operation, we follow the path for writing a **one**.[2] In this circuit a **one** corresponds to T1 **off** and T2 **on**. A "high" input is applied to transis-

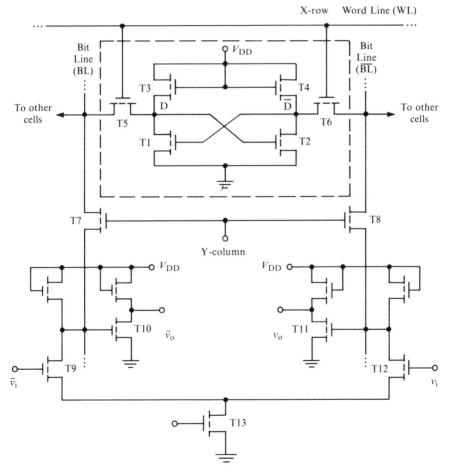

Fig. 5.7 A static random-access memory with input and output circuitry. Reprinted after Ref. [2] by permission of Prentice-Hall, Inc., Englewood Cliffs, NJ.

tors T12 and T13 and the Y-column line. This turns transistors T7, T8, T12, and T13 on. The Bit Line ($\overline{BL}$) is now essentially at ground potential, and the Bit Line (BL) is driven "high." The Word Line (WL) is pulsed "high," turning transistors T5 and T6 on. This puts point $\overline{D}$ in the "low" state close to ground potential. We neglect here the voltage drops across the **on** transistors.

The gate voltage on T1 is "low" and transistor T1 is **off**, automatically putting point D voltage at $V_{DD} - V_{T3}$. This voltage, applied to the gate of T2, drives T2 into its **on** state. Now the voltages to T5, T6, T7, T8, T12, and T13 can be removed and the memory will remain in its logic **one** state, with T1 **off** and T2 **on**. It will remain in this state as long as V_{DD} remains.

To write a **zero**, the procedure would be similar except that the "high" input would be applied to T9 instead of T12. This would result in T1 being **on** and T2 being **off**.

The "read" cycle is similar to the "write" cycle. Let us assume the memory to be in the logic **one** state. To read its memory content, transistor T13 remains **off**. Both X-row and Y-column lines are pulsed "high," turning T5, T6, T7, and T8 **on**. Point D, and therefore Bit Line BL, is "high" for a stored **one**. This causes T10 to be turned **on** and the output voltage $\overline{v}_o$ to be "low." Similarly, since $\overline{D}$ is "low," the output voltage v_o will be "high." It is, of course, only necessary to read one of the two outputs. For example, v_o is "high" for a **one** and "low" for a **zero**.

The cell in Fig. 5.7 is the basic cell and only one of a number of versions in use today. They all make use of the flip-flop. In some designs, transistors T3 and T4 are replaced by high-resistance polysilicon resistors. Some cell simplification results, and less silicon area is consumed, if the resistors are placed on top of the cell. The resistors must, of course, be properly isolated by appropriate insulating layers from the rest of the circuit.

One leg of the cell is always **on** with current flowing through it. This leads to static power dissipation as we saw in the previous chapter. A CMOS cell eliminates static power dissipation, because current flows only during switching if the small reverse-biased junction leakage current is neglected. The switching-dissipation power is

$$P = CV_{DD}^2 f \tag{5.8}$$

where C is the capacitance that must be charged during switching and f is the operating frequency. Clearly, the drain voltage is very important, and lower V_{DD} reduces power dissipation significantly.

A CMOS SRAM cell is shown in Fig. 5.8, and its operation can be derived in a straightforward manner using the concepts of the CMOS inverter presented in Section 5.3. The number of transistors is the same as in Fig. 5.7, but the fabrication process complexity has increased, because both p- and n-channel transistors must be fabricated on the same chip. Nevertheless, the CMOS SRAM is becoming the dominant technology because of its lower power dissipation and greater noise immunity. Process complexity is frequently a secondary consideration when significant circuit or system advantages can be gained, provided that the complexity still allows economically acceptable yields during the manufacturing process.

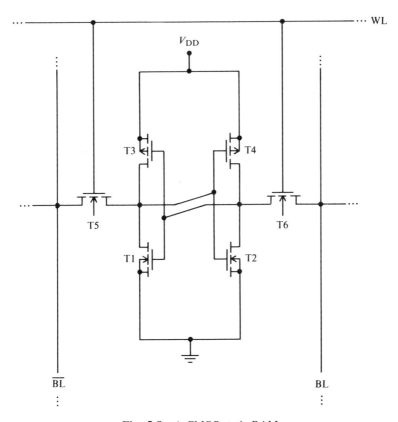

Fig. 5.8 A CMOS static RAM.

5.5 DYNAMIC RANDOM-ACCESS MEMORIES

Dynamic RAM's differ from *static RAM's* in two major ways: first, they offer higher circuit density and are cheaper; and second, they require more complex timing and logic circuits for their operation. As the memory size increases, it becomes increasingly more attractive to use DRAM's in spite of their greater complexity. The main factors in their increased use are their lower cost and smaller size.

The DRAM cell that paved the way for large-scale use of dynamic random-access memories was the three-transistor cell of the 1103 chip[5] introduced in 1970. It did not take long for it to be replaced by the one-transistor cell, invented earlier in 1966.[6] The one-transistor cell has become the standard unit of today's high-density DRAM's, and we will describe it in some detail. For a good review, see Ref. [7].

The basic design of the one-transistor cell is shown in Fig. 5.9. It resembles the input circuit of the CCD, and its operation can, in fact, be described with CCD concepts. The device in Fig. 5.9a and d consists of an n^+ input diffusion or diode (the Bit Line), two gates (the first is the Word Line and the second the storage gate, or Plate), and a

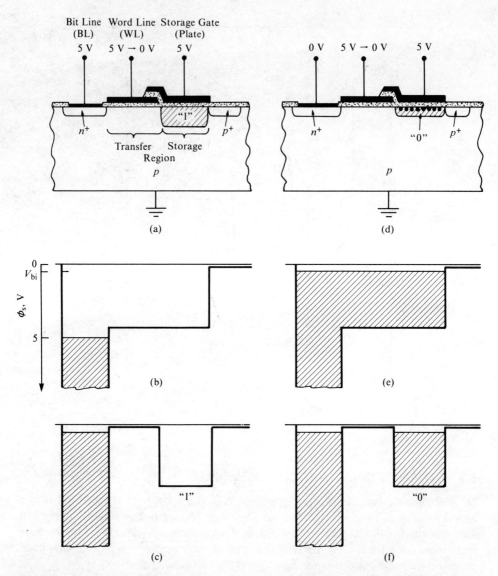

Fig. 5.9 A basic dynamic RAM cell, showing (a) a stored **one** and (d) a stored **zero**. The writing of a **one** is shown in (b) and (c), and the writing of a **zero** is shown in (e) and (f).

p^+ channel stop. The purpose of the channel stop is to confine the inversion layer to the storage gate and to prevent charge from spreading to the right. The gates are shown to be overlapping.

Let us assume that the substrate is grounded and that 5 V is applied to the storage gate. In an actual circuit, a substrate voltage is generally applied, but for our "concept" explanation, we disregard that. To write a **one**, 5 V is applied to the Bit Line, and the Word Line is pulsed "high" by applying a 5-V pulse to it. Both gates are now at 5 V. Since there is a voltage drop across the oxide, the surface potential under the gates is less than 5 V, and any charge under either gate flows into the diode, as shown in Fig. 5.9b. When the WL pulse returns to zero, an empty potential well remains under the storage gate, as in Fig. 5.9c. This empty well represents a binary **one** and is shown as the deep-depletion space-charge region in Fig. 5.9a and the empty well in Fig. 5.9c.

To write a **zero**, the diode voltage is reduced to zero and the WL is pulsed "high." Electrons from the n^+ region fill the potential wells under both gates, as shown in Fig. 5.9e. For zero diode voltage, the surface potential of the n^+ region is equal to the diode built-in voltage, V_{bi}, as indicated in Fig. 5.9. V_{bi} is on the order of the surface potential under a strongly inverted MOS-C gate — i.e., approximately twice the Fermi potential ($\phi_s \approx 2\phi_F$; see Section 1.4).

When the WL pulse returns to zero, a charge packet is isolated under the storage gate. This is shown as the binary **zero** in Fig. 5.9f and the inversion layer in Fig. 5.9d. A comparison of Fig. 5.9a with Fig. 5.9d, or c with f, shows the **one** to correspond to the nonequilibrium, deep-depletion MOS-C state, and the **zero** to correspond to the inverted, equilibrium condition. Being in a nonequilibrium state, the **one** is "volatile." As a result of thermal ehp generation, the empty potential well gradually fills up with charge and the **one** becomes a **zero**. This is the very nature of DRAM's. The **zeros** remain **zeros** while the **ones** change into **zeros**. To prevent this from happening, the circuit is periodically refreshed to maintain each of the storage sites in its correct memory state.

Early one-transistor DRAM cells consisted of a MOSFET with a floating n^+ drain, instead of the gate-induced drain of Fig. 5.9. We know from the discussion of Fig. 3.13 that a floating drain can be reverse-biased to the potential of an adjacent source if the gate is pulsed to a sufficiently high potential. Such a device has the advantage of not requiring a separate Plate line, but its charge-storage capacity is less than that of an MOS-C.

The stored charge is an important quantity, because a **one** must be clearly distinguishable from a **zero** during the "read" operation. The **zero** corresponds to the inversion charge in a full potential well. For the MOS-C DRAM, the charge/unit area is, from eq. (1.48),

$$Q_{\text{MOS-C}}(0) \approx V_G'C_o \tag{5.9}$$

For a given gate voltage, the charge decreases with decreasing area. Higher-density memories have smaller-area memory cells, and various techniques are employed to increase the total charge per cell.

One of these techniques is the use of double ion-implanted regions in the *high-capacity* (Hi-C) DRAM cell,[8] shown in Fig. 5.10a. The use of ion implantation is discussed in more detail in Section 6.2. Here we merely mention that ion implantation is

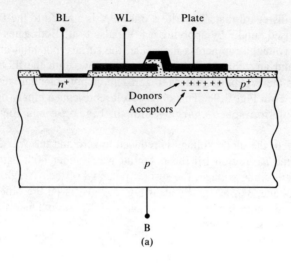

(a)

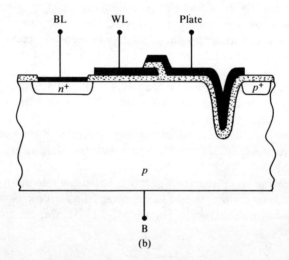

(b)

Fig. 5.10 DRAM structures with increased charge-storage capacity: (a) the high-capacity cell, and (b) the trench capacitor cell.

a method of introducing dopant atoms of very precisely controlled depth and concentration into a semiconductor. *Acceptor* atoms are implanted into the storage region of the Hi-C DRAM cell. The resulting higher doping concentration increases the scr capacitance, but it does not increase the charge-storage capacity of the cell, because the surface potential difference between an empty and a full potential well decreases.[8] However, an additional *donor* implant changes the surface potential. The donor atoms in the semiconductor are located very close to the Si/SiO_2 interface and to first order act as fixed positive oxide charges. The surface potential change due to the donors, in conjunction with the increased scr capacitance due to the acceptors, results in an enhancement of charge-storage capacity of typically 50% over a conventional cell.

The Hi-C DRAM achieves its higher charge-storage capacity by virtue of a clever dopant scheme. The structure shown in Fig. 5.10b relies on a geometrical factor. A hole is etched into the semiconductor substrate prior to cell fabrication. Then an oxide is grown on the surface in the hole and subsequently the hole is filled with a polysilicon storage electrode. Such a structure is called a *trench* or *corrugated capacitor.*[9] The storage area is increased by the three-dimensional nature of the cell. This type of DRAM design is presently under active investigation and is a leading contender for DRAM memories with densities of 1 Mbit and higher.

5.6 WRITE, READ, AND REFRESH

ROM, PROM, EPROM, and EEPROM memory cells are generally only read since the information is permanently or semipermanently programmed into them. An SRAM needs to be written and read, but not refreshed. A DRAM has to be written and read, but must also be refreshed. How is all of this accomplished?

A simplified schematic that incorporates all the essential elements of these functions is shown in Fig. 5.11. Switches S1 and S2 select the appropriate row and column. We continue with cell $(3, 5)$ used earlier in the example of Fig. 5.1. The binary codes 011 and 101 applied to the row and column decoders, respectively, are equivalent to switches S1 and S2 in Fig. 5.11. When they are closed, cell $(3, 5)$ is the only one addressed. A "high" voltage on the Word Line is applied to the gate of the transistor at that storage site, turning it on. The logic state of the cell depends on the Bit Line or Data Line voltage during writing.

The information to be written into the cell is the voltage at point A on the Bit Line. Setting switches S3 and S4 to the "Write" position ensures the voltage at "B" to be equal to that at "A." With S1 closed, the memory cell MOSFET switch is **on** and the storage capacitor, C_s, is charged to $V_A - V_P$, where V_P is the Plate potential. In other words, we can consider the MOSFET of the storage cell to be a switch that is opened and closed by the voltage on the row or Word Line. After the "Write" operation, switches S1 and S2 are opened and another cell can be written.

Let us now consider the "Read" operation. We assume that all cells have stored information and we want to read cell $(3, 5)$. Switches S1 and S2 are again closed by the appropriate binary addresses to the row and column decoders. S4 is switched to the "Read" position. The storage capacitor is connected to the sense amplifier or comparator, where the capacitor voltage is compared with the reference voltage, V_{ref}. If the capacitor voltage is larger than V_{ref}, a logic **1** is read, and if it is smaller, a logic **0** is read.

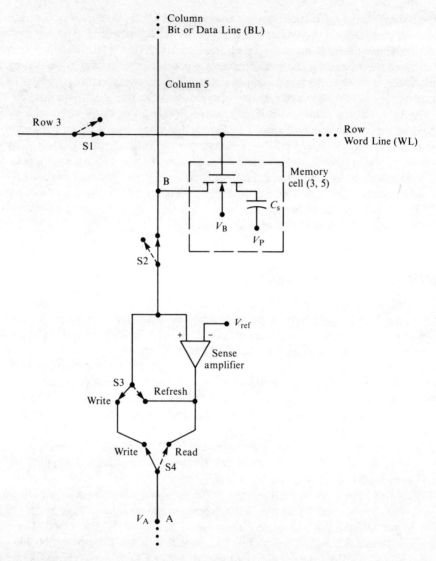

Fig. 5.11 Schematic diagram showing the writing, reading, and refreshing operations of a DRAM. Reprinted after Ref. [1] by permission of Scientific American, Inc.

A **1** originally written into the cell corresponds to the deep-depletion MOS-C state. If the information is read immediately after writing, then clearly a **1** will be read. However, the deep-depletion state will gradually disappear as a result of ehp generation. The voltage on the capacitor discharges for sufficiently long wait times, and a **0** will be read. If a **0** is originally written, corresponding to an inverted MOS-C, then it will always be a **0** upon reading, regardless of the time interval between writing and reading. We see, then, that a **1** turns into a **0**, but a **0** remains a **0**.

Clearly, the **1** needs to be refreshed. Since it is generally not known what logic value each cell contains and since furthermore the cells are read randomly, it is imperative that the entire memory be refreshed at periodic intervals. These intervals are typically a few milliseconds.

The refresh operation is also shown in Fig. 5.11. When data are read they are also refreshed by setting switch S3 to the "Refresh" position. So, by the appropriate circuitry, reading also refreshes the stored information. It should be noted that data obviously cannot be written while reading or refreshing is in progress.

5.7 THE SENSE AMPLIFIER

The *sense amplifier* is an extremely sensitive detector that is one of the key elements in the continued quest for higher-density, lower-stored-charge memories. The sense amplifier compares the charge or voltage on the storage cell with a preset value to determine its logic state. There are severe constraints imposed upon the sense amplifier by the small stored charge of today's memory cells. Many types of sense amplifiers have been suggested and tried, but only a few are used.[10] We will describe a circuit that is the basis of most variations and that was first described in 1972.[11] Our discussion follows that of Refs. [10], [12], and [13].

First we describe the voltages up to the sense amplifier and then the operation of the amplifier itself. Consider the circuit shown in Fig. 5.12. It is part of a DRAM, showing one Bit Line, three memory cells, a reference voltage, and the sense amplifier. The Bit Line (BL) is a long n^+ diffusion in the semiconductor substrate. Many storage cells are connected to the Bit Line. The BL is biased to reference voltage V_{ref} by turning on transistor T with a sufficiently large gate voltage to ensure its operation in the linear region. Then T is turned off, and the BL, set to potential V_{ref}, floats electrically.

Next, a memory cell is selected by turning on the appropriate Word Line. Charge distribution takes place between the charge stored in the memory cell and the floating Bit Line. Suppose the cell contains a **0**. Its surface potential is approximately $2\phi_F$. The Bit Line is precharged to $V_{ref} > 2\phi_F$. Obviously, the electrons in the inversion layer will flow into the Bit Line. They reduce the BL potential from its initial value $V_{BLi} = V_{ref}$ to a final value V_{BLf}.

For a **zero**-containing memory cell initially biased to V_{S0i}, with stored charge Q_{S0i} and capacitance C_{S0i} and a Bit Line with initial values V_{BLi}, Q_{BLi}, and C_{BLi}, equality of the initial and final charges gives

$$Q_{BLi} + Q_{S0i} = Q_{BLf} + Q_{S0f} \tag{5.10}$$

where the subscripts "i" and "f" stand for initial and final values, respectively. "Initial"

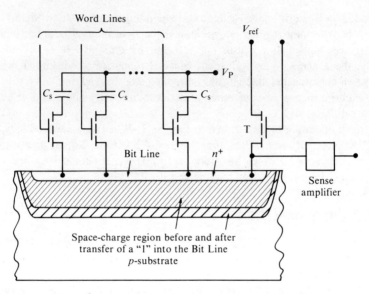

Fig. 5.12   The Bit Line, the reset transistor, and three memory cells. The shaded regions show the reverse-biased scr before and after a memory cell containing a **one** is read into the BL. For a **zero**, the scr shrinks. Reprinted after Ref. [10] with permission.

refers to the time before the cell is connected to the BL, and "final" refers to the time after the connection is made. If the charges are replaced by the voltage-capacitance products, then eq. (5.10) can be written as

$$V_{BLi} C_{BLi} + V_{S0i} C_{S0i} = V_{BLf}(C_{S0f} + C_{BLf}) \tag{5.11}$$

The sense amplifier must be able to measure the BL voltage change to detect the logic state of the memory cell. Solving for the final BL voltage gives

$$V_{BLf} = (V_{BLi} C_{BLi} + V_{S0i} C_{S0i})/(C_{S0f} + C_{BLf})$$

$$\approx (V_{BLi} R_{BL0} + V_{S0i} R_{S0})/(1 + R_{BL0}) \tag{5.12}$$

where we have assumed $C_{BLi} \approx C_{BLf} = C_{BL}$—i.e., its initial and final values are approximately equal since the BL capacitance is much larger than the storage-cell capacitance. The sense amplifier actually detects the change in the BL voltage before and after the storage cell is connected to it. The voltage change is

$$\Delta V_{BL0} = V_{BLf} - V_{BLi} = (V_{S0i} R_{S0} - V_{BLi})/(1 + R_{BL0}) \tag{5.13}$$

where $R_{S0} = C_{S0i}/C_{S0f}$ and $R_{BL0} = C_{BL}/C_{S0f}$.

The detection circuit must be able to discriminate between a **one** and a **zero**. Hence, the Bit Line voltage must change from its reference value for either logic state. This can occur only if V_{ref} is chosen to lie between the voltages V_{S0i} and V_{S1i}, the initial voltages of a **zero** and a **one**, respectively. For example, for a 5-V power supply, we find $V_{S0i} \approx 0$ V and $V_{S1i} \approx 5$ V. So V_{ref} should be around 2.5 V.

When a **one** is read, the BL is also precharged to V_{ref}, which is now lower than the memory-cell voltage. Hence, when the cell is accessed, charge flows from the Bit Line into the cell, instead of from the cell into the Bit Line, as was the case when a **zero** was read. Arguments similar to those above give the BL voltage change upon reading a **one** as

$$\Delta V_{BL1} = (V_{S1i} R_{S1} - V_{BLi})/(1 + R_{BL1}) \tag{5.14}$$

where $R_{S1} = C_{S1i}/C_{S1f}$ and $R_{BL1} = C_{BL}/C_{S1f}$.

The capacitance of the memory cell is that of an MOS-C lying between deep depletion and heavy inversion. From eqs. (1.52) and (1.53), we find for $N_B = N_A = 10^{16}$ cm^{-3}, $x_o = 500$ Å, and 5-V bias for a **one**: $C_{S0i} = 2.29 \times 10^{-8}$, $C_{S1i} = 1.08 \times 10^{-8}$, and $C_{S1f} = C_{S0f} = 1.44 \times 10^{-8}$ F/cm^2. This gives $R_{S0} = 1.6$ and $R_{S1} = 0.75$, and for $V_{S0i} \approx 0$, $V_{S1i} \approx 5$ V, and $V_{BLi} = V_{ref} \approx 2.5$ V we find

$$\Delta V_{BL0} = -2.5/(1 + R_{BL0}); \qquad \Delta V_{BL1} = 1.3/(1 + R_{BL1}) \tag{5.15}$$

The R_{BL} values lie typically around 10 or so, giving

$$\Delta V_{BL0} \approx -225 \text{ mV}; \qquad \Delta V_{BL1} \approx 120 \text{ mV} \tag{5.16}$$

The sense amplifier must be able to detect these small voltage changes. As cell sizes continue to shrink, the voltage changes are likely to decrease further because the cell capacitances become smaller. The BL capacitance, however, is not decreasing correspondingly, because the chip size is not getting smaller. If anything, the chip sizes of higher-density memories have increased. To complicate matters further, the memory array is not uniform. There are threshold-voltage variations across the array and other nonuniformities such as physical-dimension variations. They tend to degrade the already small voltage changes further. How then can these small voltages be reliably measured?

It has become common practice in almost all single-transistor DRAM's to use a *flip-flop* circuit to **sense** and **amplify** the stored information. We illustrate this concept with the simple cross-coupled flip-flop amplifier shown in Fig. 5.13a. The *sense operation* consists of a *precharge period* and a *sense period*. During precharge, transistor T8 is **off**, preventing current flow through the flip-flop. The balancing transistor T7 is turned on, ensuring that both sides of the flip-flop are at identical potentials.

If T8 were **on**, the circuit would likely settle into one of its two stable states. Ideally, of course, the node 1 and node 2 potentials should be identical. But in reality, a

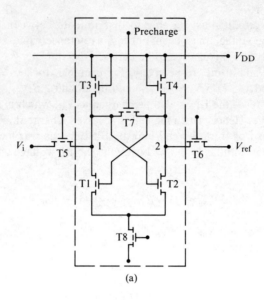

(a)

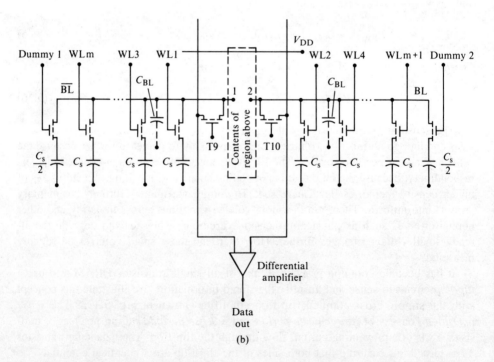

(b)

Fig. 5.13 (a) Basic balanced flip-flop sense amplifier and (b) balanced flip-flop sense amplifier with split Bit Line and half-capacitance dummy cells. Reprinted after Ref. [13] by permission of John Wiley & Sons, Ltd.

circuit imbalance can be caused by variations in the physical device dimensions or by variations in electrical parameters such as the threshold voltage. Such an imbalance would likely flip the circuit into one of its stable states. This would occur before the memory cell is addressed. If T8 is left **off**, the flip-flop in effect floats electrically and the voltages at nodes 1 and 2 are essentially identical.

After the precharge period, T7 is turned off and T5 and T6 are turned on, establishing the input voltage V_i at node 1 and the reference voltage V_{ref} at node 2. Any difference between these two causes an imbalance, and when T8 is turned on, the circuit settles into its stable state. When it does, it amplifies the small voltage imbalance between nodes 1 and 2, which is only a fraction of a volt, to the full voltage level. For $V_1 > V_2$, T1 will be **off** and T2 will be **on**, resulting in $V_1 \rightarrow V_{DD} - V_{T3}$ and $V_2 \rightarrow 0$. What the *flip-flop* in Fig. 5.13a has done is to take a small voltage difference across its two input terminals and amplify it to almost the full V_{DD} voltage difference.

Implementation of the concept of Fig. 5.13a into a real sense amplifier is shown in Fig. 5.13b. The memory Bit Lines are divided in half, with the sense amplifier in the center and equal numbers of memory cells on either side. In addition, there is a *dummy cell* on each side of the array. The dummy cell stores half the charge of a normal cell.

During the precharge period, transistor T7 is **on** to balance the flip-flop and set the two Bit Lines to a voltage of approximately V_{DD}. For the enhancement-mode loads T3 and T4, the two Bit Lines are actually set to $V_{DD} - V_T$, with V_T being the threshold voltage of T3 and T4. The dummy cells are charged to store a full potential well or logic **0** by separate circuits not shown.

After the precharge period, the selected Word Line — e.g., WL1 — together with the dummy cell on the opposite side — e.g., Dummy 2 — are pulsed **on**. Suppose cell 1 stores a logic **0**. Its charge flows onto Bit Line $\overline{BL}$, reducing the node 1 voltage from $V_{DD} - V_T$. The dummy cell also has a logic **0** and its charge flows onto Bit Line BL, reducing the node 2 voltage from $V_{DD} - V_T$. However, cell 1 contains more charge than the dummy cell because it is larger. Therefore, node 1 drops to a lower voltage than node 2. When T8 is subsequently turned on, V_1 falls close to ground potential and V_2 rises to $V_{DD} - V_T$.

With WL1 still "high," the new V_1 potential is written back into cell 1. Hence, the destructive "Read" operation ends up as a constructive "Refresh" operation without the need for additional circuitry. The Word Lines are then turned off. The cell is back in its pre-Read charge state, and transistors T9 and T10 are activated to apply voltages V_1 and V_2 to the differential amplifier and the Data Out line. The sense amplifier is then ready for the next "Read" cycle. If cell 1 had contained a logic **1**, it is straightforward to extend the analysis to show that node 1 would end up at $V_{DD} - V_T$ and node 2 at ground potential.

Note that the approach of Fig. 5.12 does not use dummy cells. It merely requires a potential of $V_{DD}/2$ on the Bit Lines. This lower voltage reduces power dissipation since, during switching, power dissipation is proportional to (voltage)^2 (see eq. 5.8). Sense amplifiers based on the concepts of either Fig. 5.12 or Fig. 5.13 are used in most memory circuits, but any given design is likely to incorporate some variation from the basic concept.

5.8 SUMMARY

In this chapter we have presented the basic concepts of semiconductor memories. The discussion is largely in descriptive terms. Many books give the relevant equations in great detail, but few discuss the underlying physical principles in any detail. We initially defined various memory terms for both nonvolatile and volatile memories. Then we treated inverters because we used them later in the discussion of static RAM's and sense amplifiers. The fairly standard six-transistor static RAM cell was used and described in some detail. Neither the inverter nor the static RAM utilizes deep-depletion MOS-C's, but they are standard components and were included for completeness. The dynamic RAM uses MOS-C's as its storage elements. Its structure, as well as the write, read, and refresh operations, were given. Finally we described the sense amplifier. It is a key element of high-density dynamic RAM's and incorporates some interesting device concepts.

REFERENCES

[1] D. A. Hodges, "Microelectronic Memories," Scient. Am., *237*, 130-145, Sept., 1977.

[2] M. M. Cirovic, *Handbook of Semiconductor Memories,* Reston Publ. Co., Reston, VA, 1981.

[3] A. B. Glaser and G. E. Subak-Sharpe, *Integrated Circuit Engineering; Design, Fabrication and Applications,* Addison-Wesley Publ. Co., Reading, MA, 1979, p. 657-680.

[4] C. L. Searle, A. R. Boothroyd, E. J. Angelo, Jr., P. E. Gray, and D. O. Pederson, *Elementary Circuit Properties of Transistors,* J. Wiley & Sons, New York, 1964, p. 67-70; J. N. Harris, P. E. Gray and C. L. Searle, *Digital Transistor Circuits,* J. Wiley & Sons, New York, 1966, p. 87-88.

[5] W. Regitz and J. A. Karp, "The Three-Transistor Cell 1024-Bit 500 ns MOS RAM," IEEE J. Solid-State Ccts., *SC-5,* 181-186, Oct., 1970.

[6] R. H. Dennard, "Evolution of the MOSFET Dynamic RAM—A Personal View," IEEE Trans. Electr. Dev., *ED-31,* 1549-1555, Nov., 1984.

[7] V. L. Rideout, "One-Device Cells for Dynamic Random-Access Memories: A Tutorial," IEEE Trans. Electr. Dev., *ED-26,* 839-852, June, 1979.

[8] A. F. Tasch, P. K. Chatterjee, H. S. Fu, and T. C. Holloway, "The Hi-C RAM Cell Concept," IEEE Trans. Electr. Dev., *ED-25,* 33-41, Jan., 1978.

[9] H. Sunami, T. Kure, N. Hashimoto, K. Itoh, T. Toyabe, and S. Asai, "A Corrugated Capacitor Cell (CCC)," IEEE Trans. Electr. Dev., *ED-31,* 746-753, June, 1984.

[10] K. H. Horniger, "Readout Methods and Readout Circuits for Dynamic Charge-Storage Elements," in *Digital Memory and Storage,* W. E. Proebster (ed.), Vieweg Publ., Braunschweig, 1978, p. 121-134.

[11] K. U. Stein, A. Sihling, and E. Doering, "Storage Array and Sense/Refresh Circuit for Single Transistor Memory Cells," IEEE J. Solid-State Ccts., *SC-7,* 336-340, Oct., 1972.

[12] C. Kuo, N. Kitagawa, E. Ward, and P. Drayer, "Sense Amplifier Design Is Key to 1-Transistor Cell in 4096-Bit RAM," Electronics, *46*, 116-121, Sept. 13, 1973.

[13] R. W. Hunt, "Memory Design and Technology," in *Large Scale Integration* (M. J. Howes and D. V. Morgan, eds.), J. Wiley & Sons, Chichester, 1981, p. 255-318.

PROBLEMS

5.1 Show that the turn-on voltage drop across a MOSFET with its drain connected to its gate is $V_G - V_T$. The current-voltage curve of such a device is shown as the enhancement-mode load in Fig. 5.2.

5.2 For the enhancement-mode load inverter of Fig. 5.2, the load transistor is always in saturation and is governed by $i_{DS2} = (k_2/2)(V_{DD} - V_{T2} - v_o)^2$. The driver transistor is either in its linear region with $i_{DS1} = k_1(v_i - V_{T1} - v_o/2)v_o$ or in saturation with $i_{DS1} = (k_1/2)(v_i - V_{T1})^2$. The boundary between the two regions is $|v_o| = |v_i - V_T|$, where we use $V_{T1} = V_{T2}$ and assume the substrate to be grounded.

Find expressions for v_o in terms of v_i for both regions of operation.
Plot v_o vs. v_i for $k_1/k_2 = 1$, 10, and 100 using $V_{DD} = 10$ V and $V_T = 1$ V.

5.3 Consider the configuration of Problem 5.2 to be an amplifier with an enhancement-mode load. Derive expressions for the voltage gain, $A_v = dv_o/dv_i$, for the two cases of Problem 5.2.

5.4 Calculate the solid v_o vs. v_i curve in Fig. 5.5b for the circuit in Fig. 5.5a. Use $k_1 = 10^{-4}$ A/V^2, $k_1 = k_2$, and $k_3 = k_4 = 0.1 k_1$. $V_{T1} = V_{T2} = V_{T3} = V_{T4} = 1$ V. $V_{DD} = 5$ V.

5.5 This problem deals with the Hi-C DRAM cell.

Draw on one figure the surface potential vs. gate voltage curves for an empty potential well for an MOS-C with $x_o = 300$ Å, and $V_{FB} = -1$ V over the gate voltage range $V_G = -5$ V to $+5$ V when:

(a) $N_B = 10^{15}$ cm^{-3}

(b) $N_A = 10^{17}$ cm^{-3} implanted into the wafer in (a) to a depth of 0.4 μm. Assume N_A to be uniform over the 0.4-μm depth — i.e., it is box-shaped.

(c) A shallow donor implant of 4×10^{12} cm^{-2} is implanted into the wafer in (b). Assume the donors to be a sheet at the surface with zero depth.

Then calculate the maximum charge density that can be stored for (a), (b), and (c) at $V_G = +5$ V. Assume the substrate to be grounded.

5.6 Point A in the circuit in Fig. P5.6 is precharged by transistor T1 to $V_{ref} = 2.5$ V, and then T1 is turned off.

Calculate the voltage change at point A — the input to the sense amplifier — when WL is pulsed on, for:

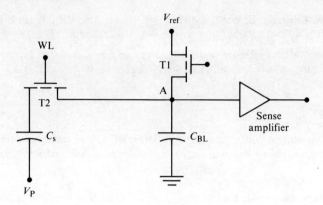

Fig. P5.6

(a) C_s in deep depletion

(b) C_s in inversion.

Use $N_B = 10^{15}$ cm^{-3}, $x_o = 500$ Å, C_s area $= 10^{-6}$ cm^2, $C_{BL} = 0.2$ pF. The flatband voltage of T2 is zero. $V_P = 5$ V, $V_{WL} = 5$ V. Assume the gate area of T2 to be negligibly small.

6 / Advanced MOSFET Concepts

6.1 INTRODUCTION

In this chapter we depart from earlier chapters and discuss only MOSFET's. In particular we discuss aspects of MOSFET's not treated in Volume IV.[1] We start by deriving the current-voltage characteristic. In Section 6.2 we address threshold voltage adjustment. We saw in earlier chapters, especially in Chapter 5, the importance of the threshold voltage in digital circuits. The threshold voltage is equally important for CCD's and other analog devices. The charge in the oxide and at the oxide/semiconductor interface, as well as the semiconductor bulk charge, contributes to the threshold voltage. Precise threshold voltage control requires accurate charge control. This is usually accomplished with ion implantation.

The MOSFET mobility is always lower than the bulk semiconductor mobility. The mobility reduction is mainly the result of increased surface scattering at the oxide/semiconductor interface. This is discussed in Section 6.3.

For gate voltages below the threshold voltage, zero drain current is predicted by current-voltage equations derived for above-threshold gate voltages. This is not observed experimentally. In Section 6.4 we derive the subthreshold current-voltage characteristic and find quite a different device behavior. Above threshold, the current is governed essentially by the channel resistance. Below threshold it is barrier-limited. A barrier-limited current depends exponentially on voltage.

As MOSFET's are made smaller with gate lengths and widths approaching dimensions on the order of 1 μm or less, short- and narrow-channel effects become important. The influence of these effects on device behavior is discussed in Section 6.5. Finally, in Section 6.6 we examine carrier injection and trapping in the oxide, weak avalanche breakdown in the reverse-biased drain space-charge region, and interface state generation and threshold voltage shifts due to "hot" carriers. These effects are found primarily in small-geometry MOSFET's.

The current-voltage characteristics of MOSFET's are derived in many textbooks. A very nice treatment can be found in Volume IV of this series.[1] We follow a derivation here that is suitable for the usual "above-threshold voltage" condition, but is also applicable for the "below-threshold voltage" or subthreshold case. For the sake of brevity, we quote only the main results here. The detailed derivation can be found in Ref. [2]. In the general case, the n-channel drain current is expressed there as

$$
\begin{aligned}
I_D = k_n \bigg\{ & [V_G'(\phi_{sL} - \phi_{s0}) - (\phi_{sL}^2 - \phi_{s0}^2)/2] \\
& + (K_s \varepsilon_0/C_o L_D)(kT/q)^2 \bigg[\int_0^{U_{s0}} F(U, U_F, 0)\, dU - \int_0^{U_{sL}} F(U, U_F, U_D)\, dU \bigg] \bigg\}
\end{aligned}
\tag{6.1}
$$

where $k_n = Z\bar{\mu}_n C_o/L$ depends on the gate length and width, the effective mobility, and the gate capacitance per unit area. $\phi_{s0} = (kT/q)U_{s0}$ and $\phi_{sL} = (kT/q)U_{sL}$ are the surface potentials at the source and drain ends of the MOSFET channel, respectively. The F function is given by

$$
\begin{aligned}
F(U, U_F, \xi) = \{ & \exp(U_F)[\exp(-U) + U - 1] \\
& + \exp(-U_F)[\exp(U - \xi) - U - \exp(-\xi)] \}^{1/2}
\end{aligned}
\tag{6.2}
$$

where $\xi = [E_F - F_N(y)]/kT$, and y is the coordinate parallel to the oxide/semiconductor interface, with $y = 0$ at the source contact. $\xi = 0$ at the source end, and $\xi \approx U_D = qV_D/kT$ at the drain end of the channel. For $\xi = 0$, eq. (6.2) simplifies to eq. (1.13).

For n-channel MOSFET's operating above threshold voltage, the normalized potentials U, U_F, and U_D are positive, and to a good approximation we can neglect most of the terms in eq. (6.2). F can be approximated by

$$
F(U, U_F, \xi) \approx [U \exp(U_F)]^{1/2}
\tag{6.3}
$$

Substituting eq. (6.3) into eq. (6.1) and integrating yields

$$
\begin{aligned}
I_D = k_n [& V_G'(\phi_{sL} - \phi_{s0}) - (\phi_{sL}^2 - \phi_{s0}^2)/2 \\
& - (2/3)[(2qK_s\varepsilon_0 N_B)^{1/2}/C_o](\phi_{sL}^{3/2} - \phi_{s0}^{3/2})]
\end{aligned}
\tag{6.4}
$$

For the general MOSFET we consider the voltages shown in Fig. 6.1, not just the gate and drain voltages as is frequently done. The strong inversion surface potential at the source end of the channel is not the usual $\phi_s = 2\phi_F$ when source (V_S) and substrate (V_B) voltages are applied. It becomes instead $\phi_s = 2\phi_F' = 2\phi_F - V_{BS}$, where $V_{BS} = V_B - V_S$. This is discussed in greater detail in Ref. [1].

For the voltage polarities shown in Fig. 6.1 we have $\phi_{s0} = 2\phi_F'$ and $\phi_{sL} = 2\phi_F' + V_{DS}$. Substituting these surface potentials into eq. (6.4) gives the drain current as

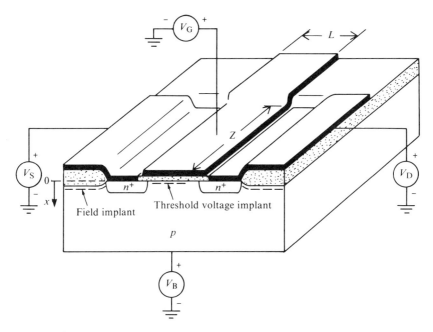

Fig. 6.1 Schematic diagram of a MOSFET, showing the source, gate, drain, and substrate voltages.

$$I_D = k_n\{(V_{GS} - V_{TS} - V_{DS}/2)V_{DS}$$
$$- (4\phi_F'V_W'/3)[(1 + V_{DS}/2\phi_F')^{3/2} - (1 + 3V_{DS}/4\phi_F')]\} \qquad (6.5)$$

with gate and drain voltages measured with respect to the source. The bulk charge equivalent voltage is $V_W' = (4qK_s\varepsilon_0 N_B \phi_F')^{1/2}/C_o$ and the *threshold voltage* is defined as

$$V_{TS} = V_{FB} + 2\phi_F + V_W' = V_{FB} + 2\phi_F + [2qK_s\varepsilon_0 N_B(2\phi_F - V_{BS})]^{1/2}/C_o \qquad (6.6)$$

For p-type substrates, V_{BS} is negative.

The *flatband voltage* is given by

$$V_{FB} = \phi_{ms} - Q_f/C_o - Q_{it}(\phi_s = 0)/C_o - (1/C_o)\int_0^{x_o} (x/x_o)Q_m(x)\,dx \qquad (6.7)$$

It depends on the gate-semiconductor work-function difference, the fixed oxide charge, the surface potential–dependent interface-state charge, and the mobile charge in the oxide. The interface-state charge is evaluated at $\phi_s = 2\phi_F$ in eq. (6.6), but at $\phi_s = 0$ in eq. (6.7).[1] If its density in the band gap were constant as a function of energy, then $Q_{it}(2\phi_F) = Q_{it}(0)$. But the interface-state density is generally not constant, and the two interface-state charge densities are likely to differ. However, both values usually are sufficiently small that they can be taken as equal with little error.

When both source and substrate voltages are zero, eq. (6.5) becomes the well-known current-voltage equation for a nonsaturated device:

$$I_D = k_n\{(V_G - V_T - V_D/2)V_D - (4\phi_F V_W/3)$$
$$\cdot [(1 + V_D/2\phi_F)^{3/2} - (1 + 3V_D/4\phi_F)]\} \tag{6.8a}$$

$V_W = (4qK_s\varepsilon_o N_B\phi_F)^{1/2}/C_o$ accounts for the bulk charge contribution to the drain current. For negligible bulk charge, the drain-current expression simplifies further to

$$I_D = k_n(V_G - V_T - V_D/2)V_D \tag{6.8b}$$

Eq. (6.8b) is sufficient for many applications, but for a proper inclusion of the bulk charge we must use eq. (6.8a).

6.2 THRESHOLD-VOLTAGE CONTROL

The threshold voltage is a very important device parameter. It is mandatory that its value not fall outside certain prescribed limits for a chip that might consist of thousands of devices. We saw in the CCD chapter (Chapter 3) that high transfer efficiency was a key device parameter. The threshold voltage is one contributor to transfer efficiency, although it was not highlighted there. Clearly, threshold-voltage variations along the CCD array produce fluctuating surface potentials for identical gate voltages. Charge transfer is impeded when there are small potential barriers when there should be none. Consequently, charge remains in small pockets along the array, perturbing the charge-transfer process.

In semiconductor memories, MOSFET's are continuously turned on and off, and charge flows from the memory cells to the sense amplifier. The sense amplifier is a delicately balanced flip-flop whose voltage-sensing capability is directly related to the threshold-voltage variation between the transistors. Hence, both analog and digital devices rely on highly uniform semiconductor device properties. It is therefore important to maintain the threshold voltage as uniformly as possible across the array, across the wafer, and from wafer to wafer.

From eqs. (6.6) and (6.7) we rewrite the threshold voltage as

$$V_{TS} = \phi_{ms} - Q_f/C_o - Q_{it}(\phi_s)/C_o - (1/C_o)\int_0^{x_o}(x/x_o)Q_m(x)\,dx + 2\phi_F + V_W' \tag{6.9}$$

Which of these parameters is easily and reproducibly changed to give the desired threshold voltage? Let us examine each term separately. The gate-semiconductor work-function difference is determined by the gate and the semiconductor work functions. The work function is the energy from the vacuum level to the Fermi level. For both metal and highly doped polysilicon gates, the gate work function is a constant. The Fermi level of the semiconductor substrate depends on the doping concentration through the relation $\phi_F = (kT/q) \ln(N_B/n_i)$. For each factor of ten in doping concentration change, the semiconductor work function, and therefore ϕ_{ms}, changes by $2.3kT/q$. Doping concentration changes perturb ϕ_{ms} by only a small amount and are not suitable for threshold-voltage control through ϕ_{ms} variations.

The fixed oxide charge varies with both wafer orientation and process temperature.[3] Every attempt is made to keep Q_f as low as possible through the use of {100}-oriented wafers and the proper oxidation and annealing temperatures. Hence, this parameter is not a useful one for controllable threshold-voltage adjustment either. The surface potential–dependent interface-state charge is reduced to low values by appropriate low-temperature anneals. For a typical manufacturing process, it has almost no effect on threshold voltage. We will see in Section 6.6 that undesirable threshold-voltage changes can occur as a result of interface-state generation by "hot" carriers during device operation. Mobile oxide charge is highly undesirable. It causes uncontrollable threshold-voltage changes as charge drifts through the oxide. The source of mobile charge appears to be mainly sodium. Oxidation in the presence of a small percentage of HCl stabilizes the sodium and makes it electrically inactive. Therefore, Q_m is also unsuitable for threshold-voltage control.

The last two terms of eq. (6.9) contain the chief threshold-controlling parameters N_B and V_{BS}. Source and substrate bias have a direct influence on threshold voltage and are used for this purpose. When MOSFET's are used as loads in inverters, as in Fig. 5.2c, for example, it is obvious that the source voltage, being equal to the output voltage, varies during circuit operation. Consequently, the threshold voltage varies.

The other two device properties suitable for threshold-voltage control are the **doping concentration** and the **oxide thickness.** Doping concentration enters through ϕ_F and $V_W{}'$, while oxide thickness enters through C_o and $V_W{}'$. We see that N_B and x_o are the chief process parameters, and that V_{BS} is the chief circuit operational parameter for threshold-voltage control.

Oxide thickness is used for major threshold-voltage control. For example, the thin gate oxide and the thick field oxide of Fig. 6.1 have different threshold voltages. However, for threshold-voltage control under the gate, oxide-thickness variations cannot be used. The oxide thickness is determined by other considerations. This leaves only N_B as a process variable for MOSFET threshold-voltage control.

From eq. (1.36) we have for the gate voltage

$$V_G = V_{FB} + \phi_s - Q_s/C_o \tag{6.10}$$

For a nonuniformly doped substrate, eq. (6.10) becomes

$$V_G = V_{FB} + \phi_s + (q/C_o) \int_0^W N_B(x)\, dx \tag{6.11}$$

if the inversion charge is neglected and only the bulk charge is considered. This is justified, as shown in Fig. 1.8. For uniform N_B, eq. (6.11) simplifies to

$$V_G = V_{FB} + \phi_s + qN_BW/C_o \tag{6.12}$$

When the gate voltage is evaluated at the onset of inversion, where $\phi_s = 2\phi_F$, that gate voltage is defined as the threshold voltage and is given by eq. (6.6).

The threshold voltage depends on V_{BS}. This dependence is known as *substrate bias sensitivity*. Let us demonstrate this by way of an example. The threshold voltage from eq. (6.6) is plotted in Fig. 6.2a as a function of the substrate-to-source voltage, V_{BS}, for three **uniform** substrate doping concentrations. V_{TS} from eq. (6.6) is repeated here:

$$V_{TS} = V_{FB} + 2\phi_F + V_W' \tag{6.13}$$

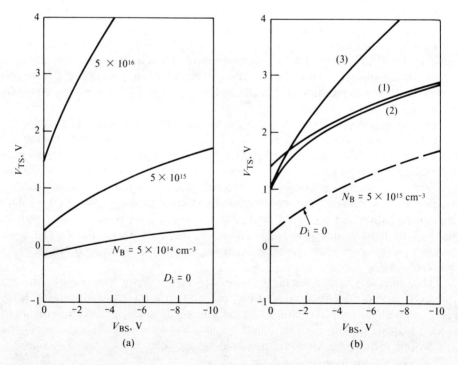

Fig. 6.2   Threshold voltage at $D_i = 5 \times 10^{11}$ cm^{-2}, $x_o = 500$ Å, $Q_f = 2 \times 10^{10}$ cm^{-2}, and $Q_{it} = Q_m = 0$, for (a) uniformly and (b) nonuniformly doped substrates. In (b), curve (1) represents eq. (6.15) and the doping distribution of Fig. 6.4a, curve (2) represents eq. (6.18) and the box-shaped distribution of Fig. 6.4b, and curve (3) represents eq. (6.13) and the uniform distribution of Fig. 6.4c.

In the flatband voltage expression, we use $\phi_{ms} = -E_G/2 - \phi_F$, which is appropriate for an n^+ polysilicon gate on a p-substrate.

The threshold voltage in Fig. 6.2a varies with V_{BS} for all three substrate doping concentrations. The variation is least for the lowest doping concentration. This can be understood from the bulk charge term V_W' in eq. (6.13). Its contribution to the threshold voltage is smallest when N_B is lowest. The threshold voltage itself is also lowest for this case. For the lowest substrate bias sensitivity, N_B should be kept as low as possible. This ensures that V_W' in eq. (6.13) will remain relatively unchanged. This leaves V_{FB} as the only variable that can be used to adjust V_{TS}. If Q_f could be altered reproducibly, the threshold-voltage-control problem would be solved. But altering Q_f is not practical. Hence, we must look for another solution, such as varying the semiconductor doping profile.

Consider first a very shallow surface layer in the semiconductor which is more heavily doped than the substrate. To first order, we approximate this shallow layer by the delta function $D_i\delta(0)$, with D_i atoms per unit area. For the substrate and the shallow layer both doped with acceptors, the semiconductor charge is $Q_s = -q\int_0^W [N_B + D_i\delta(0)]\,dx$, and eq. (6.11) becomes

$$V_G = V_{FB} + \phi_s + (q/C_o)\int_0^W [N_B + D_i\delta(0)]\,dx \tag{6.14}$$

and the resulting threshold voltage is shifted from its original value in eq. (6.13) by qD_i/C_o to

$$V_{TS} = V_{FB} + qD_i/C_o + 2\phi_F + V_W' \tag{6.15}$$

The additional term in eq. (6.15) is a constant and has the same effect as if Q_f were changed in the V_{FB} expression. In fact, one could replace V_{FB} by the new flatband voltage $V_{FB} + qD_i/C_o$.

A very shallow doping concentration can be considered a charge sheet. The threshold voltage is proportional to the charge density of this sheet. The quantities N_B and D_i, as defined in eq. (6.15), give positive threshold-voltage shifts. If D_i were a donor charge sheet, its charge would be positive and would shift the threshold voltage in the opposite direction. By adding either donors or acceptors in a thin sheet at the surface, it is possible to shift the threshold voltage to any desirable value. A threshold-voltage plot with D_i is shown in Fig. 6.2b. The threshold voltage shows a parallel shift from the $D_i = 0$ case for curves (1) and (2), but the general shape of the curve and the low substrate voltage sensitivity are retained.

A delta-function doping distribution is impossible to implement. But it can be approximated by the shallow doping achievable by ion implantation. Ion implantation has two very desirable features for semiconductor applications: (i) the depth of the implanted atoms is precisely controlled through control of the implant energy, and (ii) the doping concentration is very precisely controlled through implant dose control. These features are especially important for threshold-voltage control.

An ion-implanted profile in a semiconductor is shown in Fig. 6.3a. It is very closely approximated by a Gaussian distribution. The impurity concentration per unit volume is characterized by the *projected range*, R_p, and the standard deviation or *straggle*, ΔR_p. The ideal impurity profile is given by

$$N_i(x) = \{D_i/[(2\pi)^{1/2}\Delta R_p]\} \exp\{-(x - R_p)^2/[2(\Delta R_p)^2]\} \tag{6.16}$$

where D_i is the ion dose per unit area. The peak of the implanted profile is not at the surface, as it is for diffused profiles, but inside the semiconductor at $x = R_p$. The peak doping concentration is $D_i/[(2\pi)^{1/2}\Delta R_p] \approx 0.4D_i/\Delta R_p$. The range and straggle for the major dopant species can be found in Ref. [4].

After implantation, the implanted wafer region is heavily damaged, and the wafer must be annealed to restore crystal perfection and render the implanted ions electrically active. During this high-temperature anneal, the profile is broadened by thermal diffusion, and its shape departs from the ideal Gaussian distribution. To minimize profile broadening the ions are frequently implanted through an oxide, as shown by the example in Fig. 6.3b. The implanted ions are not subjected to the oxide-growth step and its attendant high-temperature profile diffusion broadening. Through a judicious combina-

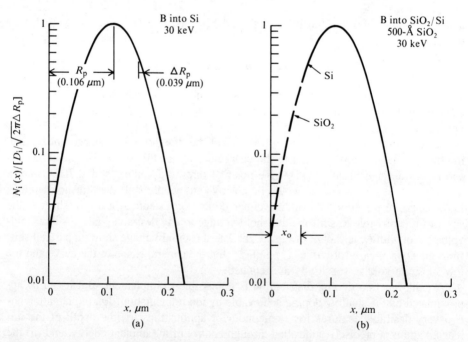

Fig. 6.3 Gaussian ion-implanted profiles for (a) B implanted into Si and (b) B implanted into Si with 500-Å SiO$_2$. $E = 30$ keV, $R_p = 0.107$ μm, and $\Delta R_p = 0.039$ μm.

tion of oxide thickness and implant energy, it is possible to locate the profile peak at or very close to the semiconductor surface.

The implanted profile expression of eq. (6.16) should be included in eq. (6.11) for threshold-voltage calculations. This requires a numerical analysis,[5] but fortunately some simplifications are possible.[6] We limit ourselves to the simplified approach to illustrate the main concept, without becoming lost in a maze of mathematical manipulations.

We show in Fig. 6.4 three idealized doping distributions. The delta function of Fig. 6.4a was discussed earlier. In Fig. 6.4b and c, we replace the actual implanted profile with a step profile, defined by[7]

$$(N_S - N_B) d_i = \int_0^W [N_i(x) - N_B] dx = D_i \qquad (6.17)$$

The total implanted dose D_i, which is in the form of an approximately Gaussian distribution, shown by the dotted curve in Fig. 6.4b, is approximated by the box-shaped distribution containing the same number of implanted atoms per unit area.

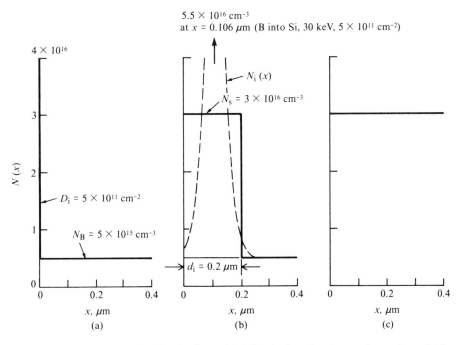

Fig. 6.4 Nonuniform doping distributions: (a) delta doping function at the surface; (b) ion-implanted profile approximated by a step profile within the scr; and (c) step profile deeper than the scr.

Figure 6.4b shows the case for a shallow ion-implanted layer. The depth d_i is less than the scr width W. The implanted atoms are all contained within the scr and all contribute to the threshold voltage. Eq. (6.11) leads to the threshold-voltage expression (see Problem 6.1):

$$V_{TS} = V_{FBi} + 2\phi_{Fi} + [2qK_s\varepsilon_oN_B(2\phi_{Fi} - V_{BS} - qD_id_i/2K_s\varepsilon_o)]^{1/2}/C_o$$
$$+ qD_i/C_o \qquad\qquad (6.18)$$

We have expressed eq. (6.18) in a form analogous to eq. (6.6) with ϕ_F replaced by ϕ_{Fi}, which is no longer uniquely defined. The inversion point is more difficult to calculate for a nonuniform doping concentration. One suitable definition is

$$\phi_{Fi} = (kT/2q) \ln(N_BN_S/n_i^2) \qquad\qquad (6.19)$$

for the box-shaped distribution.

The flatband voltage is also no longer uniquely defined for nonuniformly doped substrates, because the zero-charge condition in the semiconductor no longer corresponds to a zero electric field (flatband) at the semiconductor surface. This is the result of the built-in field due to the diffusion gradient. V_{FBi} is defined as that gate voltage for which the entire substrate is neutral. A definition of the modified flatband voltage is[8]

$$V_{FBi} = V_{FB}(\text{uniform}) + (kT/q) \ln[1 + N_i(0)/N_B] \qquad\qquad (6.20)$$

where $N_i(0)$ is the implanted doping concentration at $x = 0$. Note that for the box-shaped distribution we find $[1 + N_i(0)/N_B] = N_S/N_B$.

A comparison of the threshold-voltage expression, eq. (6.18), with the uniformly doped case, eq. (6.6), shows both V_{FBi} and ϕ_{Fi} to be changed. But the implanted concentration appears in them as the logarithm of N_S, thereby contributing only a minor effect. The bulk voltage is altered by the additional term $-qD_id_i/2K_s\varepsilon_o$. This is a little more important, but it appears under the square root. In addition, $-qD_id_i/2K_s\varepsilon_o$ is small compared with $(2\phi_{Fi} - V_{BS})$ for most nonzero V_{BS}. The most important threshold-voltage contribution comes from the linear term qD_i/C_o. For the delta-function case, it is the only contribution.

The threshold voltage for Fig. 6.4b is shown in Fig. 6.2b. We have replaced the implanted profile with the box of height 2.5×10^{16} cm^{-3} and width 0.2 μm. This gives $(N_S - N_B) = (3 - 0.5) \times 10^{16}$ cm^{-3} and $d_i = 0.2$ μm for a total dose of $(N_S - N_B)d_i = 5 \times 10^{11}$ cm^{-2} —the same as the implanted dose of Fig. 6.4a. The calculated threshold voltage is very similar for the two cases. The major discrepancy occurs near $V_{BS} = 0$, where the threshold voltage has its greatest substrate bias sensitivity. It is clearly advantageous to operate the device at a few volts substrate bias to reduce the substrate bias sensitivity. Many circuits use substrate bias for this reason.

The implanted profile for both Fig. 6.4a and b is contained in the space-charge region. If the profile is sufficiently deep not to be contained in the scr anymore, the uniformly doped case applies, and eq. (6.6) must be used. We show an example in Fig. 6.4c, where N_S remains at 3×10^{16} cm^{-3}, as in Fig. 6.4b, but has a deeper profile. The threshold voltage is shown in Fig. 6.2b, with the higher substrate sensitivity characteristic of more heavily and uniformly doped substrates. The solid curves (1) and (2) in Fig. 6.2b show the obvious desirability of using as shallow an implant as possible for lowest substrate bias sensitivity.

Substrate bias reduces the substrate bias sensitivity, but requires a separate power supply. This is a definite circuit disadvantage. However, a clever circuit design generates its own substrate bias, as shown in Fig. 6.5.[9] A square wave of 0 to 5 V amplitude drives transistor T1 into conduction during its $0 \rightarrow 5$ V rise. The node A voltage becomes clamped at one threshold voltage above ground potential. The remainder of the 5 V is dropped across capacitor C1. When the square-wave amplitude decreases, T1 turns off and node A is driven negatively, pulling the substrate with it. When the square-wave voltage increases again, the diode D1/capacitor C2 combination holds the substrate at the negative potential. The diode leakage current causes a slow capacitor

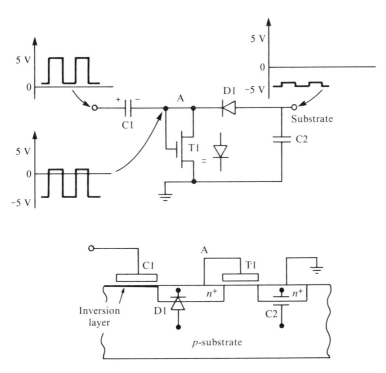

Fig. 6.5 A substrate bias generator. Reprinted after Ref. [9] by permission of McGraw-Hill Book Co.

discharge, and the square wave need only supply that leakage current, ensuring low power dissipation.

How is the threshold voltage measured? Several techniques are used. In one method, the threshold voltage is defined as that gate voltage necessary to cause a certain MOSFET drain current flow. A typical value is $I_D = 10 \ \mu$A. This is arbitrarily set. This method is not very precise, but is employed because it is easy to use. More accurate results are obtained by plotting I_D vs. V_{GS} at a drain voltage of typically 50 mV. This ensures that the MOSFET will operate in its linear region. Such a plot is shown in Fig. 6.6 for the doping distributions of Fig. 6.4b. The intercepts on the $I_D = 0$ axis are the threshold voltages. They agree very closely with the values from curve (2) in Fig. 6.2b. The linear relationship between drain current and gate-source voltage holds only at low values of V_{GS}. At higher V_{GS} values, the curve becomes sublinear due to the mobility reduction with gate voltage.

6.3 MOSFET MOBILITY

The carrier mobility in bulk semiconductor wafers depends on the doping concentration and temperature. The MOSFET channel mobility, generally known as the *effective mobility,* $\bar{\mu}_n$, depends on gate voltage as well as doping concentration and temperature. $\bar{\mu}_n$ is lower than the bulk mobility because of phonon, coulomb, and surface roughness scattering at the semiconductor/oxide interface. Surface roughness is an important con-

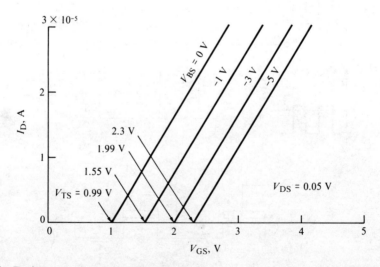

Fig. 6.6 Drain current vs. gate voltage as a function of substrate voltage. The threshold voltages indicated by the arrows are calculated from eq. (6.13). They agree well with the extrapolated curves. $N_B = 3 \times 10^{16} \ cm^{-3}$, $Z/L = 10$, $x_o = 500$ Å, $\bar{\mu}_n = 500 \ cm^2/Vs$, and $V_{DS} = 50$ mV.

tributor to mobility degradation, because the interface between the single-crystal silicon and the amorphous silicon oxide is not atomically smooth.[10] This is shown by the high-resolution transmission electron microscopy photographs in Fig. 6.7. The atomic steps at the silicon surface are clearly seen there.

Our understanding of the effective mobility–gate voltage relationship is largely based on experimental studies. Theoretical analyses are complicated by the confinement of the inversion layer to a narrow region in a potential well at the semiconductor surface. Quantum effects play an important role. The theory is further complicated by a lack of understanding of the exact roles of surface roughness, oxide charge, and interface states. The effects of all these factors are combined into the effective mobility.

The gate-voltage dependence of $\overline{\mu_n}$ can be visualized as follows. The gate voltage attracts inversion-layer electrons to the semiconductor/oxide interface. The higher the gate voltage, the more the electrons are forced against the interface. Any nonuniformities at that interface, whether actual microscopic surface roughness or charge-induced potential fluctuations, act as stronger scattering centers the higher the gate voltage. The mobility is thus continually reduced as the gate voltage increases.

Not being able to predict the effective mobility theoretically, we must rely on experimental data and empirical equations. Experimentally determined p- and n-channel effective mobilities are shown in Fig. 6.8. Mobility measurements at low drain-to-source voltages show a "universal" curve, with mobility remarkably independent of doping concentration over a wide range[11, 12] when plotted against an effective transverse electric field. The effective field, transverse to the drain-current direction, takes the electric field due to the gate voltage and the electric field due to the bulk charge density into account.

The effective transverse electric field, when averaged over the electron distribution in the inversion layer, is given by[11]

$$\mathscr{E}_{eff} = (Q_B + Q_N/2)/K_s\varepsilon_0 \qquad (6.21)$$

where Q_B is the bulk charge density in the scr under the gate and $Q_N/2$ is the average inversion charge density. An empirical fit to the two mobility curves shown by the solid lines in Fig. 6.8 results in the expressions[12]

$$\overline{\mu_n} = 1105/[1 + (\mathscr{E}_{eff}/30.5)^{0.657}] \qquad (6.22a)$$

$$\overline{\mu_p} = 342/[1 + (\mathscr{E}_{eff}/15.4)^{0.617}] \qquad (6.22b)$$

These expressions are valid at low drain-to-source voltages. When V_{DS} increases, the effective mobility is further degraded by the lateral electric field.

Eqs. (6.22) express the effective mobilities as a function of an effective electric field. This is useful insofar as it shows the gate electric field as well as the charge-induced electric field to influence the mobility. That representation is not very useful

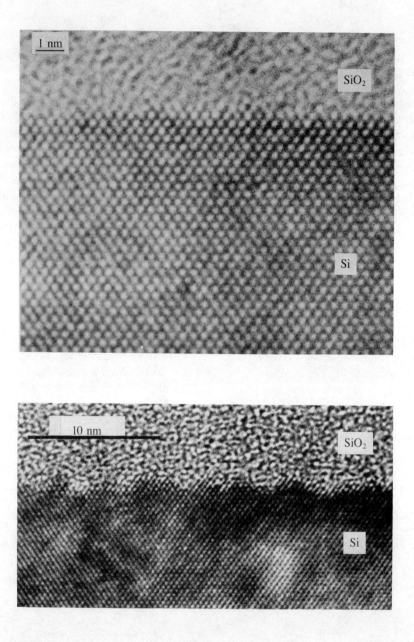

Fig. 6.7 Cross-sectional transmission electron micrographs of the Si/SiO$_2$ interface: (a) a normal interface; and (b) an interface intentionally roughened by growing the oxide in an HCl ambient. Courtesy of Z. Liliental-Weber, Lawrence Berkeley Laboratory–University of California.

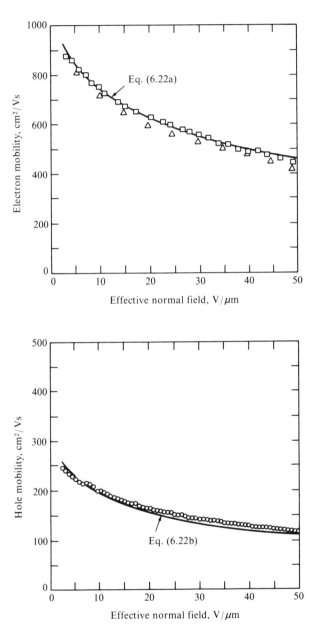

Fig. 6.8 Effective mobility for electrons and holes in silicon MOSFET's. The data points are from several researchers. The solid lines represent eqs. (6.22a) and (6.22b). Reprinted after Ref. [12] by permission of Academic Press.

for current-voltage calculations or device modeling. A more useful expression is one that contains the gate voltage explicitly. Such an analytical expression is

$$\overline{\mu}_n = \mu_0/[1 + \theta(V_{GS} - V_{TS})] \qquad (6.23)$$

where θ is an experimentally determined mobility degradation coefficient with values on the order of 0.02 to 0.08 V^{-1} (0.05 V^{-1} is a typical value), and μ_0 is the low-field mobility obtained by extrapolating the $\overline{\mu}_n$ vs. V_{GS} curve to zero gate voltage. A similar expression holds for holes.

6.4 SUBTHRESHOLD CONDUCTION

The drain current–gate voltage expression, eq. (6.5), is based on the existence of an inversion layer only for $\phi_s \geq (2\phi_F - V_{BS})$. For lower surface potentials, the inversion layer is assumed not to exist. This approximation predicts current flow only for gate voltages above the threshold voltage. For gate voltages below the threshold voltage, the drain current is predicted to be zero. This is at odds with experimental results, which show a continuously decreasing drain current below the threshold voltage.

The usual "above threshold voltage" MOSFET theory considers channel drift current to be dominant.[1] The current is essentially governed by the channel resistance, which in turn is determined by the channel charge. In contrast to *pn*-junction diode and bipolar transistor current, the MOSFET current does not depend exponentially on voltage. Why is this so? In a bipolar transistor, **majority** electrons in the emitter are forced over a potential barrier — the emitter-base junction — to become **minority** carriers in the base. Whenever a potential barrier is an impediment to current flow, the current depends exponentially on the applied voltage. This follows from the *law of the junction,* which states that the excess minority-carrier density at the edge of the scr in the quasineutral region depends exponentially on the applied voltage (see Volumes II and III in this series).

Electrons injected from the source of a MOSFET into its channel would appear to have the same problem. They also become minority carriers in the channel and have to climb a potential "hill" from source to channel. After all, the source is n^+ while the substrate is *p*-type. However, in contrast to a bipolar transistor, the MOSFET has a fourth electrode — the gate. The gate exerts additional control by essentially eliminating the potential barrier for "above threshold" conduction. As is obvious from eq. (6.5), there is no exponential dependence in that expression.

We show the potential barrier in Fig. 6.9. Note the progressive source/substrate barrier reduction as increasing gate voltage drives the device from accumulation to depletion to inversion. In accumulation and depletion, the electrons in the source see a potential barrier whose height is controlled by the gate voltage. Hence, the drain cur-

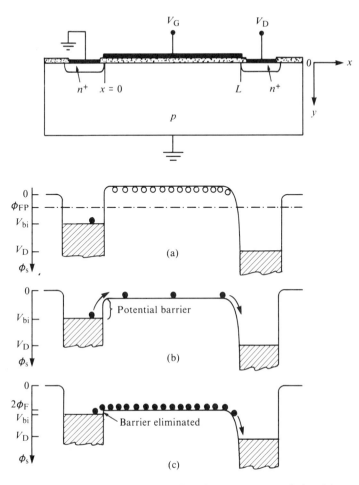

Fig. 6.9 A MOSFET with surface potential diagrams at $y = 0$ for (a) accumulation, (b) depletion, and (c) inversion.

rent should depend exponentially on gate voltage. In fact, the gate-source voltage acts very much like the base-emitter voltage of a bipolar transistor. A MOSFET operating in the "below threshold" or *subthreshold* regime has been described as a bipolar transistor in disguise.[13] It should not be surprising, therefore, that the classical MOSFET theory fails to predict the subthreshold current.

In subthreshold or weak inversion, the channel charge and drain current are both small. There is, therefore, only a slight potential gradient from source to drain. Most of the applied drain voltage appears across the reverse-biased drain scr. In eq. (6.1) we can to first order assume $\phi_{s0} \approx \phi_{sL}$. This reduces the equation to

$$I_D = k_n(K_s \varepsilon_0 / C_o L_D) (kT/q)^2 \int_0^{U_{s0}} [F(U, U_F, 0) - F(U, U_F, U_D)] dU \quad (6.24)$$

After some calculations (see Problem 6.4), eq. (6.24) simplifies to

$$I_D = (k_n C_B / C_o) (kT/q)^2 \exp[q(\phi_{ss} - 2\phi_F)/kT][1 - \exp(-qV_{DS}/kT)] \quad (6.25)$$

where $C_B = \{qK_s\varepsilon_0 N_B/[2(\phi_{ss} - V_{BS})]\}^{1/2}$.

Eq. (6.25) shows the dependence of drain current on surface potential and drain voltage. For V_{DS} larger than a few kT/q, the second term in the right bracket can be neglected and the drain current becomes independent of drain voltage. Its dependence on surface potential is of an exponential nature. To get its gate-voltage dependence, we must find a relationship between gate voltage and surface potential.

As we saw earlier, in the discussion of threshold voltage, the MOSFET voltages are generally referred to the source. The surface potential and gate voltage in eq. (1.39) are referred to the grounded substrate. In other words, $\phi_s = \phi_s - V_B = \phi_{sB}$ and $V_G = V_G - V_B = V_{GB}$. We now write the surface potential with respect to the source as $\phi_{ss} = \phi_{sB} - V_{SB} = \phi_{sB} + V_{BS}$ and use eq. (1.39) with $Q_N \approx 0$ and $V_{GS} = V_{GB} + V_{BS}$ to arrive at

$$\phi_{ss} = V_{GS} - V_{FB} - V_0\{[1 + 2(V_{GS} - V_{FB} - V_{BS})/V_0]^{1/2} - 1\} \quad (6.26)$$

This equation shows the nearly linear relationship between surface potential and gate voltage. This linearity holds only if the $V_0\{\ \}$ term is small in comparison with $V_{GS} - V_{FB}$. With this approximation, the drain current should be nearly exponential with gate voltage when eq. (6.26) is substituted into eq. (6.25).

Calculated drain current–gate voltage curves for several substrate bias voltages are shown in Fig. 6.10 for a MOSFET with the doping profile of Fig. 6.4c. Note the straight line on this semilogarithmic plot for gate voltages below and slightly above the threshold voltage. For higher gate voltages, the usual drain-current equation [eq. (6.5)] applies.

The curves of Fig. 6.10 illustrate the exponential subthreshold behavior, with the subthreshold slope given by

$$\text{slope} = d(\log I_D)/dV_{GS} = \{1 - [1 + 2(V_{GS} - V_{FB} - V_{BS})/V_0]^{-1/2}\}/(2.3kT/q) \quad (6.27)$$

The 2.3 comes from the conversion of $\ln(x)$ to $2.3 \log_{10}(x)$. Eq. (6.27) shows a slope increase with substrate bias. This is in fact observed in Fig. 6.10. The dependence on doping concentration is not shown, since the doping was held constant. But from the

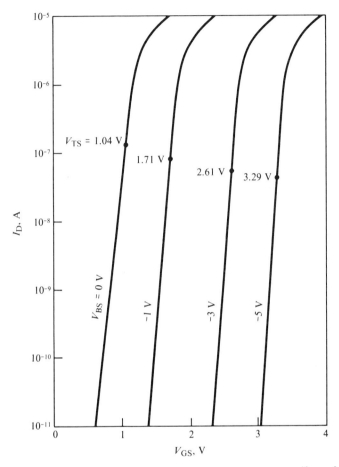

Fig. 6.10 Subthreshold MOSFET $I_D - V_{GS}$ curves for $N_B = 3 \times 10^{16}$ cm^{-3}, $Z/L = 10$, $x_o = 500$ Å, $\bar{\mu}_n = 500$ cm^2/Vs, and $V_{DS} = 50$ mV.

equation we see that the slope decreases with increased doping. It has been suggested that the subthreshold slope be used to determine the doping concentration.[14]

A more detailed derivation of the subthreshold drain current–gate voltage equation, taking into account the dependence of the interface-state density on surface potential, shows the slope to depend on the interface-state density as well.[15] A measure of the slope has been used to measure the interface-state density of MOSFET's.[16] This method has the distinct advantage of not requiring a special MOS capacitor test structure, as is frequently used for interface-state-density measurements. A MOSFET can be used directly.

The subthreshold slope is sometimes given as the change in gate voltage, dV_{GS}, required for the drain current to change by one decade. From eq. (6.27) we find, for $d(\log I_D) = 1$,

$$dV_{GS} = (2.3kT/q)/\{1 - [1 + 2(V_{GS} - V_{FB} - V_{BS})/V_0]^{-1/2}\} \qquad (6.28)$$

In the limit, this equation reduces to

$$dV_{GS} = (2.3kT/q) \approx 60 \text{ mV} \qquad (6.29)$$

at room temperature. Any nonidealities in the device — interface states, for example — cause dV_{GS} to increase beyond the 60 mV/decade value. dV_{GS} is a device-quality indicator and for that reason is sometimes used during device or process development.

6.5 SHORT- AND NARROW-CHANNEL EFFECTS

In all MOSFET derivations presented so far in this chapter, we have implicitly considered the gate charge to equal the sum of the electron charge trapped on interface states, Q_{it}, plus the channel charge, Q_N, plus the ionized bulk charge, Q_B, as shown in Fig. 6.11a. We assume here no fixed or mobile oxide charge. We have also assumed the gate area to equal the active area in the semiconductor. That is, if we wanted to convert the above charge densities to actual charges, we would merely multiply each by the gate area. Another way to look at this is to say that the gate controls the entire semiconductor under the gate.

We know this not to be strictly true. Figure 6.11a is drawn for zero source and drain voltage. Even then we see the shaded parts of the scr to be controlled by the source and drain, and not by the gate. For positive drain voltages, the reverse-biased drain scr extends further under the gate, and the gate controls even less charge. If an additional substrate bias is applied, then a similar situation develops at the source as well. For long-channel MOSFET's, this effect is usually neglected, although it is clearly not zero.

One effect on device behavior — the effect of the drain controlling some of the semiconductor charge — is found in the I_D-V_D curves of Fig. 6.11c. These curves should ideally be horizontal with infinite output resistance. But they have a slight slope due to channel-length modulation by the drain. Now consider the short-channel device of Fig. 6.11b. The shaded regions, not under gate control, have become a significant fraction of the scr. If the gate loses control of the semiconductor charge, this is bound to have repercussions on device behavior. One such effect is shown in Fig. 6.11d. The output characteristics are much less ideal than those in Fig. 6.11c. Their slopes have increased, resulting in lower output resistance, and the current increases sharply at lower drain voltage. This is indicative of the onset of avalanche breakdown.

Another consequence of short channels can be found in eq. (6.6). A part of the threshold voltage is due to the bulk charge. But if the gate no longer controls all of the

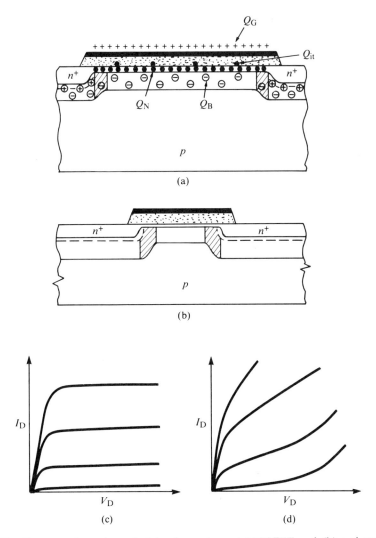

Fig. 6.11   Cross sections through (a) a long-channel MOSFET and (b) a short-channel MOSFET. The drain current–drain voltage curves are shown for (c) the long-channel device and (d) the short-channel device.

bulk charge, then the bulk charge term in the threshold voltage expression must be modified. Consequently, the threshold voltage will decrease as channel length diminishes. This is a major concern for short-channel devices.

Analogous considerations for the *channel width* show just the opposite effect, as illustrated in Fig. 6.12. A cross section through the MOSFET perpendicular to the

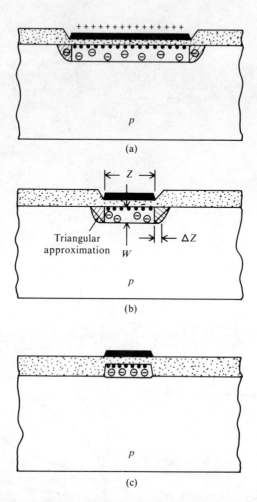

Fig. 6.12 Cross sections through (a) wide-channel, (b) conventional narrow-channel, and (c) recessed narrow-channel MOSFET's.

drain-current flow shows the gate width, Z, the inversion layer, and the bulk charge for a wide gate structure in Fig. 6.12a. The shaded lateral scr width beyond the gate gives an effective bulk charge width **larger** than the actual gate width. As the gate width shrinks, the lateral scr bulk charge component assumes a larger fraction of the total bulk charge. This can be seen by comparing Fig. 6.12a and b.

An enhanced bulk charge component gives a higher threshold voltage, according to eq. (6.6). This is a major concern for narrow-channel devices. One might think that a clever device design could, perhaps, take advantage of the decreasing threshold voltage of shorter channels and the increasing value for narrower channels. While it is true that the two effects oppose each other, a complete cancellation is generally impossible, and each must be treated independently in device design.

6.5.1 Short-Channel Threshold Voltage

Let us now consider these effects quantitatively. The relevant device parameters for the short-channel effect are shown in Fig. 6.13.[17] Both source and drain junctions are characterized by the junction depth r_j. We assume the lateral junction diffusion under the gate to be identical to the downward diffusion. This is a reasonably good approximation, although lateral diffusion is found experimentally to be slightly less than vertical diffusion. The voltage drop across the gate-induced scr is approximately $2\phi_F - V_B$ when both source and drain are grounded. The voltage drop across the source and drain junctions is $V_{bi} - V_B$. The built-in potential is typically 0.6 to 0.7 V, so that $V_{bi} \approx 2\phi_F$. Consequently, we find the three scr widths approximately equal—i.e., $W_S \approx W_D \approx W_C = W$.

The key in this derivation is the introduction of the trapezoidal region in Fig. 6.13.[17] The bulk charge in that trapezoidal region is assumed to be controlled by the gate, while the charge beyond that region is controlled by the source and drain. Based on this geometrical approximation, the bulk charge inside the trapezoid is

$$Q_B'L = qN_BW(L + L')/2 \tag{6.30}$$

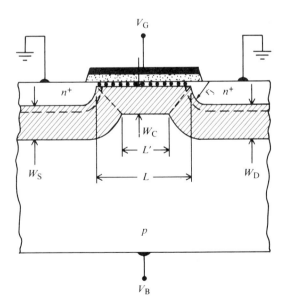

Fig. 6.13   Short-channel threshold voltage model.

where Q_B' is the **average** bulk charge per unit area for a channel length L. A trigonometric analysis (see Problem 6.5) gives

$$(L + L')/2L = 1 - [(1 + 2W/r_j)^{1/2} - 1]r_j/L \qquad (6.31)$$

and in the threshold-voltage expression, eq. (6.6), the bulk-charge term, V_W', becomes $V_W'\{1 - [(1 + 2W/r_j)^{1/2} - 1]r_j/L\}$. The short-channel threshold voltage change, defined by $\Delta V_T = V_T(\text{short channel}) - V_T(\text{long channel})$, is

$$\Delta V_T = -V_W'[(1 + 2W/r_j)^{1/2} - 1]r_j/L \qquad (6.32)$$

As L decreases, the threshold voltage and the threshold-voltage change become more negative. There is also a dependence on junction depth, with diminishing effect on threshold voltage the shallower the junction. Lastly, ΔV_T shows a dependence on the scr width W. The higher the doping concentration, the smaller the scr width and, therefore, the less the threshold voltage is affected. This is in fact utilized when MOSFET's are scaled to smaller dimensions. The devices are more heavily doped to reduce W, and the junctions are made shallower to reduce r_j, as the gate length is reduced.

Eq. (6.32) does not contain a dependence on drain voltage, because we assumed the scr width of the drain to be identical to that of the source and the channel region under the gate. With a drain-voltage bias, the drain scr increases. The three scr widths are no longer equal, and eq. (6.32) becomes[15]

$$\Delta V_T = -V_W'\{[(1 + 2W_S/r_j)^{1/2} - 1] + [(1 + 2W_D/r_j)^{1/2} - 1]\}r_j/2L \qquad (6.33)$$

where W_S and W_D depend on the source, drain, and substrate voltages.

The effect of short channels on the subthreshold behavior is a slope increase of the log $I_D - V_G$ curves with reduced channel length. This is undesirable, because the slope is a measure of the gate-voltage change necessary to reduce the drain current from its conducting-state value to some threshold-current level. In digital devices, which are either **on** or **off**, this gate-voltage change should be as small as possible to ensure device switching for small gate-voltage changes. For long-channel MOSFET's, the slopes are shown in Fig. 6.10. Short-channel effects tend to degrade this aspect of device performance.

6.5.2 Narrow-Channel Threshold Voltage

The channel width also affects the threshold voltage, due to the additional charge component in the lateral scr width. For uniformly doped substrates, we approximate the lateral charge components by the triangular shapes indicated in Fig. 6.12b. The total gate-controlled charge, assuming no short-channel effects, becomes $qN_B L(Z + 2\Delta Z) = qN_B L(Z + \xi W) = qN_B LZ(1 + \xi W/Z)$ instead of $qN_B LZ$, without the lateral components. ξ is a fitting parameter that accounts for the fact that the **lateral scr** width may be less than the vertical one because of the thicker field oxide and the field ion implantation. Hence, the additional charge components contribute the charge increment

$$\Delta Q_B = qN_B(1 + \xi W/Z) \qquad (6.34)$$

leading to the threshold-voltage change $\Delta V_T = V_T(\text{narrow-channel}) - V_T(\text{wide-channel})$:

$$\Delta V_T = \xi V_W'W/Z \qquad (6.35)$$

This expression shows narrow-channel effects giving rise to more positive threshold voltages. This effect is appreciable only for gate widths on the order of the scr width. Slightly different expressions are derived if the lateral scr component is approximated by a quarter circle or square.[18] The triangular approximation is slightly more realistic, especially for devices that are made with channel-stop implants in the channel region surrounding the gate. For more precise calculations, numerical analyses are required.[19]

The narrow-channel threshold-voltage effect is reduced for recessed oxide structures. Such a device is shown in Fig. 6.12c. When there is no lateral semiconductor, additional lateral charge cannot be induced, and the threshold voltage should be independent of channel width. Simulations and experiments[20] show this to be the case.

For devices exhibiting both *short-* and *narrow-channel* effects, neither the short-channel nor the narrow-channel models alone suffice to predict the threshold voltage accurately. Combining both models in a three-dimensional volume approximation of the space-charge region gives the threshold-voltage change[21] as

$$\Delta V_T = V_W'\{\xi W/Z - [(1 + 2W/r_j)^{1/2} - 1][1 + \xi W/Z]r_j/L\} \qquad (6.36)$$

For a more detailed expression, where the various device voltages and actual doping concentration are considered, numerical computer analyses are required. We have used approximations here because they make the analysis simple while retaining insight into the device operation and modeling. They also give quite good agreement with experimental data.

What are generally considered to be deleterious effects can occasionally be used to advantage. The narrow-channel threshold-voltage effect is one such case. We saw in Chapter 3 that the implementation of a two-phase CCD requires a surface potential discontinuity under each gate. In effect, the threshold voltage varies in the two halves of each gate. If the CCD transfer channel were to be modulated in width, as shown in Fig. 6.14a, with the narrow part sufficiently narrow to show narrow-channel effects,

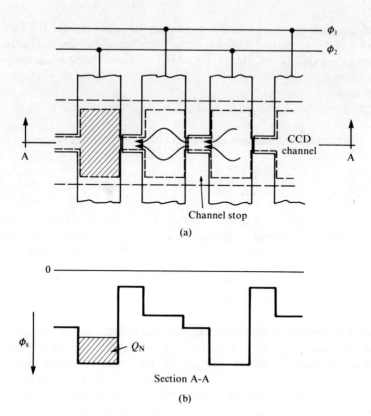

Fig. 6.14   (a) A narrow-channel CCD and (b) its surface potential.

then the surface potential would have the shape of Fig. 6.14b because the threshold voltage in the narrow-channel region is higher than that in the wide-channel region. Such a CCD has been implemented.[22]

6.6   HOT-CARRIER EFFECTS

In thermal equilibrium, electrons find themselves near the bottom of the conduction band with energy $E - E_c \approx kT$, where T is the device temperature. The carriers move continuously at their thermal velocity and constantly collide with the lattice. These collisions are often treated by invoking the concept of phonons. A *phonon* is not a lattice vibration as such, but rather a unit quantum excitation of a normal mode of vibration. If a normal vibrational mode is excited by a unit amount of energy, a phonon is created, and if it is de-excited by a unit amount of energy, a phonon is destroyed. Upon collision between an electron and the lattice, energy is transferred from the electron to the lattice or vice versa. When the lattice imparts energy to the electron, the electron is said to absorb a phonon. The emission of a phonon is a loss of energy from the electron to the lattice. In any collision, energy and momentum must be conserved. At thermal equilibrium, phonons are absorbed and emitted with no net energy gain or loss.

In nonequilibrium, there is a net gain or loss. For example, a current flow is possible only if the carriers are more energetic than those in thermal equilibrium. However, those electrons and holes that flow in quasineutral regions gain only a small amount of energy, and their energy remains close to kT. We illustrate this by showing how far the electrons are above the bottom of the conduction band. In Fig. 6.15a we show the band diagram of a quasineutral region. The slight band bending is equivalent to a small electric field. The electrons are shown to remain near E_c as they flow through the semiconductor.

An entirely different situation is found in the scr of a reverse-biased junction, shown in Fig. 6.15b. When electrons enter the scr, they continue to move along the arrow for a short distance. This takes them above E_c, and their energy increases continually until they collide with the lattice and lose energy by phonon emission. They find themselves above the bottom of the conduction band with energy $E - E_c = kT_e > kT$, where T_e is an *effective temperature*. T_e can be significantly higher than room temperature, even though the device itself is at room temperature. Such energetic electrons are known as *hot electrons*.

In long-channel MOSFET's, the inversion-layer electrons move through most of the channel at small or moderate lateral electric fields. However, when they enter the scr of the reverse-biased drain, they become **hot**. For sufficiently large drain voltages, breakdown is observed. In short-channel MOSFET's, several other undesirable effects manifest themselves.

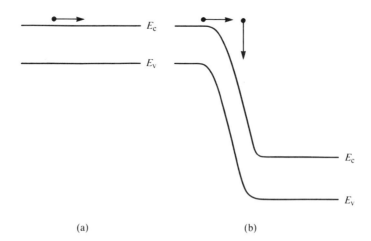

(a)   (b)

Fig. 6.15   Electrons (a) near E_c for low electric fields and (b) above E_c for high electric fields.

6.6.1 Velocity Saturation

The I_D-V_D curves are nearly constant in MOSFET's when the drain voltage exceeds the saturation drain voltage V_{Dsat}. The potential across the channel is $V_{Dsat} - V_S$, and the electron velocity is given by $v_n = \overline{\mu}_n \mathscr{E}_x$. The velocity is proportional to the lateral electric field, $\mathscr{E}_x$. For short-channel devices, the electric field can become sufficiently high for the velocity to become constant and independent of the electric field. This is known as the *saturation-limited velocity, v_{sat}*.

To compare the current-voltage behavior of a conventional long-channel MOSFET with one limited by saturation velocity, we derive two simplified equations by neglecting the terms due to the scr bulk charge. A general expression for the current is

$$I_n = -qAnv_n \tag{6.37}$$

The electron volume density in a MOSFET channel is $n = Q_N/qx_{ch}$, where $Q_N = -C_o(V_G - V_T)$ is the channel charge density and x_{ch} is the channel thickness. We assume zero source and substrate potentials. The channel area is Zx_{ch}. This gives the drain current as

$$I_D = ZC_o(V_G - V_T)v_n \tag{6.38}$$

What is the electron velocity v_n? For a long-channel device it is $v_n = \overline{\mu}_n \mathscr{E}_x$, where $\mathscr{E}_x$ is the lateral electric field along the channel from the source to the pinch-off point near the drain. Pinch-off occurs at the voltage $V_{Dsat} = V_G - V_T$. For a gate length L, we have for the average electric field $\mathscr{E}_x = (V_G - V_T)/2L$ and the saturation drain current becomes

$$I_D = (Z\overline{\mu}_n C_o/2L)(V_G - V_T)^2 \qquad \overline{\mu}_n \mathscr{E}_x\text{-limited} \tag{6.39}$$

For electric fields above about 3×10^4 V/cm for electrons and 10^5 V/cm for holes in silicon, velocity saturation limits the carrier velocity to v_{sat}. Replacing v_n with v_{sat} gives the drain current

$$I_D = ZC_o(V_G - V_T)v_{sat} \qquad v_{sat}\text{-limited} \tag{6.40}$$

To compare eqs. (6.39) and (6.40), we must compare $\overline{\mu}_n(V_G - V_T)/2L$ with v_{sat}. For a typical effective mobility of 500 cm^2/Vs and a saturation velocity of 10^7 cm/s, we get

$$250(V_G - V_T)/L \rightleftarrows 10^7 \text{ cm/s} \tag{6.41}$$

where "$\rightleftarrows$" stands for "compared with." Solution of eq. (6.41) gives $L = 1.25$ μm for $(V_G - V_T) = 5$ V. In other words, for $L \leq 1.25$ μm, velocity saturation is dominant and the drain current becomes independent of channel length. For longer-channel MOSFET's the traditional current expression holds for the parameters used here.

Eq. (6.40) gives equal drain-current increments for equal gate-voltage increments in contrast to the square-law device of eq. (6.39). This linear relationship is desirable for some applications. For example, the transconductance, $g_m = \partial I_D / \partial V_G$, is gate voltage–dependent for the $\overline{\mu}_n \mathscr{E}_x$-limited case but becomes constant when the device is v_{sat}-limited. This has advantages in some circuits, because a MOSFET amplifier gain is proportional to g_m.

6.6.2 Snapback Breakdown

The I_D-V_D characteristics of a long-channel MOSFET and a short-channel MOSFET are shown in Fig. 6.16. Assuming the devices not to be saturation velocity–limited, eq. (6.39) predicts a higher current for the short-channel device because the current is inversely proportional to channel length. What is not predicted by the conventional MOSFET theory is the S-shaped breakdown curve.

An explanation of this type of breakdown is found in second-order effects normally neglected. Consider the MOSFET of Fig. 6.17. The drain current flows through two quite different regions from source to drain. Over most of its passage, it flows along the channel through a region of relatively small electric field.

Once the channel electrons enter the scr region of the reverse-biased drain, they experience electric fields of 10^5 V/cm or greater. It is well known that when electric fields approach 3 to 5×10^5 V/cm, the junction current increases dramatically due to avalanche breakdown. But avalanche breakdown does not suddenly begin at some

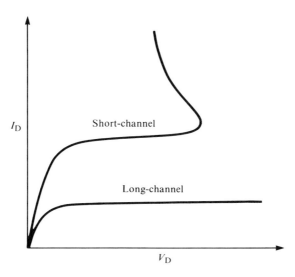

Fig. 6.16 Schematic diagram of drain current–drain voltage characteristics for long-channel and short-channel MOSFET's.

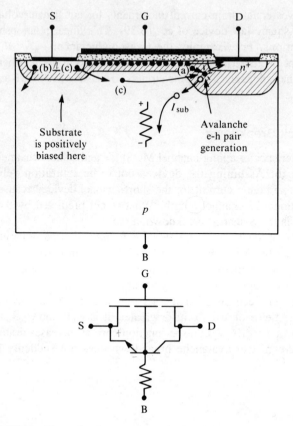

Fig. 6.17 A MOSFET with avalanche generation in the drain scr. The bipolar transistor is in parallel with the MOSFET.

well-defined electric field. Rather, it is a gradual process that takes place at low levels at lower fields, schematically illustrated by electron (a) in Fig. 6.17. However, the generated avalanche current is usually a small fraction of the drain current and therefore is negligible.

For short-channel devices we have an additional complication. The electrons generated by the avalanche process flow into the drain and add to the drain current. The avalanche-generated holes flow through the substrate as I_{sub} to the substrate terminal. A voltage develops across the substrate by the avalanche-generated substrate hole current. This voltage drop drives the potential of the substrate near the source more positive than that of the substrate terminal B. The source-substrate junction becomes forward biased when the voltage near the source approaches 0.6 to 0.7 V. The source then injects minority electrons into the substrate.

The injected electrons diffuse away from the source in all directions. Some will flow to adjacent devices [electron (b) in Fig. 6.17] and may create problems. For example, if there is a DRAM cell within a minority-carrier diffusion length, the injected electrons can cause the cell to discharge, changing its logic state from **1** to **0**. Some of the electrons flow into the drain [electron (c)], where they cause further avalanche generation. Recall that avalanche generation requires not only the necessary high electric fields but also carriers to sustain the avalanche process. The more carriers there are, the more effective is the avalanche process.

We have a regenerative or positive feedback mechanism here. Weak avalanche causes the source-substrate junction to be forward biased. The injection and subsequent collection of the electrons by the drain scr further enhances avalanche generation. The substrate current rises as a result, and the source becomes further forward biased, leading to further electron injection. Such feedback systems are inherently unstable. Once the feedback gain reaches unity, the current rises uncontrollably, limited only by a resistance in the current loop.

The negative-resistance or "snapback" portions of the curves come about for the following reason. The source-substrate-drain forms a bipolar transistor in parallel with the MOSFET, as shown in Fig. 6.17. The source is also the emitter, the substrate is also the base, and the drain is also the collector. It is a bipolar transistor with a nearly floating base because the substrate potential near the source (emitter) is determined by the avalanche-generated substrate current, not by the externally applied substrate voltage. It is well known that open-base bipolar transistors often exhibit negative-resistance or "snapback" breakdown.

Let us see how this occurs. For an open-base transistor, the base current is zero and the collector current is given by

$$I_C = \alpha I_E + I_{CBO} = \alpha I_C + I_{CBO} \tag{6.42}$$

where α is the current-amplification factor and I_{CBO} is the open-base collector leakage current. For zero base current, $I_C = I_E$. When biased near breakdown, the collector current is multiplied by the multiplication factor M (see p. 44 to 45 in Volume III of this series for a breakdown discussion), and eq. (6.42) becomes

$$I_C = M(\alpha I_C + I_{CBO}) \tag{6.43}$$

Solving for I_C gives

$$I_C = MI_{CBO}/(1 - \alpha M) \tag{6.44}$$

Breakdown is defined as that condition when $I_C \to \infty$. For a simple pn junction, where the current in avalanche is given by $I = MI_{leak}$, $M \to \infty$ at breakdown. Eq. (6.44) shows, however, that in the open-base transistor, in contrast to a pn junction, breakdown occurs for a much lower M — namely $M \rightarrow 1/\alpha$. A much lower multiplication factor suffices for large currents to flow.

The multiplication factor is related to the breakdown voltage, V_{BD}, and the applied voltage, V_{CE}, by the relationship [see eq. (4.2) in Volume II of this series]

$$M = 1/[1 - (V_{CE}/V_{BD})^m] \tag{6.45}$$

where the exponent m lies in the range of 3 to 6. At low collector currents, the current-amplification factor α of most bipolar transistors increases with collector current. Breakdown then proceeds as follows.

Consider the collector-emitter voltage being increased from zero. The collector current is initially low, and the multiplication factor is unity at these low voltages. As V_{CE} is increased, it will reach a voltage where $M = 1/\alpha$. Breakdown begins and causes a significant current increase. However, with rising collector current, α increases and, to maintain the breakdown condition, $M = 1/\alpha$, M must decrease. But an M decrease requires a V_{CE} decrease. So we have a situation where increases in collector current are accompanied by decreases in collector-emitter voltage. In other words, a negative-resistance or snapback breakdown takes place. Its two key requirements are that the base be open and that α increase with collector current.

The short-channel MOSFET behaves very much like an open-base bipolar transistor. The source and drain are also the emitter and collector, and while the substrate or base is not truly open, the substrate potential near the source is no longer determined by the substrate bias, but by the substrate current. It biases itself to some poorly defined potential, thereby acting almost like an open base.

The source current is given by an expression similar to eq. (6.44), which we do not derive here, but merely quote from Ref. [23]:

$$I_S = [(M - 1)I_D + (V_{BS} - 0.65)/R]/[1 - \alpha(1 + kM - k)] \tag{6.46}$$

where 0.65 is taken as the source-substrate voltage necessary for the source to be significantly forward biased. R is the sum of substrate and any external resistance, and k is that fraction of electrons collected by the drain that cause avalanche breakdown to the total number of electrons collected by the drain.

Breakdown, defined as I_S becoming very large, now occurs for $M \rightarrow [1 + \alpha(k - 1)]/k\alpha$. $k = 1$ applies for the bipolar transistor. But for the MOSFET, both substrate current and drain current flow, while the open-base bipolar transistor is truly a two-terminal device. In spite of this, we find the breakdown mechanisms to be qualitatively very similar.

One solution to this snapback-breakdown problem is the use of an epitaxial layer on a low-resistivity substrate. The low-resistivity substrate prevents any significant voltage from being developed across it. The source therefore does not become forward biased. For a nonepitaxial substrate, the circuit containing the MOSFET must be designed so that this type of breakdown does not occur. If it does occur, there is the danger of device destruction once the current becomes too large, because it is difficult to control the device once it enters this snapback mode of operation. Another complication is the change of the current path from one in which the current flows over the entire width of the device under normal operation to one in which the current constricts to a small part of the channel width.[24] The danger of device destruction then increases signficantly.

If the source becomes forward biased, it injects minority electrons into the substrate. They diffuse over distances of about a diffusion length and, as mentioned earlier, can cause problems in other devices located within this distance. One can reduce this problem by providing appropriate minority-carrier sinks around the minority-carrier injector.

A recent observation has brought out another problem. *Photon generation* takes place in the weak-avalanche drain region. It is not clear what the mechanism is; however, the implication is potentially serious. These avalanche-generated photons have an energy near the silicon band gap. Hence they have a relatively small absorption coefficient and can propagate large distances through the material before being absorbed.

The absorption length has been estimated as 780 μm.[25] As the photons propagate through the silicon, they are eventually absorbed, generating electron-hole pairs. Minority carriers can be generated as far as about 1 mm from the drain. This is longer than typical minority-carrier diffusion lengths, and the avalanche-generated **photons** can therefore cause circuit disruptions over longer distances than minority-carrier injection from the forward-biased source. It is more difficult to prevent photon propagation. Minority-carrier sinks effective for reducing minority-carrier diffusion are not effective against photons. Some type of optical sink is required.

6.6.3 Interface-State Generation and Threshold-Voltage Shift

In addition to snapback breakdown, there are several other "nuisance effects" that have been observed in short-channel devices. We will briefly discuss interface-state generation and threshold-voltage shift, both caused by hot carriers.

When electrons flow from source to drain, they gain energy — especially when they enter the high-electric-field region near the drain. This has two consequences. First, some of these energetic electrons interact with the oxide/silicon interface and generate interface states.[24] The mechanism by which this takes place is not well understood. But conceptually one can think of the electrons having sufficient energy to break some of the weak silicon-hydrogen bonds in the oxide at the SiO_2/Si interface formed when hydrogen diffuses there during the final low-temperature anneal. The resulting dangling bonds are thought to be interface states. The second consequence is *hot electron* injection into the oxide. Some of the electrons flow through the oxide to be collected by the gate, and some become trapped in the oxide.

Either one of these mechanisms affects the MOSFET threshold voltage. This is clearly seen from eq. (6.9), repeated here:

$$V_{TS} = \phi_{ms} - Q_f/C_o - Q_{it}(\phi_s)/C_o - (1/C_o) \int_0^{x_o} (x/x_o)Q_m(x)\, dx + 2\phi_F + V_W'$$

$$(6.47)$$

Interface-state generation raises Q_{it}, while electron injection into the oxide increases Q_m. Both lead to threshold-voltage changes. Interface-state generation leads, furthermore, to increased surface-scattering centers with an attendant mobility reduction. This type of degradation is, of course, a continuous process, and the device degrades with time. This is clearly an undesirable situation, and much effort is presently under way to gain a better understanding of these effects and to try to eliminate or at least reduce them to levels at which they are of little consequence.

6.7 SUMMARY

We have described several aspects of MOSFET's not generally covered in introductory texts. After deriving the MOSFET current-voltage expression, we described threshold-voltage control by substrate bias and ion implantation in some detail. Mobility degradation due to gate voltage and substrate dopant charge was shown by "universal" effective mobility — effective electric field curves. It is interesting to note that the MOSFET mobility has changed very little over the years in spite of the many advances in silicon-device processing. This constancy is a reflection of the basic atomic-interface roughness.

Next we discussed the subthreshold current-voltage behavior. We showed the exponential drain current–gate voltage relationship to originate from the potential barrier at the source-channel junction. The effects of short and narrow channels on threshold voltage were described. Short channels are typically those with channel lengths less than approximately 1.5 μm. Finally, we briefly discussed several effects attributable to hot carriers. These include channel charge velocity saturation, snapback breakdown, photon generation, interface-state generation, and threshold-voltage shifts. All of them are undesirable. Some are not well understood; some can be minimized by appropriate device or circuit design.

The main equations of this chapter are summarized here. The current-voltage characteristic above threshold is

$$I_D = k_n\{(V_{GS} - V_{TS} - V_{DS}/2)V_{DS}$$
$$- (4\phi_F'V_W'/3)[(1 + V_{DS}/2\phi_F')^{3/2} - (1 + 3V_{DS}/4\phi_F')]\}$$

where $k_n = Z\overline{\mu}_n C_o/L$. The threshold voltage for uniformly doped substrates is given by

$$V_{TS} = V_{FB} + 2\phi_F + V_W' = V_{FB} + 2\phi_F + [2qK_s\varepsilon_0 N_B(2\phi_F - V_{BS})]^{1/2}/C_o$$

When ion implantation is used for threshold-voltage adjustment, V_{TS} becomes

$$V_{TS} = V_{FBi} + 2\phi_{Fi} + [2qK_s\varepsilon_0 N_B(2\phi_{Fi} - V_{BS} - qD_id_i/2K_s\varepsilon_0)]^{1/2}/C_o + qD_i/C_o$$

The mobility degradation with gate voltage can be expressed by

$$\overline{\mu}_n = \mu_0/[1 + \theta(V_{GS} - V_{TS})]$$

The subthreshold drain current is given by

$$I_D = (k_n C_B/C_o)(kT/q)^2 \exp[q(\phi_{ss} - 2\phi_F)/kT][1 - \exp(-qV_{DS}/kT)]$$

where the surface potential is related to the gate voltage by

$$\phi_{ss} = V_{GS} - V_{FB} - V_0\{[1 + 2(V_{GS} - V_{FB} - V_{BS})/V_0]^{1/2} - 1\}$$

These two equations clearly show the nearly exponential relationship between drain current and gate voltage. The short- and narrow-channel threshold-voltage change is

$$\Delta V_T = V_W'\{\xi W/Z - [(1 + 2W/r_j)^{1/2} - 1][1 + \xi W/Z]r_j/L\}$$

REFERENCES

[1] R. F. Pierret, *Field-Effect Devices,* Vol. IV in *Modular Series on Solid State Devices,* Addison-Wesley, Reading, MA, 1983.

[2] R. F. Pierret and J. A. Shields, "Simplified Long-Channel MOSFET Theory," Solid-State Electr., *26,* 143-147, Febr., 1983.

[3] B. E. Deal, M. Sklar, A. S. Grove, and E. H. Snow, "Characteristics of the Surface-State Charge (Q_{ss}) of Thermally Oxidized Silicon," J. Electrochem. Soc., *114,* 266-274, March, 1967.

[4] D. H. Lee and J. W. Mayer, "Ion-implanted Semiconductor Devices," Proc. IEEE, *62,* 1241-1255, Sept., 1974.

[5] J. R. Brews, "Threshold Shifts due to Nonuniform Doping Profiles in Surface Channel MOSFETs," IEEE Trans. Electr. Dev., *ED-26,* 1696-1710, Nov., 1979.

[6] K. Shenai, "Analytical Solutions for Threshold Voltage Calculations in Ion-Implanted IGFETs," Solid-State Electr., *26,* 761-766, Aug., 1983.

[7] V. L. Rideout, F. H. Gaensslen, and A. LeBlanc, "Device Design Considerations for Ion Implanted n-Channel MOSFETs," IBM J. Res. Dev., *19,* 50-59, Jan., 1975.

[8] F. van de Wiele, "On the Flatband Voltage of MOS Structures on Nonuniformly Doped Substrates," Solid-State Electr., *27,* 824-826, Aug./Sept., 1984.

[9] D. G. Ong, *Modern MOS Technology: Processes, Devices and Design,* McGraw-Hill, New York, 1984, p. 219-220.

[10] Z. Liliental, O. L. Krivanek, S. M. Goodnick, and C. W. Wilmsen, "Correlation of Si-SiO$_2$ Interface Roughness with MOSFET Carrier Mobility," Mat. Res. Soc. Symp., *37,* 193-197, 1985; S. M. Goodnick, D. K. Ferry, C. W. Wilmsen, Z. Liliental, D. Fathy, and O. L. Krivanek, "Surface Roughness at the Si(100)-SiO$_2$ Interface," Phys. Rev., *B32,* 8171-8186, Dec. 15, 1985.

[11] A. G. Sabnis and J. T. Clemens, "Characterization of the Electron Mobility in the Inverted (100) Si Surface," IEEE Tech. Dig., Int. Electr. Dev. Meet., 18-20, 1979.

[12] J. A. Cooper, D. F. Nelson, S. A. Schwarz, and K. K. Thornber, "Carrier Transport at the Si-SiO$_2$ Interface," in *VLSI Electronics* (N. G. Einspruch and R. S. Bauer, eds.), Academic Press, New York, *10,* 323-361, 1985.

[13] E. O. Johnson, "The Insulated-Gate Field-Effect Transistor — A Bipolar Transistor in Disguise," RCA Rev., *34,* 80-94, March, 1973.

[14] J. M. Shannon, "DC Measurement of the Space-Charge Capacitance and Impurity Profile Beneath the Gate of an MOST," Solid-State Electron, *14,* 1099-1106, Nov., 1971.

[15] W. Fichtner and H. W. Poetzl, "MOS Modelling by Analytical Approximations. I. Subthreshold Current and Threshold Voltage," Int. J. Electron, *46,* 33-55, Jan., 1979.

[16] G. DeClerck, "Characterization of Surface States at the Si-SiO$_2$ Interface," in *Nondestructive Evaluation of Semiconductor Materials and Devices* (J. Zemel, ed.), Plenum Press, New York, 1979, p. 105-148.

[17] L. D. Yau, "A Simple Theory to Predict the Threshold Voltage of Short-Channel IGFETs," Solid-State Electron., *17,* 1059-1063, Oct., 1974.

[18] L. A. Akers and J. J. Sanchez, "Threshold Voltage Models of Short, Narrow and Small Geometry MOSFETs: A Review," Solid-State Electron., *25,* 621-641, July, 1982.

[19] C. R. Ji and C. T. Sah, "Two-Dimensional Numerical Analysis of the Narrow Gate Effect in MOSFET," IEEE Trans. Electr. Dev., *ED-30,* 635-647, June, 1983.

[20] M. Sugino, L. A. Akers, and J. M. Ford, "Optimum p-Channel Isolation Structure for CMOS," IEEE Trans. Electr. Dev., *ED-31,* 1823-1829, Dec., 1984.

[21] G. Merckel, "A Simple Model of the Threshold Voltage of Short and Narrow Channel MOSFETs," Solid-State Electron., *23,* 1207-1213, Dec., 1980.

[22] Y. Daimon-Hagiwara, "Two-Phase CCD with Narrow Channel Transfer Regions," Jap. J. Appl. Phys., *17,* Suppl. 17-1, 255-261, 1978.

[23] F. C. Hsu, P. K. Ko, S. Tang, C. M. Hu, and R. S. Muller, "An Analytical Breakdown Model for Short-Channel MOSFET's," IEEE Trans. Electr. Dev., *ED-29,* 1735-1740, Nov., 1982.

[24] C. M. Hu, S. C. Tam, F. C. Hsu, P. K. Ko, T. Y. Chan, and K. W. Terrill, "Hot-Electron-Induced MOSFET Degradation–Model, Monitor and Improvement," IEEE Trans. Electr. Dev., *ED-32,* 375-385, Febr., 1985.

[25] S. Tam, F. C. Hsu, P. K. Ko, C. Hu, and R. S. Muller, "Spatially Resolved Observation of Visible-Light Emission from Si MOSFET's," IEEE Electr. Dev. Lett., *EDL-4,* 386-388, Oct., 1983.

PROBLEMS

6.1 For the box-shaped doping distribution of Fig. 6.4b, derive the threshold-voltage equation given by eq. (6.18).

6.2 Using the threshold-voltage equation derived in Problem 6.1, calculate the V_{TS} vs. V_{BS} curves over the same range of V_{BS} as in Fig. 6.2 for the box-shaped distribution of Fig. 6.4b for the following conditions: $N_S = 2.5, 3, 3.5, 4, 4.5$, and 5×10^{16} cm^{-3}. In each case you will have to find d_i such that $(N_S - N_B)d_i = 5 \times 10^{11}$ cm^{-2}. For $V_{BS} = -2$ V, plot V_{TS} vs. d_i to show the dependence of the threshold voltage on the shape of the assumed box distribution. $Q_{it} = Q_m = 0$. Use $Q_f/q = 2 \times 10^{10}$ cm^{-2}; n^+ polysilicon gate with $E_F = E_c$; $x_o = 500$ Å; $N_B = 5 \times 10^{15}$ cm^{-3}.

6.3 The effective mobility vs. gate voltage data of a MOSFET are given below:

V_G(V)	$\overline{\mu}_n$(cm^2/Vs)	V_G(V)	$\overline{\mu}_n$(cm^2/Vs)
1.0	522.3	5.5	439.7
1.5	539.8	6.0	429.4
2.0	537.9	6.5	419.5
2.5	520.4	7.0	411.0
3.0	503.3	7.5	402.8
3.5	488.0	8.0	393.9
4.0	474.1	8.5	385.8
4.5	461.8	9.0	378.2
5.0	450.5	9.5	369.7

For these measurements, $V_S = V_B = 0$ and $V_T = 0.62$ V.

Plot $\overline{\mu}_n$ vs. V_G. Then find μ_0 and θ as defined in eq. (6.23). On the $\overline{\mu}_n$ vs. V_G data, plot eq. (6.23) to show the fit between theory and experiment. Hint: μ_0 can be obtained by extrapolating the $\overline{\mu}_n$ vs. V_G data to $V_G = 0$. θ can be obtained by plotting $\mu_0/\overline{\mu}_n$ vs. V_G.

6.4 Derive eq. (6.25).

6.5 Derive eq. (6.31).

6.6 Derive eq. (6.33). Then let $W_S = W_D = W_C$ and show that this simplification leads to eq. (6.32).

6.7 This problem deals with the current-voltage characteristics of MOSFET's.

Plot I_D vs. V_{DS} from $V_{DS} = 0$ to 10 V for
  (a) eq. (6.8b)
  (b) eq. (6.8a)
  (c) eq. (6.5)
Use ϕ_{ms} appropriate for a highly doped n^+ polysilicon gate ($E_F \approx E_c$ in polysilicon), $Q_f/q = 2 \times 10^{10}$ cm^{-2}, $Q_{it} = Q_m = 0$, $x_o = 500$ Å, $N_B = 10^{15}$ cm^{-3}, $V_S = 0$, $V_B = -3$V, $V_G = 5$ V, $\overline{\mu}_n = 450$ cm^2/Vs, $Z = 20$ μm, and $L = 3$ μm.

Appendix I

LIST OF SYMBOLS

A_G gate area (cm^2)

A_J junction area (cm^2)

A_s lateral space-charge region area (cm^2)

B bandwidth (Hz)

c velocity of light (2.998×10^{10} cm/s)

c_n bulk-state electron-capture coefficient (cm^3/s)

c_{ns} interface-state electron-capture coefficient (cm^3/s)

c_p bulk-state hole-capture coefficient (cm^3/s)

c_{ps} interface-state hole-capture coefficient (cm^3/s)

C capacitance per unit area (F/cm^2)

C_B bulk space-charge region (scr) capacitance per unit area (F/cm^2)

C_{BL} bit line capacitance per unit area (F/cm^2)

C_{BLi} initial bit line capacitance per unit area (F/cm^2)

C_{BLf} final bit line capacitance per unit area (F/cm^2)

C_{eff} effective capacitance per unit area (F/cm^2)

C_F final MOS-C capacitance per unit area (F/cm^2)

C_{FB} flatband capacitance per unit area (F/cm^2)

C_i initial deep-depletion (DD) MOS-C capacitance per unit area (F/cm^2)

C_m intermediate DD MOS-C capacitance per unit area (F/cm^2)

C_N inversion-layer capacitance per unit area (F/cm^2)

C_o oxide capacitance per unit area (F/cm^2)

C_{sat} saturation MOS-C capacitance per unit area (F/cm^2)

C_s semiconductor capacitance per unit area (F/cm^2)

C_{si} initial DD MOS-C semiconductor capacitance per unit area (F/cm^2)

C_{sF}	final DD MOS-C semiconductor capacitance per unit area (F/cm^2)
C_{sm}	intermediate DD MOS-C semiconductor capacitance per unit area (F/cm^2)
C_{s0i}	initial storage capacitance per unit area of a logic **0** (F/cm^2)
C_{s0f}	final storage capacitance per unit area of a logic **0** (F/cm^2)
C_{s1i}	initial storage capacitance per unit area of a logic **1** (F/cm^2)
C_{s1f}	final storage capacitance per unit area of a logic **1** (F/cm^2)
C_T	MOS-C capacitance per unit area at $\phi_s = 2\phi_F$ (F/cm^2)
d_i	equivalent ion-implantation depth (cm)
D_i	ion-implantation dose per unit area (cm^{-2})
D_{it}	interface-state density $(cm^{-2}\ eV^{-1})$
D_n	electron-diffusion constant (cm^2/s)
$\mathscr{E}$	electric field (V/cm)
$\mathscr{E}_{eff}$	effective MOSFET transverse electric field (V/cm)
$\mathscr{E}_s$	surface electric field (V/cm)
$\mathscr{E}_{xf}$	CCD fringing electric field (V/cm)
$\mathscr{E}_{xs}$	CCD self-induced electric field (V/cm)
e_n	bulk-state electron-emission coefficient (s^{-1})
e_{ns}	interface-state electron-emission coefficient (s^{-1})
e_p	bulk-state hole-emission coefficient (s^{-1})
e_{ps}	interface-state hole-emission coefficient (s^{-1})
E	energy (eV)
E_c	lowest conduction-band energy (eV)
E_F	Fermi energy or Fermi level (eV)
E_G	band gap energy (eV)
E_i	intrinsic Fermi energy (eV)
E_{it}	interface-state energy (eV)
E_T	G-R center energy (eV)
E_v	highest valence-band energy (eV)
f	frequency (Hz)
f_c	clock frequency (Hz)
f_p	low-pass filter cut-off frequency (Hz)
f_s	spatial frequency of optical excitation pattern (cycles/cm)
F	photon flux density incident on the semiconductor $(photons/cm^2s)$
F_i	photon flux density inside the semiconductor $(photons/cm^2s)$
F	normalized electric field (see eq. 1.13)
F_N	electron quasi-Fermi level (eV)
F_P	hole quasi-Fermi level (eV)

g_m	transconductance (S = Siemens)
G	CCD delay-line gain
G	steady-state bulk generation rate ($cm^{-3} s^{-1}$)
G_s	steady-state surface generation rate ($cm^{-2} s^{-1}$)
G_{scr}	steady-state scr generation rate ($cm^{-3} s^{-1}$)
G_{qn}	steady-state quasineutral region generation rate ($cm^{-3} s^{-1}$)
h	Planck's constant (6.626×10^{-34} Js)
$h(t)$	CCD delay-line transfer function
$H(f)$	CCD delay-line transfer function
i_{DS}	drain-source MOSFET current (A)
i_L	load current (A)
I_C	collector current (A)
I_{CBO}	collector-base leakage current with open emitter (A)
I_D	drain current (A)
I_E	emitter current (A)
I_{GIJ}	gate-induced junction current (A)
I_J	junction current (A)
I_s	surface current (A)
I_S	source current (A)
I_{sub}	substrate current (A)
j	$= \sqrt{-1}$
J	current density (A/cm^2)
J_{coll}	collected photocurrent density (A/cm^2)
J_d	displacement current density (A/cm^2)
J_N	electron current density (A/cm^2)
J_{scr}	scr current density (A/cm^2)
k	Boltzmann's constant (8.617×10^{-5} eV/K)
k	fraction of drain electrons causing avalanche breakdown
k_n	$= Z\bar{\mu}_n C_o/L$ (see eq. 6.1)
K_o	oxide dielectric constant (3.9 for SiO_2)
K_s	semiconductor dielectric constant (11.8 for Si)
L	MOSFET, CCD gate length (cm)
L_D^*	extrinsic Debye length (cm)
L_D	intrinsic Debye length (cm)
L_n	electron-diffusion length (cm)
M	avalanche multiplication factor
n	number of elemental CCD transfers

n	electron concentration (cm^{-3})
n_1	defined in eq. (1.64a)
n_{1s}	similar to n_1, but at the surface
n_i	intrinsic carrier concentration (cm^{-3})
n_{it}	electron-occupied interface-state density (cm^{-2})
n_0	equilibrium electron concentration (cm^{-3})
n_s	electron concentration at the surface (cm^{-3})
n_T	bulk G-R center concentration occupied by electrons (cm^{-3})
N	number of CCD stage transfers
N_A	acceptor doping concentration (cm^{-3})
N_B	net doping concentration $= N_A - N_D$ (cm^{-3})
N_{Bi}	initial DD MOS-C net doping concentration (cm^{-3})
N_{BF}	final DD MOS-C net doping concentration (cm^{-3})
N_{Bm}	intermediate DD MOS-C net doping concentration (cm^{-3})
N_c	effective conduction-band density of states (cm^{-3})
N_D	donor doping concentration (cm^{-3})
N_i	ideal ion-implanted concentration (cm^{-3})
N_{it}	interface-state density (cm^{-2})
N_S	equivalent ion-implanted surface concentration (cm^{-3})
N_T	bulk G-R center concentration (cm^{-3})
p	hole concentration (cm^{-3})
p_1	defined in eq. (1.64b)
p_{1s}	similar to p_1, but at the surface
p_0	equilibrium hole concentration (cm^{-3})
p_s	hole concentration at the surface (cm^{-3})
p_T	bulk G-R center concentration occupied by holes (cm^{-3})
p_y	CCD cell or pixel spacing (cm)
P	number of CCD clocking phases
P	optical power density (W/cm^2)
q	magnitude of electron charge (1.602×10^{-19} coul)
Q	charge density ($coul/cm^2$)
Q_{av}	average initial CCD charge density ($coul/cm^2$)
Q_B	bulk charge density ($coul/cm^2$)
$Q_B{}'$	average bulk charge density, defined in eq. (6.30) ($coul/cm^2$)
Q_f	fixed oxide charge density ($coul/cm^2$)
Q_G	gate charge density ($coul/cm^2$)
Q_{it}	interface-state trapped charge density ($coul/cm^2$)

Q_m	mobile oxide charge density (coul/cm^2)
Q_N	electron surface charge density (coul/cm^2)
Q_{NF}	final electron surface charge density (coul/cm^2)
Q_{Nm}	intermediate electron surface charge density (coul/cm^2)
$Q_{N,m}$	maximum charge density of a CCD well (coul/cm^2)
Q_P	hole surface charge density (coul/cm^2)
Q_s	semiconductor charge density (coul/cm^2)
Q_{s0i}	initial storage charge density of a logic **0** (coul/cm^2)
Q_{s0f}	final storage charge density of a logic **0** (coul/cm^2)
Q_{s1i}	initial storage charge density of a logic **1** (coul/cm^2)
Q_{s1f}	final storage charge density of a logic **1** (coul/cm^2)
Q_z	CCD charge per unit width (coul/cm)
$\mathcal{R}$	responsivity (A/W)
r	MOS-C gate radius (cm)
r_j	junction depth (cm)
R	steady-state recombination rate (cm^{-3} s^{-1})
R	voltage sweep rate (V/s)
R	reflectivity
R	MOSFET substrate and external resistance (Ω)
R_p	ion-implantation projected range (cm)
s	surface generation velocity (cm/s)
s'	effective surface generation velocity (see eq. 2.12) (cm/s)
s_1	surface generation velocity of a back contact (cm/s)
s_0	surface generation velocity of a depleted surface (cm/s)
s_r	surface recombination velocity (cm/s)
t	time (s)
t_c	stage delay time (s)
t_d	$= N t_c$ CCD delay time (s)
t_F	recovery time of a pulsed MOS-C (s)
T	temperature (K)
T_e	effective electron temperature (K)
U	normalized potential $= q\phi/kT$
U_D	normalized drain voltage $= qV_D/kT$
U_F	normalized Fermi potential $= q\phi_F/kT$
U_{FN}	normalized electron quasi-Fermi potential $= q\phi_{FN}/kT$
U_{FP}	normalized hole quasi-Fermi potential $= q\phi_{FP}/kT$
U_s	normalized surface potential $= q\phi_s/kT$

$\hat{U}_s$	sign ($\pm$) of U_s
v_i	input voltage (V)
v_o	output voltage (V)
v_L	load voltage (V)
v_n	electron velocity (cm/s)
v_{sat}	saturation-limited velocity (cm/s)
v_{th}	thermal carrier velocity (cm/s)
v_{tr}	trigger voltage (V)
V_B	substrate voltage (V)
V_{CE}	collector-emitter voltage (V)
V_{BD}	breakdown voltage (V)
V_{bi}	built-in pn junction potential (V)
V_{BLi}	initial bit line voltage (V)
V_{BLf}	final bit line voltage (V)
V_{BS}	substrate-source voltage (V)
V_D	drain voltage (V)
V_{DB}	$= V_D - V_B$ (V)
V_{DD}	drain power supply voltage (V)
V_{DS}	$= V_D - V_S$ (V)
V_{Dsat}	saturation drain voltage (V)
V_{FB}	flatband voltage (V)
V_G	gate voltage (V)
V_G'	$= V_G - V_{FB}$ (V)
V_{GB}	$= V_G - V_B$ (V)
V_R	guard-ring voltage (V)
V_{GS}	$= V_G - V_S$ (V)
$V_i(f)$	input voltage (V)
V_n	n-channel voltage in BCCD (V)
$V_o(f)$	output voltage (V)
V_0	defined in eq. (1.39)
V_{ox}	oxide voltage (V)
V_{ref}	reference voltage (V)
V_S	source voltage (V)
V_{sat}	saturation voltage (V)
V_{SB}	$= V_S - V_B$ (V)
V_{s0i}	initial voltage of a logic **0** (V)
V_{s1i}	initial voltage of a logic **1** (V)

V_T	threshold voltage (V)
V_{TS}	defined in eq. (6.6)
V_W	$(4qK_s\varepsilon_0 N_B \phi_F)^{1/2}/C_o$
$V_{W'}$	$(4qK_s\varepsilon_0 N_B \phi_F')^{1/2}/C_o$
W	space-charge region (scr) width (cm)
W_{BD}	breakdown-limited maximum scr width (cm)
W_C	scr width under the channel (cm)
W_D	scr width under the drain (cm)
W_F	final scr width for MOS-C in heavy inversion (cm)
W_i	initial DD MOS-C scr width (cm)
W_m	intermediate DD MOS-C scr width (cm)
W_S	scr width under the source (cm)
W_T	scr width for MOS-C at $\phi_s = 2\phi_F$ (cm)
x_{ch}	MOSFET channel thickness (cm)
x_n	n-channel thickness in BCCD (cm)
x_o	oxide thickness (cm)
Z	MOSFET gate width (cm)
α	CCD stage transfer inefficiency
α	bipolar transistor common-base current gain
α	optical absorption coefficient (cm^{-1})
Δn	excess electron concentration (cm^{-3})
Δp	excess hole concentration (cm^{-3})
ΔR_p	ion-implantation straggle (cm)
$\Delta\Phi$	phase shift
$\Delta\phi_s$	defined in eq. (3.44)
ε	CCD elemental transfer inefficiency
ε_0	permittivity of free space (8.854 $\times$ 10^{-14} F/cm)
η	CCD transfer efficiency
η	quantum efficiency
λ	CCD charge loss
λ	wavelength (cm)
θ	mobility-degradation coefficient
ϕ	potential (V)
ϕ	CCD gate connection as phase
ϕ_F	Fermi potential (eV)
ϕ_F'	$= \phi_F - V_{BS}/2$
ϕ_{FN}	electron quasi-Fermi potential (V)

ϕ_{FP}	hole quasi-Fermi potential (V)
ϕ_{min}	defined in eq. (3.43)
ϕ_{ms}	metal-semiconductor work function difference (V)
ϕ_R	reset gate phase
ϕ_s	surface potential (V)
ϕ_{sB}	$= \phi_s - V_B$ (V)
ϕ_{sS}	$= \phi_s - V_S$ (V)
ν	frequency of light (Hz)
ω	$= 2\pi f$ (rad/s)
ρ	charge density (coul/cm^3)
σ_n	bulk-state hole-capture cross section (cm^2)
σ_{ns}	interface-state electron-capture cross section (cm^2)
σ_p	bulk-state hole-capture cross section (cm^2)
τ	defined in eq. (3.26)
τ_c	capture-time constant (s)
τ_e	emission-time constant (s)
τ_g	generation lifetime (s)
τ_g'	effective generation lifetime (see eq. 2.11) (s)
τ_n	$= 1/c_n N_T$ (s)
τ_p	$= 1/c_p N_T$ (s)
τ_r	recombination lifetime (s)
τ_s	effective interface-state electron-capture time constant (s)
μ_n	electron mobility (cm^2/Vs)
$\bar{\mu}_n$	effective electron MOSFET mobility (cm^2/Vs)
$\bar{\mu}_p$	effective hole MOSFET mobility (cm^2/Vs)
μ_0	low field mobility (cm^2/Vs)

Appendix II

ABBREVIATIONS AND SYMBOLS

BBD	bucket-brigade device
BCCD	bulk-channel charge-coupled device
BJT	bipolar junction transistor
BL	bit line
CCD	charge-coupled device
CMOS	complementary metal-oxide semiconductor
CTD	charge-transfer device
C-V	capacitance-voltage
DD	deep depletion
DRAM	dynamic random-access memory
EAROM	electrically alterable read-only memory
EEPROM	electrically erasable programmable read-only memory
EPROM	electrically programmable read-only memory
ehp	electron-hole pair(s)
GaAs	gallium arsenide
Ge	germanium
G-R	generation-recombination
HF	high-frequency
Hi-C	high-capacity
LF	low-frequency
MOS	metal-oxide semiconductor
MOS-C	metal-oxide-semiconductor capacitor
MOSFET	metal-oxide-semiconductor field-effect transistor
MTF	modulation transfer function

NTSC	National Television System Committee
pixel	picture element
PROM	programmable read-only memory
qn	quasineutral
RAM	random-access memory
RePROM	reprogrammable read-only memory
ROM	read-only memory
SCCD	surface channel charge-coupled device
scr	space-charge region
Si	silicon
SIMS	secondary ion mass spectroscopy
SRAM	static random-access memory
TV	television
WL	word line

Appendix III

SEMICONDUCTOR SYMBOLS

The electronic symbols for a variety of semiconductor devices are:

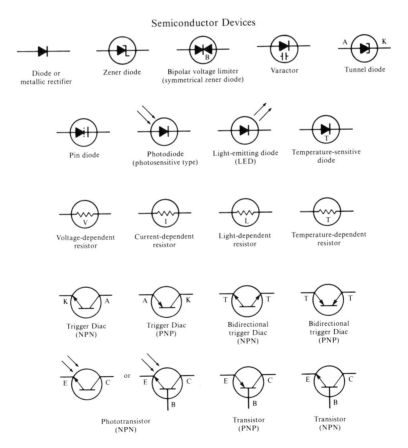

Semiconductor Devices

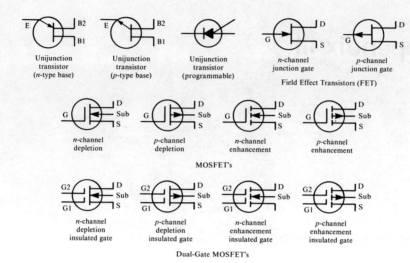

Unijunction transistor (*n*-type base)

Unijunction transistor (*p*-type base)

Unijunction transistor (programmable)

n-channel junction gate

p-channel junction gate

Field Effect Transistors (FET)

n-channel depletion

p-channel depletion

n-channel enhancement

p-channel enhancement

MOSFET's

n-channel depletion insulated gate

p-channel depletion insulated gate

n-channel enhancement insulated gate

p-channel enhancement insulated gate

Dual-Gate MOSFET's

From *Handbook of Electronic Tables and Formulas,* 5th Edition, 1979, Howard Sams & Co., Inc., p. 149. Used by permission of the publisher.

Index